By Oriana Fallaci

If the Sun Dies

Oriana Fallaci

Translated from the Italian by Pamela Swinglehurst

If the Sun Dies

Atheneum   New York   1967

English translation copyright © 1966 by Atheneum House, Inc.
Published in Italian under the title *Se il Sole Muore*,
copyright © 1965 by Rizzoli Editore
All rights reserved
Library of Congress catalog card number 66–23576
Published simultaneously in Canada by McClelland & Stewart Ltd.
Manufactured in the United States of America by
Kingsport Press, Inc., Kingsport, Tennessee
Designed by Harry Ford
First Printing September 1966
Second Printing February 1967

To my father who doesn't want to go to the Moon
because on the Moon
there are no flowers nor fishes nor birds

To Theodore Freeman who died, killed by a goose
while he was flying to go to the Moon

To my friends the astronauts who want to go to the Moon
because the Sun could die

This note is to thank a friend.
The friend is Ben Raeburn
who first encouraged me to write this book
and whose faith was a help to me throughout.

To the Reader

Many times, while writing this book, I was asked whether I was writing fiction or fact. In other words, was this book a novel or reportage? The question embarrassed me because the answer I was forced to give seemed somehow solemn, and I find solemnity rather disturbing. But once in a while one cannot avoid being solemn, so I said what I say now. This book is neither a novel nor reportage. It is the diary of a journey inside my conscience and my memory, of a dialogue that opens on the conflict with my father, then develops across the abyss that divides two generations. Where will the space race bring us? Where are we running and why? What is the price of continuing life if the Sun dies? My father wants to know, and I do too. But our approaches are different: he belongs to a generation firmly anchored to the Earth and the past; I belong to a generation facing a future of dizzy horizons and thirsty for new ideals. The Earth has become too small for us: we must look for other myths and other dreams.

The book is ruthlessly autobiographical; none of its characters has been invented. And since many of them are clamorously known through the daily press, everyone has been called by his real name as in actual reporting. This raises the question whether I have been objective or not. The reply is that I have not been: I do not believe in objectivity. As far as I know, objectivity exists only in mathematics where two plus two make four, period. Within conscience or memory, objectivity cannot exist, and to demand it would be grotesque. A true portrait of a man cannot be achieved without the beliefs, the feelings, the tastes of the painter. Look at that tree. For you it is a tree; for me it is perhaps a plastic form or a shadow. Look at that landscape. For you it is divine, full of butterflies and fruit; for me it may be empty as a desert. And who remembers whether a certain dialogue took place near a rocket or a cheese sandwich? Who wants to remember? Not me. That journey was a fight with my fears, with my doubts: not a report for some statistical bureau. I recall now that the creatures my father was afraid of, when he was in prison under threat of execution, were not the mice but the cockroaches that drank his wounds. Is there any difference? I would like to ask the mice, the cockroaches, the men of this book to forgive me if I put them in one chapter instead of another, in one situation instead of another. To my total lack of objectivity these liberties make them truer than the truth. And God knows how much truth I have put in, with how much pain and grief.

Along with the question of the book's being a novel or a journalistic report, I used to be asked whether this book favored America or not. To the blind, the deaf and the impatient I might suggest that the answer can be found in the last pages, when I arrive at such a merciless conclusion and tell my father that my choice has been made. However, placing the problem in those terms seems to me tendentious and wrong. Clearly, America is for me an example, a symbol, an interpretation of tomorrow's world. When a child, I often read that America-is-not-a-country-but-a-state-of-mind. Perhaps I read it too much: as a woman, I am now convinced it is true. And though I do not have American citizenship—I am a Florentine—I feel fully authorized to discuss that state of mind. When I discuss America, is it not to discuss us, myself, my ancestors who emigrated from Europe and created America? Who is a guest in this country? I don't feel like a guest; I am merely at home with a new address. Because Americans never slam the door in your face. Remembering perhaps that it was never slammed upon them, they open it always. For years I have come back to this country as a needle drawn by a magnet, a mysterious call of love, and not once have I been rejected. When the moment came to collect information for this book, I recalled that another country had not done badly in space. And I went to the Soviet Embassy in Rome to ask for a visa, to explain what I wished to see. I was received by a gallery of marble ears, motionless lips. I spoke and they didn't answer. It was like holding a conversation with the statues among which I was born. Then, exhausted, enraged, I turned my shoulders and took a plane to Houston, Texas. They had real ears and real lips in Houston. Not statues at all. They listened, they answered, they complicated matters, they made me sign papers and treated those papers like jewels, but soon after: op-la! they opened every door down to the last bolt, offering up the most private intimacy. I have often been surprised, even scandalized, by this casual generosity, this lack of secrecy. Yet I liked it, and I was madly grateful. Without being aware perhaps, those givers saw America as I see it, as something that does not belong to Americans only.

So, having reached the ceremony of gratitude, I must thank them publicly: scientists, astronauts, NASA employees, all the people who accepted me and helped me—my friends. Yes, friends now, and I often wonder: how could it happen? On one side of the miracle, there I was, with my father, my museums, my irony, my passions, my regrets, my rebellions, my solitude; on the other side, there they were, with their youth, their future, their equipment, their innocence, their discipline, their teamwork. How could it happen? I don't know, but I do know that they had great patience. It is not easy being goaded by an objector to objectivity. It is even less easy to have urgent obligations, like going to the moon, to Mars, to Alpha Centauri, and yet to give time to someone involved with problems that apparently can wait. Can they wait? I am speaking of the research into a dream, an ideal, of the dialogue with a conscience, of the decisions to be made when reality exceeds bravery and technical conquests and impinges upon the field of ideas.

Oriana Fallaci

Part One

I.

You couldn't see the stone, so thick and lush was the grass. I tripped over it and fell flat, alongside the road. Nobody came to help me. But then who could? There was nobody walking along the road, nobody along the roads of the whole city. Nobody existed, nobody with feet and legs, with a body on his legs, a head on his body. Only automobiles existed, sliding by, smooth, controlled, always at the same speed, at the same distance, never a man inside, nor a woman. There were human forms behind the steering wheels, yes, but so straight they were, and still, that they could not be men or women; they were automatons, robots. Isn't modern technology perfectly able to make robots identical to ourselves? Isn't the first rule for robots "remember that you must never interfere with the actions of humans unless they ask you to"? And was I asking anyone to intervene? On the contrary. Stretched out on the grass by the roadside, my cheeks burning with embarrassment, I was only hoping that they wouldn't notice me and laugh at me. And the robots obeyed, sliding by, smooth and controlled, always at the same speed, at the same distance, not even asking their computers whether the woman lying there was dead or alive and if she was alive why she wasn't getting up. I wasn't getting up because I had noticed something absurd. The grass didn't smell like grass.

I stuck my nose into it and sniffed. No, it didn't smell like grass, it had no smell at all. I grasped a blade and tugged. No, it didn't come out and it didn't break. I scrabbled underneath with my fingernail, looking for a speck of earth. No, you couldn't even get hold of a speck of earth. How odd. Yet it was the color of earth, it had the consistency of earth. And the grass that was planted in it was the same color as grass, it had the consistency of supple fresh grass, even watered with an ingenious sprinkler system to keep it green and make it grow; my God, I couldn't be delirious, dreaming, the grass was grass, yes, of course it . . . Was it grass? I sniffed it again. Again I grasped a blade between my thumb and forefinger and tugged. Again I scrabbled underneath with my fingernail, looking for a speck of earth, and like a dagger-thrust in my brain the doubt became certainty. The grass was plastic. Yes. And perhaps all the grass I'd seen there, the grass plots along the avenues, along the highways, in front of the houses, the churches, the schools, looked after by gardeners, watered, treated like real grass, grass that grows and dies, was all plastic. A huge shroud of plastic, of grass that never grows or dies, a mockery.

I jumped up as if I'd been stung by a thousand wasps, hurried back to my hotel, flung open the door of my suite and almost fell over the cactus plant that adorned the living room. It was a big cactus, green, lush, bristling with thorns, and on top there was a flower. I felt the flower, I bent it and twisted it. It remained intact. I poked my finger between the thorns, squeezed the fleshy part, hoping for a drop of liquid. I felt only the sponginess of rubber. I squeezed the thorns with both hands, desperately praying that they would prick me, that they would tell me I'd made a mistake. They only tickled me gently, the thorns were made of aluminum with rounded points. And the plant in the corridor? False too. And the hedge in the garden? False of course. And probably those trees too around which there were never any flies or birds, every blade of grass, every branch, every leaf was false in this city where nothing green sprouted and grew and died. The daisies, the azaleas, the rhododendrons, the roses in that vase . . . The vase was on the TV and I approached it without hope. I gently removed a rose, raised it to my face, let it drop, and the rose went crack: it shattered on the floor in a thousand splinters of glass. On the floor a cold frost, a spark of light remained. I had reached Los Angeles, first stage of my journey into the future and into myself.

———————————

It had all started with a spark of light: do you remember, Father? The spark of light ran across the TV screen, so small and weightless that I could have picked it up on the tip of my little finger and put it in the palm of my hand. It wasn't even so very bright, do you remember? It glimmered very feebly like the fireflies that glimmer on August nights along the hedges and get caught by the children and finish up inside a jar. It often vanished into the darkness just like the fireflies, and the TV was like a hedge that had swallowed it up and would never give it back, my spark of light. Impatient, angry, I would have liked to search behind that smooth glass, move aside the mechanisms and the leaves, to catch it again and put it in a jar. But there it was, coming back again, obstinately coming alight again out of nothingness, very much more than a spark of light: it was a star. The first star made by men. A crude thing if we could have seen it close up, Father, no bigger than a demijohn, and with a ridiculous wrathful name: Sputnik. But it was a star, and men had taken a billion years to make that star, and from that star would be born other stars, bigger and stronger, able to go higher, to carry us with them—until we too would be able to leave the Earth and plunge into the infinite, become weightless fireflies: "Father! Isn't it extraordinary, Father?" I shouted.

You were reading the newspaper. With exasperating slowness you lowered your paper. You showed me two ancient blue Earth eyes, a skeptical ancient Earth face, and you grumbled: "What's so extraordinary about it?"

"But to go to the Moon, Father! Don't you see what it means, that spark of light? We'll go to the Moon, to the other planets!"

With even more exasperating slowness you folded the newspaper and put it on the table. "The thought of it makes me wince. What's the use of going to the Moon? Men will always have the same problems, on the Moon or on the Earth; they will always be sick and wicked, on the Moon or on the Earth. They tell me that on the Moon there are no seas, no rivers, no fish, no woods, no fields, no birds. I couldn't even go shooting or fishing."

Yes, your love is exclusively for things that are rooted in this Earth and you cannot understand about the caterpillar waiting to turn into a butterfly. I've never managed to get you up in an airplane, only once I almost persuaded you: when you wanted to see the Botanical Gardens in London. I brought you the brochure of the Botanical Gardens together with the plane ticket and you leafed happily through the brochure but gave me back the ticket: "Can't we go by train?" "It would take too long, Father." "Then I won't go." Mother came in your place but she kept her seat belt fastened throughout the entire flight, thinking it was a parachute, and from time to time she kept saying: "Your father's right, what's all this hurry?" For you speed is hurry, and you don't like airplanes. I'd guarantee that in your heart of hearts you think the same as Grandfather, who thought that planes were evil birds to be struck at with his stick. During the bombing Grandfather wouldn't take shelter in the cellar, remember? He would put on his hat and go out into the street, brandishing his stick at the sky and shouting: "Bastards! Bastards!" So I didn't answer you, but stayed there watching my spark of light, which was suddenly extinguished, swallowed up by a face that described its trajectory, its position, and then I felt the same disappointment as on those mornings in my childhood when I would run to see my firefly in its jar and the firefly would have gone, in its place a small coin, and someone saying see, the firefly has turned into money, and I would be angry and answer that I wanted the firefly, I didn't want money, and everyone would laugh. The little coin seemed to laugh too as it clinked spitefully when I hurled it to the floor, and I felt that nobody understood me, I felt ridiculous, I couldn't find words, if I found them I was ashamed to say them. Haven't I always been ashamed to say them all these years, every time a new star left the Earth with a man named Gagarin or Shepard or Titov or Glenn or Popowski or Cooper? He would go up, and I would be going up with him. He would float through space and I would be floating through space with him. He would return and I would be returning with him. But how can one express certain things, Father? Nothing holds one back like embarrassment, the fear of indulging in rhetoric. Irony is easy, faith is difficult, and nobody makes a fool of you if you're ironical, but everybody is ready to deride you if you recite an act of faith. On the one hand there was myself, the child who believes in the stars, and on the other hand there was you, the adult who believes in the Earth.

"Oh! It's vanished, Father!"

"What has?"

"The Sputnik."

"Don't be foolish. Stop bothering me."

"But, Father—"

"I've already told you I'm not interested, it's no concern of mine."

"I can understand that you might not be interested. But not that it isn't your concern: it certainly is your concern, Father. It concerns the blind too, and the deaf, and—"

"Blind, deaf—what are you talking about! I love the Earth, do you understand? I love the leaves and the birds, the fish and the sea, the snow and the wind! And I love green and blue and all the colors and the smells, and that's all there is, do you understand? That's all we have, and I don't want to lose it on account of your rockets, do you understand?"

You grew white with anger. And your every muscle warned me to be quiet, not to go on with my nonsense. But I couldn't keep quiet any longer: it was as if a war, a gulf, had opened up between us. And I told you, though I don't know if these were my words, that I love the Earth too, Father. It's my home and I love it. But a home you can never leave isn't a home at all, it's a prison, and you have always told me that man isn't made to stay in prison, he's made to escape from it and too bad if he risks getting killed escaping. I said to you that if it's true that man comes from the sea where once he was a fish, then the sea was his prison too and to leave it seemed madness. But he did leave it, and slowly, painfully dragged himself to the shore, and collapsed in the air. He couldn't breathe in the air, Father. His gills begged for water, water, and in that emptiness without liquid he drowned and suffocated and died; the Earth was a hell for him, a white nightmare of light that blinded him, stuck to him like suckers, but slowly, painfully, trying and dying and trying again, for millions of years, he managed not to drown in the air, not to be blinded by the brightness, not to stay stuck to the shore. He developed suitable lungs and learned to breathe the air. He developed suitable eyes and learned to look into the brightness. He developed suitable limbs and learned to move on the ground. He developed a suitable spine and learned to stand on his feet. He developed hands with fingers and learned to take hold of things. And so one day he came to realize that he could do more: that he could think. And thinking brought him the knowledge that he was a man. And he was so happy being a man that he invented things which nature had not invented. He rubbed two stones sharply together and made fire. He sliced up tree trunks and made wheels. He put together the fire and the wheels and made a train. He discovered that he could go fast and far, and he became envious of the birds, he stole their wings, put them on the train, and he flew, higher, always higher, until he became envious of the stars and made rough copies of the stars and shot away on them to see beyond the closed door of the sky. For the love of God, Father, if a door is closed don't you have the urge to open it and see what's behind it? Isn't the story of man a story of closed and open doors? Father, answer me.

You shook your head. "You can open it, of course. You're able to open it, so you open it. But if that door is the last door, where will it take you? I'll tell you where: headlong into the void. The future you're dreaming of is nothing more than a headlong leap into the void. You'll go hurtling down at the first step, and it's as well for me that I won't be there to watch and weep."

That was exactly what you said, then you stood up and went away down the corridor with dragging footsteps. It was an autumn afternoon, remember, and we were in our house in the country. Through the windows came the fragrance of mushrooms and resin, the woods were aflame with red and violet heather, the bunches of grapes hung heavy with juice on the vines. It would soon be time for the grape harvest, the grapes would boil in the vats, and in the intoxicating tranquillity the chestnuts would start to fall with little round thuds. In the kitchen Mother would cook blackberry jam. "Heavens, it's burning, it's catching!" "Mother, can I taste it?" "Keep away, I told you!" Haven't you ever noticed how beautiful our cypress trees look from the kitchen window? It makes you want to stroke them, if you stretch out your finger you seem to feel their paintbrush tips, smooth as velvet.

I truly don't know why that should have been the very day I decided to make this journey among the men who are preparing our future. Perhaps it was what you said about the void: "a headlong leap into the void." We have always been fascinated by the void. The deeper, the darker it is, the more we are attracted to it: like a mysterious love call. And there's no use putting off the moment of departure: I had been putting it off for years, and now here I am, amid the plastic grass, the rubber plants, the glass roses, the robots—a body on two legs, a head on a body, seeking the answer to your answer, Father.

———

Calmly and unhesitatingly I bent to pick up the cold frost that had been a rose. But suddenly I was pricked by a splinter, a drop of blood appeared on my finger, and I was filled with the great dismay of a child who dreams of escaping from home but, when he's escaped, wishes he hadn't. It's fine to run away if it seems the right thing to do. When you close the door behind you, you feel more alive, the road is a boundless prairie and the train is a long promise. But when the train starts to move, the compartment becomes an airless cage, a tunnel taking you who knows where. Suddenly you feel ill, tormented by a thousand threats, you miss your warm soft bed, your good comfortable home, and you don't know what you want any longer. We are all afraid of the future and we all regret the past and we are all unsure at the beginning, Father. And that is why this book must often be an obsessive swing between yesterday and tomorrow: two worlds which by now separate us in a timeless time. That is why I shall often turn to you in this book. Read it and think about it, Father, whether it amuses you or irritates you: everything in it, from the first page to the last, is what truly happened to me, or is what I truly saw or felt or thought. The names of the people and the places are real. The dates and the conversations I report are real. My doubts and my enthusiasms and my cowardice are real: I have invented nothing and kept very little out of it. This book, Father, is the diary of a year in my life: and I offer it to you by way of continuing the conversation that started on account of that spark of light.

2.

A great turmoil could be heard inside, shouts, screams, instructions: Daddy you open it, no Daddy I'll open it, no Mother'll open it, no Mother isn't opening it, then who's opening it? Then the crimson door was flung wide open and he was there in front of me. A barefoot giant, tanned, with fair hair the color of ripe wheat and blue eyes the color of a clean sky: protected by two thick lenses so they wouldn't get dirty. Just the sight of him was more warming than a lighted fire in winter, and as he warmed you he cured you of all bitterness, and as he cured you he told you a thousand possible fairy tales, of silver mountains and emerald skies, of blue hills and moonstone valleys, of Mars as he imagined it. His laughter was—how shall I describe it?—like the laughter of a happy young boy who lacks nothing: neither mother, nor father, nor toys, nor the faith that tomorrow is Sunday, and Sunday is a day of sunshine, and tomorrow is always Sunday.

"Hey! Here she is! Hey!"

In a whirlwind of hair and spectacles, like the beads of a broken necklace, his four little daughters came rolling out of the kitchen: the biggest was about fourteen, the smallest about six. And after them came a fifth blonde: his wife. The necklace strung itself together with five beads of identical color and different sizes, then rattled off its greeting.

"Hi," said the first blonde.

"Hi," said the second blonde.

"Hi," said the third and fourth and fifth blondes. And drew me into a living room lined with books.

"I should have telephoned, I know."

"For goodness' sake! Father hates the telephone."

"He hates it to death."

"He can't stand it."

"He always breaks it."

"Ray hasn't been converted to the telephone very long," explained his wife, who was called Maggie, "and every now and then he breaks it, out of guilt. It was broken today, for instance."

"As far as that goes, he hates planes too," said the first blonde.

"In fact, he's never been in a plane," said the second blonde.

"And he doesn't even drive a car."

"He's flunked his driving test thirty-three times."

"Ray rides a bicycle," explained Maggie, rather ashamed. "He's forty-four and he still rides a bicycle."

Sprawled on a sofa, Bradbury waited patiently for the blondes to express all their opinions. When they had finished, he revealed his gravest fault.

"I don't even have a television set."

"All the kids around here have one and we don't!"

"All he cares about are Verne's books."

"We'll grow up idiots."

"Ignorant."

"Like you, Father."

"Idiot? Ignorant?" Bradbury raised an eyebrow.

"He's not an idiot. A lot of Father's books are used as school textbooks, you know," one blonde admitted.

"Most of his stories appear in anthologies, a hundred and thirty of them, along with Steinbeck, Saroyan, Hemingway, Poe. He's not an idiot," admitted another blonde.

"But he is ignorant. His books are full of mistakes."

"Father, I've found another mistake, Father," announced the youngest.

"Yes," said Bradbury.

"In your book *Martian Chronicles.*"

"Yes," said Bradbury.

"On page 194."

"Yes," said Bradbury.

"When the moons of Mars rise in the east."

"Yes," said Bradbury.

"No," said she.

"What do you mean, no?" said Bradbury.

"The moons of Mars rise in the west, Father."

"I've found a bigger mistake," announced the eldest.

"Yes," said Bradbury.

"Father, you remember the farmer who's planting apples on Mars?"

"Yes," said Bradbury.

"When he's waiting for the rain?"

"Yes," said Bradbury.

"It doesn't rain on Mars, Father."

"Little pedant. I don't even know that water is composed of oxygen and hydrogen, and they complain about moons rising in the east. What do I care if the moons of Mars rise in the west or the east, if it rains or it doesn't rain on Mars? I don't aim to furnish breviaries for mathematicians and physicists. But, they say, a writer of science fiction ought to know some things. Well, they've been calling me a science-fiction writer all my life and I still don't know what it means. For some time they've been calling me the writer of the space age: that sounds a little more respectable, but I still don't know what it means. All I know is that twenty years ago they all laughed at me: they used to say you're ridiculous, you're absurd. What do you mean, astronaut, spaceport, going to the Moon, are you mad? Then, suddenly, wow! the space age exploded and everything I'd been writing came true. But they weren't at all sorry, they didn't make any apology. They went on saying: Your work isn't art, it's Cinerama. Well, what's Cinerama got? Between ourselves, who invented Cinerama but old Michelangelo? Didn't he do the Sistine Chapel? And what's the Sistine Chapel if it isn't Cinerama in painting? So if old Mike painted in Cinerama, why can't I write about the future in science fiction? I use science fiction to interpret the times I live in, the children of my children will live in, to illustrate the perils . . ."

The blondes went away, and I looked at him in concern.

"The perils?"

"Sure. TV, for example."

"TV?"

"Yes. What do you think they're all doing at this moment, millions of Americans, Italians, French, Japanese and so on? They're watching TV. Like zombies. They aren't thinking. They aren't moving. They aren't living. They're just watching. The TV thinks for them. Lives for them. Lives? It's poisoning them with its imbecility. It's conditioning them to apathy: but they don't realize it. Because they're only watching, watching, watching. All the dangers of the world are enclosed in that damn box that stands like an altar in the middle of the house, and they kneel dumbly before it as before an altar. By means of the TV any Hitler could turn a peaceful nation into a land of wild beasts in the space of three days: you wouldn't have to go anywhere to attend his meetings or watch his eyes—they would enter every dining room, every bedroom. But they don't realize it, they don't even suspect it, they don't give it a thought because all they're doing is watching. And if someone . . ."

"And if someone falls down on the grass and notices that the grass isn't made of grass . . ." I told him about the grass.

"I know, I know."

"And if somebody has a vase of roses and its petals aren't petals at all, but flakes of glass . . ."

"I know, I know."

"And machines everywhere. Nothing but machines . . ."

I sounded like a patient describing his symptoms to a doctor, and then it hurts me here and here and then here, hoping the doctor will tell him it's nothing and the doctor tells him it's very serious, it's fatal. At the third "I know, I know" I looked at him in even greater concern.

"You know? You tell me you know?"

"I know. So what? What does it matter? For me to accept the plastic it's enough that a piece of plastic makes a good raincoat and keeps my daughter from catching pneumonia. As for the telephone, it's enough that the telephone can be used to send for the fire department. It's enough for me that TV shows a good movie. And it's enough that a microphone can record what I say at a moment when my brain is functioning. So fascists talk into the microphone too? We have to be patient. So stupid people watch TV too? Bores call on the phone, so I get mad and break it? And they substitute plastic for grass? We have to be patient. I know that the Sun over Los Angeles is gray because of the smoke from the exhausts. I know that automobiles serve to make the impotent feel virile. But if out of a thousand imbeciles there's one man who says: it's not going a hundred miles an hour that makes a man virile, it's not necessary to look virile all day long, it's enough to be so once every twenty-four hours and to go on foot, then I shout that man is marvelous, he's marvelous because he's created machines. I have no fear of machines: they make mortal man immortal. Music is handed on by records, books are printed on machines, ideas are recorded on tape. The tragedy of man is not only that he dies, it's that his brain grows old and dies. But the machines he invented can halt and hold his brain before he dies, they can lock up the truth the moment it's spoken and give it back intact, and so the gift that man had to offer doesn't die with him. Oh, if only Christ had had a tape-recorder! Then I'd have the proof to enable me to shout at those false Christians that the truth was His, not theirs. If Buddha had had radio! If Homer had had a linotype machine! If Leonardo had had an electronic computer! If Sappho had recorded her poems on uninflammable material! Oh, if Shakespeare had made a movie! Nobody will ever convince me that machines are dangerous or wicked; it's men who are dangerous and wicked. Movies fog the mind? But they can also awaken it. That's why I love Verne; he's a moralist like myself, an optimist like myself. He too lived at a time when everyone seemed to have lost the desire to do or to dare anything, and he gave them back that desire. For God's sake, in his book *From the Earth to the Moon* he said: 'Let's make a fine rocket and for God's sake let's go to the Moon.' For God's sake, and in his book *Twenty Thousand Leagues Under the Sea* he said: 'Let's make a fine submarine and for God's sake let's go underwater.' Think of Captain Nemo who cried with demonic passion: 'Be better among yourselves, don't worry about your relations with God, worry about your relations with each other!' Think of Robinson Crusoe who said: 'Yes, I am alone. The Earth is against me, the universe is against me, but I have a head, huh! I have two hands, huh! I can survive, I can live, huh!' So I like everything that can help to make us better, from plastic to rockets. And I'm tired of hearing people grumble."

"All right, Mr. Bradbury, but a writer's job isn't only to exalt what little there is that's beautiful: it's to seek out the bad and the ugly, and to denounce it. The job of man isn't to be content, it's to rebel. We can seek truth only through rebellion."

"But at a certain moment we have to find this truth. There comes a moment when society says to the writer O.K., boy, perfectly right; however, since you're so clever and can destroy so well, since you've demolished everything, our hopes, our illusions, tell us how we can build them up again. Then, my dear, you either shut up or you tell them how to build again. I have attacked society a great deal, with the enthusiasm of a freshman. But you can't go on being a freshman forever and you can't go on having a fever forever. Fever is illness and it doesn't last forever. When the thermometer goes up to a hundred and five you either get better or you die. I've had my hundred and five degrees and I came out of it beginning to appreciate good health. It's for old people to grumble, hope is for the young, and maybe I'm an eternal child, but I see the space age with the enthusiasm of our children, an innocent enthusiasm that makes me shout, what does it matter if the first rocket was Russian or American, if the first man to land on the Moon or Mars was called Popovic or Smith? The important thing was having it, that rocket, the important thing was sending the man up there!"

"I agree, Mr. Bradbury. But one may surely be allowed a little fear—just a little fear. Where are we going? What are we doing? Are we doing right? Shall we take our plastic grass and our glass roses to Mars too? For the rockets I too have enthusiasm. But when they're up, who's to stop them? They go on by themselves, because man has made something that has gone beyond his control and can live without him."

He suddenly grew red all over. He quivered like a thin sheet of metal in the wind. He boiled and bubbled with all the passion of the world.

"Fear? Have you ever seen a rocket taking off? It stands there, so big that the men around it look tiny, like flies, they light a little spark, and a great bellow tears the air to shreds, a white cloud spreads, and it lifts off, up into the infinite, and you blaspheme: God, we've caught you by the coattails! And as you utter this polite blasphemy, you no longer fear the rocket because you remember that it was man who built it, it was man who lighted the spark that fired the rocket. The rocket without man is a glove without a hand. Fear? But this is the most beautiful age that humanity has had the good fortune to live in, the most audacious, the most privileged, the most stupendously blasphemous, this is the greatest age in history. When they say: look, isn't that rocket marvelous? I answer: man who built it is marvelous, the age I live in is marvelous, our ideas are marvelous, ideas that are no longer static, abstract, frozen, but that burn and fly! Yes, we used to think of Beauty and we would sculpt statues, paint pictures, build palaces. We used to think of God and we raised churches, spires, offered up prayers. Now we think of Beauty, we think of God, and we create something that burns and flies upward: engines, machines. Until now we've been asleep, like tortoises hibernating in the winter. We've been asleep, but now we're waking, fresh and rested and intelligent, we're inventing our rockets, we're leaping beyond the Earth, we're breaking the chains that bound us to the Earth, we're leaving our prison behind us . . . ."

"My father replies that we are made to live here. We need air to breathe, water to drink, we suffocate without air and water: so why go?"

"For the same reason that makes us bring children into the world. Because we're afraid of death and darkness, and because we want to see our image reflected and perpetuated to immortality. We don't want to die, but death is there, and because it's there we give birth to children who'll give birth to other children and so on to infinity. And this way we are handed down to eternity. Don't let us forget this: that the Earth can die, explode, the Sun can go out, will go out. And if the Sun dies, if the Earth dies, if our race dies, then so will everything die that we have done up to that moment. Homer will die, Michelangelo will die, Galileo, Leonardo, Shakespeare, Einstein will die, all those will die who now are not dead because we are alive, we are thinking of them, we are carrying them within us. And then every single thing, every memory, will hurtle down into the void with us. So let us save them, let us save ourselves. Let us prepare ourselves to escape, to continue life and rebuild our cities on other planets: we shall not long be of this Earth! And if we really fear the darkness, if we really fight against it, then, for the good of all, let us take our rockets, let us get well used to the great cold and heat, the no water, the no oxygen, let us become Martians on Mars, Venusians on Venus, and when Mars and Venus die, let us go to the other solar systems, to Alpha Centauri, to wherever we manage to go, and let us forget the Earth. Let us forget our solar system and our body, the form it used to have, let us become no matter what, lichens, insects, balls of fire, no matter what, all that matters is that somehow life should continue, and the knowledge of what we were and what we did and learned: the knowledge of Homer and Michelangelo, of Galileo, Leonardo, Shakespeare, of Einstein! And the gift of life will continue."

So he said, Father. And to me it sounded like a most beautiful prayer. Even now as I try to repeat it with words like the words he used, and I can't make it quite the same, it still sounds to me like a most beautiful prayer: infinitely more sacred than the prayers my mother taught me as a child, making the sign of the cross. Perhaps because he spoke it in a low voice, his eyes half shut. This man who rides a bicycle and doesn't possess TV. Perhaps because he kept his head lowered, he no longer seemed like himself, but like a priest who recites the Pater Noster and believes in it. Perhaps because I was pricked with guilt toward you, and was seeking a great justification, a forgiveness, the very acceptance of this man's ideas meant betraying you, Father. Later I would have accepted them very much less. Like a pendulum that never hangs straight but always swings, from one doubt to another, I would even have rejected them and turned more than once to you. But the taste of that prayer always remained with me. I have it still.

3.

I couldn't sleep. That demon with the innocent eyes had played with my nerves, stretching them, testing their resistance, flaying them. And now they were lying in a tangle of twisted string, too tired to face the effort of going to sleep, incapable of telling my brain: That's enough now, stop thinking and leave her in peace. My thoughts rushed onward, only slightly slowed by a little blonde shouting: "Dad, I'm hungry."

The little blonde had come in uttering her cry at the end of the prayer. Wrenched out of his mysticism, no longer a priest but an American father, Bradbury had obediently stood up, observing that he was hungry too, I must be hungry too, all blond boys and girls must be hungry, so we would eat. The meal had been peaceful, enlivened by trivial chatter about things on which we found ourselves happily in agreement: love of old books, antipathy toward critics, inability to appreciate today's Picasso. Of old books he said that they were like wine, with the passing of time they changed in taste and smell, so that he was able to tell the year a book had been published by giving it a little lick and sniffing it. Of critics he said that they are nearly always unsuccessful writers, and consequently sour, you can keep on good terms with them only if you accept their bad advice: he didn't accept it and so they took no notice of him. Of Picasso he said that the older he gets the worse he paints, some of his pictures are real messes, but nobody says so for fear of seeming ignorant, and the world goes on kidding itself that his paintings are really very beautiful. A peaceful meal, in short, without any reference to lichen and balls of fire. But at the door, while Maggie was getting ready to take me back to my hotel (she does drive a car), the subject had cropped up again.

"We've certainly said a mouthful, eh, Miss Fallaci?"

"Yes, Mr. Bradbury. And I feel a bit the worse for wear."

"But why? They are things that should make you feel happy, and stronger, and braver."

"What? The thought that it falls to us of all people, the privilege of continuing the miracle of existence? If it's a privilege at all, then it's a very tragic privilege. A very tragic responsibility."

"Glorious, not tragic."

"Tragic, Mr. Bradbury. The most tragic that the human race can imagine. God! To renounce the body, the form we have, to take on a body and a form that we can't even imagine . . ."

"Listen, it isn't such a great form, not when you look at it closely. Have you ever wondered what a bug would think of it if a bug could think? Or a bird?"

"I have wondered. And I've concluded that we don't present a very fascinating sight. Quite possibly they find it very revolting, this vertical octopus full of tentacles and holes. A bird is far more attractive than we are. But we're used to it, aren't we? To being like this. And I don't feel ready to turn into a bird, or a bug, or lichen."

"None of us are ready. Nor shall we ever be. But that's our destiny, all the same: to change. We're changing already, physically, psychologically, spiritually, whether you like it or not. Change comes slowly, as slowly as spring turns to summer to autumn to winter. You never realize the exact moment when spring becomes summer: we get up one morning and it's hot, summer has come while we were sleeping."

"Ray! Ray, please! It's midnight," his wife was complaining.

"O.K., Maggie. O.K. I tell you what we'll do, Miss Fallaci: you come back tomorrow and we'll have another little chat. At nine, at eight, before we go to the beach."

"Ray! Oh, no! Nooo!"

Nice Maggie. Nice and full of patience: you need a lot of patience to love an intelligent man. And courage too. She convinced me of this as she drove me back.

"Miss Fallaci, there's something I want to say to you."

"Yes, Mrs. Bradbury."

"While you two were talking, I was listening. I've never heard Ray say those things. Never, in the twenty years we've known each other. I've read the same things, more or less, in the books he writes, but I've never actually heard them. It kind of shocked me."

"Me too, Mrs. Bradbury."

"Kind of frightened me."

"Me too, Mrs. Bradbury."

"But do you think some of it might be true?"

"Yes, I do."

"Heavens. And we'll turn into lichen?"

"If things go the way he says, I think we will."

"Well, I don't like the idea at all. And so one day they'll make us leave: Up, quick, the Earth's exploding, we must get away, and they'll take us who knows where. And so one day we'll arrive who knows where and we'll manage by turning into lichen . . ."

And so I couldn't sleep. I kept thinking about the lichen and the things he'd said and I couldn't sleep. "And if the Sun dies, if the Earth dies, if our race dies . . ." Strange, Father, but I'd never thought about the death of the Earth, of the Sun. I'd thought about my own, and about the death of the people I love, but not about the death of the Earth and the Sun. I'd always thought of them as immortal because they'd been there for billions of years before me and they'd be there for billions of years after me. But not even they are immortal, even they will die. Soon, very soon, if you think that billions of years are nothing to the Sun and the Earth, like the difference between ourselves and a butterfly: to us twenty-four hours seem very short, but to a butterfly who lives from one dawn to the next, twenty-four hours are a lifetime. Soon, very soon . . . together with the mountains and the seas, the valleys and the deserts, the sounds and the colors, the days and the nights, and all that we call the riches of the world. And at the thought that the Sun would die, that the Earth would die together with the riches of the world, I felt empty, wild with anger, Father, as I do when I think that you will die, that Mother will die, that I will die. I have never understood death. I have never understood those who say that death is normal, death is logical, everything comes to an end and therefore so shall I. I have always thought death is unjust, illogical, that we shouldn't have to die just because we are born. Nor have I ever understood those who say you don't really die, you become something different, you become a tuft of grass and you nourish a fish, a bird, another man, so then you live through them. I've never understood it because, for me, to live means to move with this body and this mind. Then what do I care about becoming a Martian on Mars, a Venusian on Venus, an Andromedian on Andromeda? Are they ugly, these tentacles we call arms, legs, fingers, toes? So what do I care if they are ugly? They're all I know and I don't want anything else. I want these arms and legs, I want this Earth. Is this Earth a prison? All right. I'm quite comfortable in it, it is warm and safe like the maternal womb. And you were right, Father. Right? But you can't stay in your mother's womb forever. If you stay there forever, you die, and she dies too. You stay there until you're made, and when you're made she spits you out, expels you by force into a world you never even imagined. Maybe you didn't want to see it, you were comfortable crouching there in that womb, in that warmth. You didn't have to make the effort to eat, to sleep, your mother did everything for you, her skin, her tissues protected you more than a shell, more than the atmosphere that surrounds the Earth and repels meteorites. And yet you had to leave that womb, you had to accept the shape of a body you had not imagined, to eat in a new way, to sleep in distress, to protect yourself in grief. And this change was no abuse, nor was it any cruelty: it was the only way of continuing your life. And the only way the Earth can continue her life is by spitting you out, vomiting you up into the sky, beyond the atmosphere into worlds you cannot imagine and which in their turn will spit you out into the other worlds, cold and hostile. Where was it I had read about the birth of a baby? That article I had almost learned by heart. In *Life*. By Albert Rosenfeld . . . After the baby has spent his appointed 266-or-so days in the tranquillity of his mother's womb, he is abruptly shoved out by a 100-pound propulsive force into the hostile world, full of startlingly unfamiliar conditions. The first shock is the drop in temperature from the mother's cozy 98° F. to a room temperature some 20° lower. His eyes, which have been open to nothing but darkness, are suddenly assailed by light. He moves from a wet world to a dry one . . . But this was the story of a journey to Mars, to Venus, to other planets, the story of our destiny that is to be born, to keep on being born, in a thousand different ways and always in the same way. This was what Ray Bradbury had said. So it was Ray Bradbury who was right, not you, Father. Having reached this conclusion, I found some peace, I fell asleep at last, awoke next morning bursting with curiosity, and soon found myself hastening back to him in a taxi, like a pin drawn to a magnet.

"Mother, she's back, the-one-who-keeps-him-talking-and-he-likes-it."

"Mother, will we be able to leave at noon?"

"Good morning, Miss Fallaci."

"Good morning, Mrs. Bradbury."

"Maggie, my dear, will you make us some coffee?"

"Coffee for the gasbags!"

"That was very rude. I'll spank you for that!"

"Father! Mother spanked me!"

"Can't we ever have a moment's peace and quiet in this house?"

The house thundered with cries, thumps, invocations, joy, youth, and the blondes were all ready to go except for Maggie, who was still wandering around in her hair-curlers with the bewildered air that means

I-can't-stand-it-any-more-I'll-go-mad-I-tell-you. The trip to the beach
had been planned for some time, and to judge by the paraphernalia
scattered all over the living room—dozens of ties, sunsuits, shoes,
pounds of creams and oils—you would have thought the Bradburys
were preparing to go to Mars to perpetuate the miracle of creation,
Amen. With all this going on, it was quite clear that there was no corner suitable for us to talk in. We took refuge in the cellar—and how
difficult it is to free oneself of certain burdens, Father.

As long as I live I shall never be able to free myself of those sinister
angels of marble and bronze and wood and canvas, sculpted and drawn
and painted, frozen in the act of puffing out their cheeks and blowing the
trumpet; of those melancholy saints, enraged, transfixed, depicted at the
moment of macabre martyrdom, St. Sebastian with an arrow through
his neck, St. Lucia with her eyes placed on a tray; of those Madonnas
dressed in blue and white, always caught in the act of suckling the
Child; of those Christs crucified, naked or clothed and with a heart in
the left hand. As a child I would enter the church, and as well as the
damp and the cold and the smell of sweat and incense and the whisper-
ings of the penitents forced by the priest to recite thirty Pater Nosters,
forty Ave Marias, fifty Salve Reginas, ask the Lord's forgiveness,
shame on you, I would be submerged in the nightmare of saints and
angels, Christs and Madonnas, would stand hypnotized and stare at that
heart, those eyes, but how had Jesus managed to take out his heart and
hold it in his hand, how had St. Lucia managed to tear out her eyes and
put them on a tray, and the paganism of a mistaken religion would
crush me like a cloak of lead. And so I would run to the altar, and
kneeling there beneath the candles, the lace, the jewels, the precious
cloths, the shimmer of gold and silver, the flowers I would have liked
to steal to take to my mother, I would force myself to believe in the
beautiful legends and mouth a Pater Noster, Ave Maria, Salve Regina,
Requiem Aeternam, full of false gratitude to Our Lord who in seven
days had created the Earth, first the waters, then the plants, then the
living creatures, then man and then woman: but there always came
a moment when unbelief blossomed again, a skepticism toward the
great magic, and with it terror. The terror of being punished, of sinking into Hell, of burning, and my hands would sweat, my knees would
tremble, forgive me God, but how could You create in seven days,
how could You have done it, and I would be lost in such absurdities.
I never told anyone, not even you. I never had the courage. And so
I grew up in the fear of angels, saints, the Virgin Mary, Child

Christs and Christs Crucified, of Paradise, Hell and Purgatory, of what they call Good and what they call Evil, and these burdens stayed with me, stuck to me, even when I wanted to thrust them away, to shake them off, like a fingernail that keeps on growing, growing, no matter how often you cut it, until the day you die: and isn't it like this for everyone? Isn't it like this for you too? Your hobby is mosaics. And what do you always produce with those little bits of yellow red green and blue glass, Father? Always angels, saints, Child Christs and Christs Crucified, Madonnas. You expend your effort for them, never for a cloud, a flower or a bird. In that cellar in Cheviot Drive, Cheviot Hills, I was finally able to vomit out to somebody my awful nightmare, my dream of liberation. The rockets, the spacecraft— do you find it grotesque?—they can serve also for that.

"Ready, Mr. Bradbury?"

"Of course."

"It's this, Mr. Bradbury. Without a doubt the space age is taking us further away from the old structures of religion. The beautiful fairy tale of Adam and Eve is no longer enough even for a child. The affirmation of the Old Testament, *God created Man in His own image,* will be contradicted ipso facto as soon as we come face to face with intelligent creatures physically quite different from ourselves. The great adventure on which we have embarked, whether by our own will or by fate, leads us to wonder whether we are breaking the shackles of religion as well as the force of gravity."

He took off like a rocket.

"My dear, it was not the space age but the train that began to take us away from the old structures of religion. The train, the reinforced concrete, the cranes, the stupendous heresies we committed when we came to settle in America and didn't like the location of those mountains and rivers and cut down the mountains and diverted the rivers. And we didn't like the voids which had now taken the place of the mountains and the rivers, so we put up skyscrapers in them; we didn't like the time and space given us by nature, so we built supersonic planes, we learned to break the sound barrier. All these are blasphemous activities and as soon as we learned to perform miracles we blasphemed. But of course it changes everything. Just think of the wonderful heresy we commit, pulling God by the coattails every time a rocket goes up. Wow! We're playing with the elements of the universe like Frankenstein, but nobody, not even the Catholic Church, dares to say, like Frankenstein's assistant:

"You're getting involved in things that are better left to God." When Galileo said: "The Earth revolves," the Catholic Church threw him in prison; it took centuries before the priests would admit yes, in fact, as far as revolving goes, it revolves. But today the Pope declares: "God does not forbid man to go into space, God is happy for us to visit other worlds." Isn't that blasphemy? Any Pope in the past would have lost his job in half an hour for saying such a thing! Naturally it follows that this is only a slight concession, a feeble attempt at a rough-and-ready conciliation of dogmas with reality. Needless to say, if they don't change their reasoning, all the churches will lose their jobs. They'll lose them through their own stupidity, because we can't do without religion. If every religion disappeared tomorrow morning, we'd have to invent others, or others would have to appear spontaneously, to explain the new facts to us. Do I make myself clear? The scientists give us facts, but they never give us the reason behind the facts. We can't exist without the reason. When a man is dying of an incurable disease and you don't know what to do, whether to treat him and prolong his suffering or kill him so that he'll suffer no longer, the scientists don't make any suggestions regarding your decision, they only give you the means to treat him or kill him. I know about this because I had this dilemma six years ago with my father, it was the most awful dilemma of my life. Science offered me the means of killing him painlessly or treating him painfully, and that was all it offered me. I didn't know what to do. No, we can't do without religion. But by religion I don't mean what the churches offer us today. That's no longer enough. Nor are Darwins enough, nor the astronauts enough. We have to formulate new structures in accordance with the new times, for vaster seas. Be quiet, don't interrupt me. So I was saying that it's no longer enough to explain the origin of the Earth, of our solar system, of our galaxy, this negligible speck in the universe. We have to go further, to the origins of the origins of the origins, to a moment in the history of the universe that was billions and billions of light-years ago, when matter reproduced itself and learned to smell, to touch, to see, to taste the miracle of its own existence. It's no longer enough to concern ourselves with the Earth, to ask ourselves who created the Earth; we are alive in space, not only on the Earth. It's no longer enough to say that everything is God, the air, the stones, the void. God has grown curious and is breaking the silence, wanting to understand Himself, learn where He came from. It's no longer enough to say that God created the universe. We have to ask ourselves who created God. Who created God?"

From the floor above us came a great thud, like something exploding, and the house shook. I suddenly thought of Charlie Chaplin, the night when he flings open the window of his room in London and shouts at the sky: "God! You don't exist!" and is answered by a streak of lightning which comes crashing through the window into the room. Then I closed my eyes and waited, cringing; it would take the lightning a moment to reach the cellar. One . . . two . . . three. On three the piercing cry of a blonde reached us.

"Fa-ather! Susan has fallen off the wardro-obe!"

Bradbury got up and ran to Susan. Between the cries and the sobs could be heard the argument inspired by divine punishment.

"How many times have I told you not to get up on the wardrobe?"

"Why are you scolding her? Can't you see she's dead?"

"Oh, she's just unconscious."

"She's not even unconscious, she's faking. The hypocrite."

"Susan. Oh! Susan! Baby!"

"If your baby would stop climbing onto the wardrobe and if you could watch her . . . !"

"If you weren't always talking in the cellar!"

"I stay in the cellar because there's never any room for me anywhere else!"

"It's not true. You stay in the cellar to talk about God!"

"Susan!"

"Father!"

"She's opening her eyes."

"Miracle! She's alive again!"

Bradbury came down again, heaving a sigh.

"Where were we?"

"We had reached a point of considerable imprudence, Mr. Bradbury."

He burst into delighted laughter. The better to laugh, he leaped up, banging his head against the water pipes.

"That's number two!"

"Perhaps we'd better change the subject, Mr. Bradbury. We Italians have a proverb: Things happen in threes."

"We have it in America too," he grieved as he rubbed his head.

"And the third thunderbolt might land on me."

"You're innocent," he said, still rubbing his head.

"No, because I was going to answer your question."

"What question?" He went on rubbing his head.

"The question: Who created God?"

"Ah!" he said with scant interest.

He had given himself a hard knock.

"Mr. Bradbury, I was going to say: man. It's man who created God. Or created the notion of God. We can't do without God, and when He isn't there we invent Him. Yes, Mr. Bradbury. Man created God!"

He was off like a rocket again.

"No! I go further than that. I say that *we* are God. We excrements of the universe, we sparks in the infinite. There's no point in searching for God elsewhere, because God is ourselves, and I don't accept the idea of God as something superhuman, transcendental, something incorporeal playing with his toys, stars and men. I don't accept the idea of God as something far removed. I see God as something that grows and expands through senses and thoughts, that wants to be mortal in order to die and be born again, and wants to move on, to push ahead with the human race, to spread and expand it throughout the whole cosmos! God is this flesh, this voice. That's what I mean when I say that God has grown curious, when I speak of matter that can reproduce itself. And if the churches don't work around to saying this, or something like this, the churches won't survive: they'll collapse, together with their lovely fairy tales of Adam and Eve, of man made 'in His image and after His likeness,' of the Earth created in seven days."

I got in quick as he paused for a second.

"Mr. Bradbury, have you ever discussed these things with priests and theologians?"

"Once, years ago, when I was writing *Martian Chronicles*—the chapter about the balls of fire, the ancient Martians who are in the form of light balls of pale blue fire. Remember the story of Father Stone who was stubbornly looking for sin on Mars, and he looked for it but he couldn't find it, while Father Peregrine wasn't looking for it but was saying that there is no Evil on Mars, there's not even any sin, because the Martians are good—do you remember? Remember when, to prove his theories to Father Stone, Father Peregrine flung himself off a mountain, saying the balls of fire will save me, and in fact they did save him? Well. As a boy I was educated by the Baptists, alas, and this business of Original Sin has always stuck in my gullet without enlightening me in the least. Have you ever understood why, according to the Catholics, we come into the world stained with Original Sin? No? Neither have I, it's illogical. Eve picks the apple, she eats it, and so I am born damned. What's her apple got to do with me? Anyway I wanted to know the viewpoint of a Catholic on the following problem: Did the Martians commit Original Sin or did they not? I telephoned a priest in Beverly Hills. Dear Father, good morning, how are you, I'm fine, you're fine, may I come and see you about a rather unusual matter? He said yes, of course, so I went and I asked him: Listen, Father, how would you act if you landed on Mars and found intelligent creatures in the form of balls of fire? Would you think you ought to save them or would you think they were saved already? Wow! That's a hell of a fine question! the Father exclaimed. And he told me what he would do. In short, what I make Father Peregrine do. He was young and intelligent, on the ball, that priest. We talked for a whole day, shut up inside that sacristy, and he never once threatened to have me burned in St. Peter's Square."

"Tell me, Mr. Bradbury. Did you discuss Christianity as a code for living? Did you consider whether, leaving theology aside, the essence of Christianity would have survived there? Whether it could have been applied there? Did you discuss whether the commandment that says *Thou shalt not kill* would be valid on other planets in the millions of years to come? Did you discuss whether love, forgiveness and charity would also have some meaning on Venus and Mars and Alpha Centauri?"

And suddenly this child of joy grew sad. He forgot the Easter bells, forgot his wows bursting like thousands of fireworks, forgot his sense of humor and his smiles, and was suddenly an old man disappointed in advance in his unbounded optimism, in his blind faith for mankind.

"Yes. Naturally. We decided that it would be very, very difficult. Even impossible. Let us suppose, Father, I said to him, that you are an Earth man and I am a Venusian. Now, I'm a Venusian and I'm a thinking creature, good and righteous and vastly more intelligent than you. I haven't the remotest intention of hurting you. But I am made like a huge spider—ten feet tall, coal black, all covered with hair, with a lot of big legs and three eyes. Now, Father, you've landed on Venus and I'm looking at you with my three eyes. Just looking at you. What do you do? He answered me as I would have answered the same question: "Bradbury, do you think I would welcome your curiosity and your suspicion? Bradbury, do you think I'd believe in your human kindness? And that I would not therefore unload my radioactive gun on you? And that I wouldn't then hunt down your brothers and your children to exterminate them before they frightened me?" And he was right, by God, he was right. Why, we can't even believe in the humanity of a Negro! We haven't even grasped that there's a creature identical to ourselves locked away inside that black skin! We let Buddhists burn themselves. And more. We've exterminated the American Indian and even today we make movies called westerns that never show a decent Indian who doesn't deserve to be butchered. We kill off dolphins even though we know they have a brain like ours and a language like ours, all they lack is legs to escape on, fingers to fire a harpoon at us! And you'd fool yourself that we could act like Christians toward creatures made like insects and serpents, monsters covered with scales? No, no, no. There's only one way for the concept of Christianity to resist."

"What way, Mr. Bradbury?"

"The way I said before—by convincing ourselves that humanity is not just a body with two arms and two legs. Humanity is an idea, a way of acting, something that moves and reasons, whatever its outward form: whether spider or lichen or balls of fire! Damn these mosquitoes!"

And he squashed a mosquito on his arm. There's no harm in that, Father, I agree: I've always thought that Elijah delicately refrained from killing the fly not because he thought the fly was human but because squashing flies gave him the creeps. However, he squashed it, that wretched mosquito that was only looking at him, and no celestial thunderbolt struck him, or me, to punish us. Every angel in Paradise is prepared to let a child fall off a wardrobe when two sinners take the name of God in vain; not one angel in Paradise will cause you to bang your head against the water pipes because you've squashed a mosquito. Or perhaps the Lord God realized that we weren't wicked, this Bradbury and I, we were only trying to reason it all out a bit. After this I said goodbye to Maggie and the blondes, and to Bradbury, took a taxi and went away into the cloud of smoke.

In front of a church at Beverly Hills there was a notice which read:

CHURCH OUT OF USE
TO BE SOLD OR RENTED

I asked the taxi driver if this was a joke in bad taste and he said no, it wasn't a joke, it was very fashionable to live in ex-churches in Los Angeles, and in any city in America I'd see notices like it. He'd live in it himself if he could, the trouble was that churches are expensive and it costs lots of money to heat them in the winter.

4.

"My name's Herb Rosen. Just call me HR. Or just R."

"O.K., R. Call me OF or just F."

"Fine, F. What do you know about ST?"

"Nothing, R. ST has never been my strong point."

"Bad, F. Very bad. I'll have to tell you a bit about ST."

"Oh, please don't trouble, R."

"How else will you understand the STL?"

"Quite right, R. Then, can I have a little HO?"

"Do you mean H_2O?"

"I thought HO would be shorter."

"Good, F! Gotta abbreviate. Girls, bring a little HO."

Great confusion ensued. The girls were used to wasting time saying H_2O and they didn't understand what HO was. R had to explain that HO was water abbreviated and they said there was no abbreviated water, there was only ordinary water: we lost more time than if we'd said: "A glass of water, please." However, I eventually had my glass of water and I was ready for a lesson on ST (Space Technology), which, I'd better explain, Father, is the science concerned with launching a craft into space, keeping it there, making it fly, bringing it back down to Earth. I was ready and willing. Bradbury had given me a second injection of faith and this morning the pendulum of my uncertainties was still on his side, not yours. I could even face HR, with his wicked-looking face, his icy eyes, his toothbrush mustache, that were enough to frighten a Nazi. I could even like the STL (Space Technology Laboratories), a hallucinating box of black glass beside which the building of the Montecatini in Milan seems pure rococo; black glass takes the place of bricks, cement and steel, and in the STL there are no walls or windows or roofs. Only that black glass that no lightning could shatter or fire burn, and no spy could penetrate. It holds the secrets of the journey to the Moon, and what goes on inside it is a guarded mystery. Technicians who've been working there for years do not know how their work is to be used. Anyone who does know runs the risk, by the most harmless indiscretion, of being accused of treason. Armed police follow you all the time, the most you can see are the electronic brains that in five minutes produce answers which five thousand mathematicians wouldn't be able to produce in thirty years. The people here talk the same language—a code composed of abbreviations. Words waste time, Father, and time is precious. Every minute costs millions of dollars.

". . . and finally, the trajectories. Do I make myself clear, F? Obviously it is the job of the electronic brain to provide the trajectories."

"May I see one, R?"

"But you're inside one, F!"

"Inside?"

"Inside. This room is an electronic brain, the walls, the floor and the ceiling are its cranium. These metal boxes are the membrane that supports its gray matter. Batteries, gears, pistons, electric wires, levers are its blood vessels and nerves. Can't you hear the sound? That's him thinking, working."

"Heavens, it makes me feel like a bacterium."

"You are. Compared with him, you're a wretched bacterium. He can solve any problem in differential and integral calculus. Can you? He can correct any error in the course of a spacecraft, keep it going in the right direction and stop it. He can learn by heart hundreds of books of mathematics, physics, astrophysics, chemistry, meteorology. He can do simultaneous translation into any language, compose music, write poetry. He's so much more intelligent than we that if he had a tongue and some saliva he'd spit in our faces as soon as look at us, he'd reduce us to being his slaves."

The ice had melted and R's eyes were gleaming with a violent carnal passion, looking at the tangle of gears and wires as if they were the most beautiful woman in the world, stretched out naked on a bed.

"Tell me, R, if you asked this brain to learn by heart the whole of the Library of Congress, would he do it?"

"Of course he'd do it."

"And how long would he take to learn the *Iliad* and the *Odyssey?*"

"Ten or fifteen minutes."

"And *The Divine Comedy?*"

"Fifteen or twenty."

"And the whole of Shakespeare?"

"About the same. Why?"

"Because, since the Library of Congress is destructible, and anyway not big enough to contain everything even on microfilm, it mightn't be a bad idea to use the brain to save certain riches."

"Riches? Nonsense, you mean. The whole idea is a lot of nonsense too."

"A lot of nonsense?"

"Obviously. It's uneconomical. You know how much it costs to make him memorize a physics textbook?"

"And isn't Shakespeare maybe worth as much as a physics textbook?"

"A physics textbook is useful, indispensable. What's so useful about Shakespeare?"

"Isn't he?"

"About as useless as the Parthenon or the Sistine Chapel or anything else that came before technology."

"Useless?"

"Useless. But don't worry: technology is ready to wipe it all out."

"All?"

"All: laws, systems, cities. Do you really think we can tolerate such ghosts much longer? We'll get the world clean again like you clean a saucepan—like that. We'll knock everything down and start again from the beginning. We've had enough of those madmen who want to turn the Earth into a museum. Enough of museums. Enough of the mania for old rubbish. If we hadn't burned Rome down, Rome wouldn't be there now. If we hadn't pulverized Hiroshima, Hiroshima wouldn't be there now. Away with the dust and the rot and the stink."

"R . . . HR . . . Rosen . . . Mr. Rosen! Do you know what you're saying?"

"We'll destroy and build again. We'll bring death to remake life; existence is conditioned to die, men die to make room for other men, if we hadn't uprooted the trees New York and San Francisco and the other big cities wouldn't exist today. There wouldn't be any churches and skyscrapers. Fact is the skyscrapers are old too, the vertical development of Manhattan is increasingly antiquated and, to make a long story short, New York has to be wiped out. It isn't practical."

"Mr. Rosen! What the hell are you saying?"

"San Francisco has to be wiped out. It isn't logical."

"What the hell are you saying?"

"Paris has to be wiped out. It's a mess."

"What the hell are you saying?"

"Florence has to be wiped out. It's not rational."

"No! Not Florence, by God!"

"You surely don't want to hang on to those narrow streets and crooked houses? New streets. New houses. New churches. That's what we need. Charges of dynamite."

Charges of dynamite . . . Do you remember, Father? That white horse coming down the road from Rome in the middle of the night, his hoofs sliding on the asphalt like drops of water on glass that slide suddenly to a spot and then go sliding on again. On the horse rode a German officer, and his head was nodding as he was very sleepy. Only when the horse was on the point of falling did he raise his head, assume that erect cruel attitude, warning of what he was about to do. Behind the horse came a mule pulling a small gun, and along the pavements, hugging close to the walls, the soldiers filed past, with bulging kit bags, tommy-guns on their arms, dragging boots. They were covered with mud and shame, they were thirsty, and under every window they cried: "Wasser! Water! Wasser!" The windows remained shut and they smashed them with their guns and then they would go on walking, dragging along in their boots straight down toward the bridge. Our beautiful bridge, the most beautiful bridge in the world.

". . . What's all this cult of stones and cracks and decrepit collections? Clean it up, baby. Be logical. Charges of dynamite. And . . ."

The day before, you knew, they had mined it. They had moved the people out of the nearby houses without letting them take their belongings, and then they had mined it. The officer on the white horse was leading the last group of the rear guard. When he had gone past, and the mule with the gun had gone past, and the soldiers shouting "Wasser! Water!" had gone past, then one hand two hands three hands would light the fuses and our bridge would blow up. Our beautiful bridge, the most beautiful bridge in the world. It was the night between the 10th and the 11th of August and the city was about to change hands. The curfew had started at five in the afternoon, and for hours, for centuries, we were locked in behind those windows that looked directly onto the street, not far from the bridge. Mother was praying, you were smoking in silence. When the first load of dynamite exploded, a mirror fell down and shattered. But the noise was so great that the mirror shattered without a sound.

". . . and wars also serve the purpose. What was Coventry? A cold nest of lice. Now the cathedral even has central heating. Charges of dynamite, that's what we need."

More than a noise, a rumbling roar. The roar of a hundred thunderclaps together bursting and drawing away and coming back and bursting again. Your friend Gomez recorded it and kept up a running commentary. I still cry when I listen to that record, Father. "But of all sounds the most tragic is that of the mines. Our microphone isn't always able to contain it and the recording needle leaps in terror . . ." A roar. "Which bridge will have blown up in the night? The sky above the Arno is all red . . ." Another roar. And another. And another, and another, and another, and another, and the voice of Radio London: "The Americans, supported by British units of the Guards, entered the outskirts of the city of Florence early yesterday. Advance patrols pushing forward to make contact with the enemy have established that five of the six bridges over the Arno had been destroyed. One of them, the bridge of Santa Trinità, was one of the most perfect examples of Renaissance architecture." Our beautiful bridge. Now it was lying in fragments of stone, and the statues of the Seasons had been hurled down to the bottom of the river, among the fish and the mud. They fished them out again one day, but Spring was decapitated and her head was never found, it doesn't exist any more. We have rebuilt the bridge, all new and clean. But Spring's head doesn't exist any more. And our beautiful bridge, too, doesn't exist any more.

". . . they'll bring well-being, health, life."

"I beg your pardon, R. I wasn't following you."

"I was saying that charges of dynamite will bring well-being, health, life."

"You're joking, surely, R?"

"I'm not joking at all: if the bridges and churches aren't demolished, how can we build new ones? Where will we find room? I used to have the kind of house you like, with a sugarloaf roof, a porch, fireplaces for log fires. My grandmother left it to me. I had it demolished and in its place I now have a modern house in Japanese-Swedish style."

"You're a fine fool, HR."

"You're the one who's a fool, dear F. You're living in the past and you're blind. I'm living in the future and looking far ahead."

"Leaders sometimes come to a bad end, HR. They cross the bridge on their white horse and often finish up defeated, sometimes hanged."

"You're the one they'll hang, F. And the ones who'll hang you will be the ones you think are on your side, because you offer poetry and I offer comfort, you offer dreams and I offer reality, what you offer is useless and what I offer is useful. You're the one who's defeated, I'm the victor. If this isn't so, why should you get so excited at the idea of going to the Moon?"

All around us the brain was thinking, thinking, with a murmur of pistons and gears and wheels, and I suddenly felt that he was listening to us with irritation. "Let's go out," I whispered faintly to HR. "We're disturbing him, we're distracting him." I was ready to enter the future, to enter the Apollo spacecraft.

5.

I was shaking when they shut me inside. I felt caught in a trap, resigned to death, as you feel when you're lying on the operating table and above you are faces masked with gauze and somebody sticks a needle in your arm that sends you off into a sleep from which you might never awaken and above you there's a cold blinding white light.

There was a cold blinding white light here too, and even with the greatest effort I couldn't convince myself that I was still on Earth, in the big building that contains the Apollo spacecraft, in a city called Downey, in the state of California. Below me was the rocket; the spacecraft was attached to the top of this rocket; do you see how I mean, Father? Countdown begins and the numbers get quickly, implacably lower. On zero great flames roar out of the rocket, and the spacecraft starts madly vibrating, oscillating, then an apocalyptic thrust hurls me into the sky and I go up and up, with a slab of lead cutting off my breath, crushing my chest, and the Earth grows distant, by now I am in space with no above or below, no days or nights, no sounds or silences, no beginning or end, up and up, or down and down, on toward the distant satellite with no air or water, with no green or blue, no animals or plants, nothing of what to us is life and gives us life. For three long days and three long nights that are more than days or nights I travel on in a nothingness that is like standing still, until the Earth becomes a moon and the Moon an earth, nearer and nearer, by now so near that I am able to see its crust, its smooth expanses, its hollow craters, its sharp-pointed mountains, and nobody there to help me. Neither man nor monster nor anyone at all.

"Let me out!" I yelled. "For mercy's sake, let me out!"

They opened the hatch, laughing, and I was out in the big shed that contains the Apollo spacecraft that will carry three men directly to the Moon. It is a white cone, made of porcelain-enameled steel to resist great heat and great cold, not unlike the Martian spaceships of science-fiction films, and it is thirteen feet in diameter and nine and one-half feet high, with an entrance hatch, two portholes, made like a more spacious and larger version of the Gemini spacecraft, containing three seats and the controls. The controls are similar to those of jet planes. The seats are shaped like Egyptian sarcophagi sawed in half, or rather they are molds of the human body, with a cup to accommodate the head, a hollow to accommodate the spine, two grooves to accommodate the legs as far as the knee, and another two grooves to accommodate the legs from knee to foot. The mold is made in the horizontal position for the length of the body, in vertical position for the length of the legs as far as the knee, and again in horizontal position for the part from the knee to the foot. To understand it better, suppose you sat on a chair with its backrest lying on the floor: your back and your arms would be on the floor too, but your legs as far as the knee would be perpendicular, and from the knee to the foot they would be parallel to the floor. So, encased in their seats, fastened into their space suits, the astronauts look at the nose of the cone: this position helps them to withstand the thrust of lift-off, the invisible lead weight that crushes the body when the rocket breaks through the atmosphere and the force of gravity becomes six times greater than normal. Up in space, however, the astronauts are sitting as you do in a chair in its normal position: in fact the Apollo travels with the nose of the cone pointing directly ahead. There are three astronauts in the Apollo. Their seats are in a row, one next to the other; the third seat is movable and can be turned into a couch. When it's moved, there's enough room inside the spacecraft for a man to stand upright. In fact there is very very little room: not much more than there is in a coffin. You must beware of saying so, however. The fact is that Russian spacecraft are much more spacious and comfortable, and the Americans have a real complex about things being spacious and comfortable. Their roads are more spacious and comfortable, their houses, their automobiles, their shoes, their doubts, their ideas are too. But their spacecraft are neither spacious nor comfortable, and this causes them humiliation. On the other hand, they can't build them any more spacious because this would make them infinitely heavier, so that to lift them off they would need a better fuel, and they don't have this better fuel.

The building where they are constructing the Apollo belongs to a firm called North American Aviation's Space and Information Systems Division, which used to make only planes. Reduced war production was about to leave it on the brink of bankruptcy, but the space adventure has restored its prosperity. North American boasts the biggest contract ever given by the government to a single firm: $934,500,000. It employs eleven thousand workers and employees, and has been working on the Apollo spacecraft since 1961—a mere trifle, I was told by a proud official, if one remembered that it took more than six years to make the atom bomb, twelve years to develop television, fifteen years to perfect radar, thirty-five for radio, fifty-six for the telephone, a hundred and twelve for photography. Naturally I knew that at North American they're building the Apollo and not the Saturn rocket, that the Apollo is only a small part of the giant which will leave Cape Kennedy and the only part that will come back to Earth. No, I didn't know? But I couldn't be serious. Pale and overcome with indignation, the official stared at me as I had stared at HR when he'd been wanting to destroy Florence, Paris, London, New York. Clearly, he concluded, we'd have to start again from the beginning. I'd better follow him to the projection room, where he'd show me the animated film *Apollo Mission*. I followed him, and now pay attention, Father, the film isn't simple.

Are you ready? Well then. It is dawn on a day in the future, and the three men are shut in up there, inside the cone, motionless and defenseless. The mastodontic rocket, the Saturn, is in position on the launch pad, soaring 360 feet above the ground. A round smooth skyscraper, painted white. At first glance you would think it was made in one piece, but in fact it consists of three different stages, each with its own engines and fuel, and each stage serves to give it an extra thrust. On top of the third stage is the spacecraft with the three men. Motionless, defenseless. Dawn on a day to come, here already. Do you see it? Do you feel it? It's cold. In Africa, in Australia, in the Hawaiian Islands, in the United States—wherever there is a control base everybody is pale before the electronic computers, the television screens, the radios. Countdown is getting near the end: minus six . . . minus five . . . minus four . . . minus three . . . minus two . . . minus one . . . zero . . . lift-off! Like a volcano suddenly awakening and belching forth hell, a cyclopic gush of flame bursts forth from the five engines, the Earth and the heavens shudder violently, the rocket is enveloped in boiling vapor. Slowly the skyscraper lifts off from the launch pad and rises, accelerating, streaking up into the sky. It is propelled by the engines of the first stage, five mouths of fire that burn for two and a half minutes: when the last drop of fuel has been sucked up, the two and a half minutes have passed, and the first stage is jettisoned and the second stage ignites. Another five mouths of fire burn for six and a half minutes, taking the now halved rocket into its correct orbit, to orbit the Earth. And by orbiting the Earth it gathers speed and now, there, now it's gathered enough speed, and the six and a half minutes have passed, the fuel in the second stage is finished too: the second stage is jettisoned, it falls away into the infinite, the third stage ignites. The rocket is even shorter now (can you see it as it drops off bit by bit in the sky?) and ready to enter the celestial corridor that will lead it straight to the Moon. In the Apollo spacecraft the astronauts are as taut as wires of steel: the Moon corridor is barely forty miles wide. One inexact calculation, one wrong maneuver, and they won't reach the Moon, they won't reach anywhere, they'll get lost in a void that leads only to the void.

Now they've entered the celestial corridor. They've made it, for the moment, and they're traveling at a speed never before experienced: twenty-five thousand miles every hour. They are flying along, light as butterflies, a tiny flame in the vast blackness, but now they are about to do something very difficult, something compared with which Glenn's green retro attitudes were child's play, Father. In five minutes, when the fuel in the third stage will also be finished, the third stage will separate and open itself like a book to free the LEM, which is the craft that will land on the Moon. Then the Apollo spacecraft must turn around and mate with it nose-to-nose: to take it with it, latched on to the nose of the cone. There now, the third stage is released and has opened. A curious object is emerging through the open hatches: a kind of box with four legs that end in a round disk with suckers. The astronauts call it the Bug, never LEM: because of its legs, it looks like a big spider. In the top of the spider's head there is a hole. And this is the hole into which the Apollo spacecraft must insert its nose, latching on to it to take it with it. Will it succeed? From the Earth come orders and instructions, growing feebler and feebler. Precious phrases are lost, crumbling in the darkness, and the three astronauts pursue them in vain. Good luck, Mr. Schirra. Good luck, Mr. Cooper. Good luck, Mr. Carpenter. Good luck, Mr. X, Mr. Y, whoever you are. We are praying for you. We've never been much good at praying, have we, Father? Even when they were blowing up those bridges we couldn't manage to pray: our lips were as mute as our minds. But this time we'll try it. I'll try it, at least.

Without deviating from its course, the Apollo turns around. It moves toward the Bug, waits for it. It noses into that hole, latches itself in. It turns around again and proceeds with that strange box, down down, or up up, for three days and three nights. Three Earth days, three Earth nights: there are neither days nor nights there, black is black by day or by night, when you switch on a light terrible dangers brush past you. Meteorites, for example. A meteorite as small as a pea would be enough to make a hole in the spacecraft: if that happens, the most they can do is leap out into space and try to repair it. So let us look at them as they leap out into space, these little men, dressed in silver spacesuits, oxygen cylinders strapped to their shoulders, their heads enclosed in Plexiglas helmets. They look like divers repairing a leak in a ship, they even float as if they were in water, and they have such courage, by God! And they have courage when they go back inside, Father, and each in turn takes off his spacesuit and flings himself down on the bed of their prison. Yes, the prison bed was terrible, the night spent waiting for a dawn that might not come, I know. You lay there on the bed and watched the door: if the door opened there would be no dawn for you. For many there was no dawn: they had barely lain down to try to sleep when the door opened, and when they stood them against the wall the guns fired like meteorites in the cosmos. I know. But this bed is terrible too: because they too are probably condemned to death. They too are in prison. Is it day, is it night on the distant ball they call Earth? On one side it will be day and on the other night, but then the night will become day and the day will become night. Here, though, the night is always night. With no yesterday and no tomorrow. You lie down on the bed and what do you say to your companions who remain at the controls? Good night? Good morning? Good afternoon? Good nothing. The man lies down on the bed, in silence, and stretches out. He shuts his eyes and dreams of yesterdays and tomorrows. He dreams of his house, of his woman between the sheets, of the Earth.

Not that dreaming is permitted, or rather, prudent. Dreaming tires the brain, and to become tired is suicide: there are too many things to do. On the first day the Earth's force of gravity reduces their speed by 6500 miles an hour: they must accelerate without losing too much fuel. On the second day the Earth's force of gravity slows them by only 1500 miles an hour. But on the third day the Moon's force of gravity begins to suck them and they have to decelerate so as not to plummet down on it. They have to glide gently nearer, so, enter its orbit, so, and release the Bug when they are sixty miles above the Moon, no sooner and no later. And now the moment has come for them to say goodbye and separate: one astronaut stays in the Apollo, the other two lower themselves into the Bug, the LEM. Good luck, comrade. Good luck, comrades. The trapdoor through which they've lowered themselves is closed, the two take their places in their new prison, before the new controls. Slowly they separate themselves from the Apollo spacecraft, then they descend to ten miles above the lunar surface to decide on the point of touch-down. That crater down there. It looks good, safe. The strange craft is buzzing and steering toward it. It is already only five miles now, four, three, two, one, it hovers and comes down like a helicopter, lands in the middle of the crater, and now the strange craft called LEM looks like a seat, or like a real bug. Have we made it? We've made it. The engines shut down. Two pairs of eyes peer out through the portholes. Out through the portholes lies a windless desert, and that is the Moon. The Moon? There's nothing in sight but lava, and then rocks, and then more lava, and then more rocks. The sky is ink dotted with lights, and everything is still, the stillness of death. The astronauts look at each other through their Plexiglas helmets to find assurance of life in the looks they exchange: how much comfort there is in a blink, in a movement of the eyes. The whole Earth, with its green and its blue, is in that blink, a movement of the eyes. And the voice of their comrade who's flying around up there is suddenly the voice of father, mother, loved one; it is the most beautiful music you've ever heard.

"Apollo Command Module: this is LEM. Do you read me?"

"Roger. This is Apollo Command Module. We read you loud and clear."

"Roger. LEM here. We've done it, we've made it."

"Roger. Apollo here. Check for re-launch."

"LEM. LEM here. Re-launch checked."

"Work well, boys."

"You too. So long."

Don't tell me this leaves you cold, Father. I don't believe you. You've been alone too and you know what it means. You've been afraid too and you know what it means. But their fear, their loneliness is something beyond our knowledge. They have nothing with them, you understand me? Nothing except food and instruments and hope. You were without food and instruments and hope when you were in that prison. I know. But you had the Earth! Even if they killed you, you still had the Earth. Not those two. They don't even have the Earth. All they have of Earth is two pairs of eyes and a voice. And nothing else. If that thing manages to lift off again, if that other thing manages to get back through the sky and land, then the newspapers will scream like crows about the first to go up, the first to set foot on the Moon. Not even this matters to those two. I am you and you are me. If I live, you live. If you live, I live. If I die, you die. If you die, I die. If I get out first, you get out first. If you get out first, I get out first. Courage, brother. God protect you, brother. A hatch opens, aluminum steps lower to the ground. A man climbs down with all his load of instruments and oxygen: a strange creature enclosed in a spacesuit. Look well at him, Father.

Look at him as he puts down one foot, then the other, and stops. Look at him as he raises his head, walks. He walks so very slowly, without lifting his feet from the ground, almost dragging them, mistrustful, prudent: gravity on the Moon is only one sixth of Earth gravity, if he took a real step, an Earth step, he would fly like a ball and drop like a ball, but the drop would bounce him up again like a ball and he would fly up again, grotesque, up and down, down and up, to infinity, and nobody would be able to stop him. Look at him well. Perhaps he feels the temptation to give himself a push and become a ball. He feels so light, he feels like a feather. Even the spacesuit which had been so heavy on Earth is light here, light as a feather. Even the oxygen cylinder is light, light as a feather. Even the heavy instruments he's carrying: he feels as if he were underwater, in the sea, in his dreams of childhood. If he lost his head, he could reach that peak and fling himself off it, like an angel. He can feel wings. He's terrified and he can feel wings. Suddenly he's sorry for the third companion who stayed up there, waiting for them. All this journey just to stay up there, waiting inside a capsule. If he goes back to Earth, they'll question him too: What's it like on the Moon? Is it like the Earth? Is it more beautiful? Is it uglier? What does it feel like to walk on it? And he won't know, he'll have to say: I didn't see the Moon. I went there, but I didn't see her. Like Tantalus, I reached out my hand and couldn't touch her. I only went around and around.

So, Father, should we envy this man who is walking up and down on the Moon? This weightless man who could reach that peak and fling himself off it like an angel? Let us look at him again as he advances, measuring every step. There is no atmosphere on the Moon, you know. Without it the bombardment of meteorites is continuous. They plummet down in a blaze of comets and it's like jumping out of the trenches into the attack. The ground is lava on which you might slip and tear your spacesuit, when it isn't lava it's a blanket of dust that lies undisturbed by any wind, by now so deep and fine that you can easily sink in it. Enough of poetry. This is the landscape where the man must spend hours and hours. And do you know how? Working hard. Providing he isn't struck by projectiles from the cosmos, swallowed up

by the dust, he will set up the instruments that will put him in contact
with Earth, collect samples of rock, lava, sand, take a lot of photographs. Then, when two hours are up, he will return to the Bug and
change places with his companion, who in his turn will get out and
continue for a further two hours: and so they will continue to change
places for eight hours. There must be no unexpected occurrences, nor
must they alter the program. The scientists have said that after eight
hours the two astronauts will shut themselves inside the Bug, eat the
prescribed food, sleep the prescribed number of hours, wake at the
prescribed hour and leave.

But will it work?

It works: dreams always work, Father, and so do films. I'm telling
you about the film. Minus thirty . . . twenty . . . ten . . . four
. . . three . . . two . . . one . . . ignition—lift-off! The blazing
flames ignite, burn for six minutes and twenty seconds, the Bug separates from the fuel tank, leaves behind in the crater that chair-like,
spider-like landing stage, blasts off at a speed of four thousand miles an
hour, a box without wings or propellers, and inside it two tired
men going to look for their third companion in the lunar sky. By now
their craft is without engines, to rendezvous with Apollo they have only
the thrust that sent them up, and they cannot maneuver: it is up to
Apollo to rendezvous with them, to maneuver. The Apollo takes an
hour to get into the correct position. It orbits around the Moon and
each orbit is a bit better, a little nearer. It is barely three miles away
when the docking maneuver begins. It is the same maneuver they made
when Saturn's third stage opened like a book to liberate the Bug, only
then there were three of them helping one another and their brains were
rested with Earth sleep and from the Earth they were receiving exact
calculations. Then the Bug was empty: if they lost it they just made
fools of themselves. Now there are two men inside, two brothers, and
there must be no mistake. A mistake would mean murder. It would
mean leaving them up there forever. . . . Inch by inch the Apollo
approaches, noses into the hole, latches on. A sigh of relief and the two
astronauts enter again through the narrow hatch in the command
module, three hands touch: We've done it, boys. We've done it and
now let's try and get back, all together again. The Apollo casts off from
the now empty Bug, abandons it in the sky, fires its rocket and re-enters
the Earth corridor. A corridor forty miles wide, a thin invisible needle
from which they must not deviate by so much as a yard or they will miss
the Earth: and this time there are no scientists or electronic computers

to help them even with this. They are on their own, on their own, and to thread this needle on their own is a thousand times more difficult. This time it's like sitting on something that rocks and shakes and firing with an old gun at a nickel that's rocking and shaking too. You have to aim straight and true. If you don't aim straight and true, an inch will become a yard, a yard will become a mile, a mile will become thousands of miles, thousands of miles will become infinity, and you will become a meteorite orbiting round the Sun until one day you fall into the Sun. Help them, God, I beseech you.

Help them because they are so helpless, they are like children who have fallen down a well. They might have substituted plastic grass for real grass, glass roses for real roses, rubber plants for real plants: but they did so because they are children, and children shouldn't die. They should hit the nickel in the opposite corner of the pitch, thread themselves through the eye of the needle and continue for three days and three nights. The white cone follows the same path again, passes again through the deadly peas of fire that would be enough to make a hole in their capsule, through cosmic rays and perils. It left Earth on the top of a 360-foot skyscraper, and it's returning alone: all those millions, all the skills of years are scattered up there in the cosmos like dry bread-crumbs. And the three men inside? Look at them again, Father. They were strong and now they're exhausted. They were excited and now they're worn out. Their eyes are red, their beards have grown. They no longer have any desire to eat or drink. They only want to get back home, and in this one desire they pass the days and the nights, days that are not days and nights that are not nights, while Earth sucks them back, calls them, absorbs them, and now they are on the edge of the atmosphere, they plunge in with determination, an incandescent flying bomb, all red when it appears in the blue and plunges downward like a stone. Then the nose of the cone opens, three yellow-and-orange-striped parachutes burst open. And from these three, another three. From the next three, three more, like summer fireworks when a fan of light produces another fan of light and then a third and a fourth until the sky is a riot of colors, and you become a child again and want to yell with joy as you did in those days. They have come home, they are safe and sound! Waiting for them are the fields, their women between the sheets, the Earth. Thank you, Lord. Someone switched on the light.

It was the official again. He was asking if I'd liked the film— "Interesting, isn't it?"—and telling me I was due to meet Dr. Celentano in the Tahitian Village restaurant. "Interesting. Yes, certainly." The fog had thinned a little, Dr. Celentano was a handsome young man, a specialist in space medicine, and the Tahitian Village was a place full of shells and canoes. Among other things they served an extremely strong drink with a rum base which augmented rather than diminished a strange feeling of sadness. While we were eating roast beef and lima beans a group of fashion models paraded between the tables showing dresses made of some kind of synthetic cotton. They kept stopping in front of Dr. Celentano, very talkative, holding out a sleeve or a hip so that he could touch the fabric and announcing the price: "Fifteen dollars. Thirty-two dollars." Dr. Celentano would blush, keep his eyes fixed on the roast beef and go on talking about the Moon.

He was saying that living there would not present any problems: plastic shelters could be installed in the lunar colony and naturally I could see what an advantage this would be to sufferers from heart ailments. "Nobody can ever tell what will result from a scientific undertaking. In medicine many discoveries have been made by accident. I shouldn't be surprised if in twenty years the Moon became a great sanitorium for cardiacs. Just think of the relief it would give them to be where gravity is reduced to a sixth." Dr. Celentano was very optimistic and his smile was most convincing. He compared the lunar expedition with the journey of Christopher Columbus and kept saying that it was stupid to keep asking why: why go, why land, what for? When Christopher Columbus left, people also asked: why go, what for? Even his sailors grumbled: "What for?" In the field of research, steps are often taken without any precise justification, the why comes later. I was eating, drinking, listening, and the strange feeling of sadness vanished. Then something happened, I don't recall when or how, and my sadness returned. I think our conversation had worked around to the astronauts and Dr. Celentano asked me what I thought of them. I replied that I didn't know them, I was going to Texas to meet them in a few days, for the present I could only say that my thoughts about them were varied: at times I thought they seemed heroes, at times robots, at times martyrs. Anyway they certainly couldn't be ordinary types: a normal man couldn't emerge from such experiences with his sanity intact.

Dr. Celentano gestured impatiently. "Nonsense! Astronauts aren't heroes, nor martyrs, nor robots. They're men like any others. You could say they're athletic, but they're not as athletic as a football player or a gymnast. You could say they're intelligent, but they're not as intelligent as a scientist or a philosopher. You'd find far stronger physiques on any beach in California and far better brains on any university campus. Besides, they don't have to be geniuses, they only have to be good pilots and good engineers, with some notion of geology." And their courage, Doctor? "All humbug! They're perfectly normal in that respect too. They're soldiers, they've nearly all fought in the war. For them, going to the Moon is like going into battle. And then don't forget that they were all test pilots: you need nerves of steel to fly a plane that has never been flown before, to sit and watch an engine on fire, trying to understand why the hell it's on fire, to eject yourself with your parachute only a split second before it explodes. Being a test pilot is more dangerous than going up in the Mercury spacecraft or the Apollo spacecraft. They take infinite precautions with the spacecraft, not many with planes." And the loneliness they must withstand out in space, Doctor? "All imagination! It's no worse then being in a desert or a submarine. Doen't the crew of a submarine stay under for as long as three months? I tried it out myself in a simulator. It's not as bad as all that." Truly, Doctor? Tell me about it. "Well, it's not all that easy, of course. If you want to be honest, it's rather uncomfortable. The experiment lasted eight days, I was in the simulator with two astronauts, and on the third day we all began to feel on edge. Although we knew perfectly well that we were still on Earth, we couldn't forget that we were inside the thing and everyone else was outside. We couldn't get out of our heads the notion that they might leave us in there. So on the fourth day we began to abuse the instruments, cursing and swearing at them. On the fifth day we began to hate each other, we could no longer stand the smell and sound of each other. On the sixth day one of us complained that he wanted to get out. On the seventh day we started suffering from hallucinations: one of us saw a great hole yawning beneath his feet and wanted to plug it up but couldn't, another could see a fire and wanted to put it out but couldn't, and all three of us kept seeing human faces in place of the levers and buttons. Yes, to be quite honest, it is a bit uncomfortable. The meanest prison cell becomes a paradise in comparison. So what?"

The mannequin parade continued, somewhat absurdly. They had got through the cocktail models and were now on the evening dresses, and my brain was a hallucinating salad of spacesuits and daring décolletages, hands reaching to put out fires and bosoms reaching toward Dr. Celentano. Dr. Celentano was having particular success with the blondest blonde and she would come and loiter in front of him just at the moment when his story was reaching dramatic heights. For example, as Dr. Celentano would be saying: "One of us saw a great hole yawning beneath his feet and wanted to plug it up but couldn't," the blonde would be wiggling her behind and saying: "Ballgown with petal bodice, forty-two dollars." Instead of the hole there would be this ballgown dancing about, and the whole thing was somehow a mockery. In any event, Dr. Celentano continued, certain sacrifices were indispensable to turn trips to the Moon into normal routine: "We don't want to send only astronauts up there. We want to send up our best scientists, doctors, astronomers, geologists. The first space station, for example, must be inhabited by them, not by pilots." I asked him why, instead of three astronauts, they didn't send two astronauts and one scientist on the first expedition, and Dr. Celentano answered as follows: "Scientists? Now? But the Apollo spacecraft is unsafe, it's primitive, it's dangerous. Only the caravels of Columbus have ever been as dangerous as the Apollo spacecraft. We'd run the risk of losing our scientists. We can't send them up without being sure they'll survive, can we?" And what about the astronauts, Doctor? Shouldn't they have the same assurance? "The astronauts . . . My dear, you must get this into your head. They're only gladiators, the gladiators of the space age. And gladiators, not scientists, are sent out to die."

That was how he answered and just at that moment the blonde stopped by our table to open the show of negligees. Her negligee was black, very transparent, and consisted of three minute pieces: a bra, pants and a wrap as invisible as her modesty. The blonde gazed at Dr. Celentano as much as to say yes, I like you, boy, see you this evening, and chirped in her chicken voice: "Only twenty-two dollars." Then slowly, very slowly, she removed the wrap to reveal a pallid body, pale with the cold of the air-conditioning. Her bra was inadequate, her bosom bursting cheerfully out of it. Her pants were reduced to the minimum and strategically printed with a pretty red heart. Dr. Celentano blinked and smiled beatifically.

Only gladiators, my dear. The gladiators of the space age. And gladiators, not scientists, are sent out to die.

6.

The helicopter flew through the fine silvery dust and below me the city stretched, monotonous, without beginning or end. Little houses in rows like the cells in a beehive. Glistening swimming pools of blue water. Interminable streets as straight as gun barrels. Sliced-up, blunted mountains reduced to cube shapes. Streams of hurrying automobiles. Parking lots, automobile cemeteries. And to the west the ocean, rough and angry. I soon tired of looking and opened the package I had with me and took out of it four little transparent plastic bags: at first sight they were like feeding-bottles. The first contained a green powder, like facepowder. The second contained dry crumbs, like sand. The third contained hard white stones, like gravel. The fourth contained fine yellow threads, like hair. In perplexity my fingers felt them and I tried to convince myself that the hairs were spaghetti, the gravel lobster, the sand bread, the facepowder soup. The spaghetti, the lobster, the bread and the soup that the astronauts will eat during their journey to the Moon and back. The food of our future. The food that will nourish us on Mars, on Venus, wherever we seek another home, Father.

I had been given all this by another doctor from North American after that strange meal at the Tahitian Village: a doctor who specialized in dietetics. And, what was worse, he had made me try it, thus showing me that although theoretically space food really consists of what we eat on this planet, in fact it's a mess. First cooked like normal food, then dehydrated and frozen, finally chopped up as if for a baby or a toothless old man, it is reduced to a tenth of its former weight, then enclosed in little transparent plastic bags that have the advantage of being neither bulky nor heavy. Naturally, the specialist in dietetics had said, I must be aware that the spacecraft couldn't carry more than a certain weight, and I must also be aware that it is inadvisable to provide the nourishment for the astronauts in the form of pills. Such a process therefore solves certain problems: enough food for three men for two weeks will fit into a box no larger than a shoebox. A very rich menu, it included also steaks, mashed potatoes, chicken salad, runner beans,

fruit, cheese, orangeade, lemonade, chocolate, milk, coffee—all that
was missing was wine, because alcohol, like cigarettes and women, is a
luxury not allowed on the journey to the Moon. I understand, Doctor.
But how do they eat this stuff, what do they drink? The good man had
looked at me with surprise: come on now, couldn't I imagine? You only
have to take a little water, so, inject it through a syringe into the little
bag, shake it and squeeze it to mix it all together, and in a few minutes
the food would once more acquire its normal volume and consistency.
And then? And then stick the bottle into your mouth and suck, exactly
like a baby with a bottle. And then? Then chew it, for goodness sake,
or else it would go down the wrong way. Quick! Some water! My
lungs full of dehydrated rehydrated lobster, my eyes popping and purple
in the face, I was coughing my space inexperience all over the good
man: didn't I know that it would not be possible to eat with a spoon and
fork? In the absence of gravity the food would start flying about hither
and thither and land in the most unlikely places: what would happen if
the astronaut had to swat his peas like flies? If a strand of spaghetti
finished up on an electronic computer? Yes, Doctor, of course. Then,
having got over my attack of coughing, I had asked him to let me keep
the little bags I was looking at now, Father, imagining your face when I
show them to you: "Men are mad, mad! Is it possible, is it possible
that you can get excited in the face of such evidence of madness?"

I did up the package again and fastened my seat belt. The
helicopter was coming down into Garrett, the firm that manufactures the
system of controls for space capsules: to put it simply, the instruments
that will keep the astronaut alive. Heating and cooling systems,
oxygenization and purifier systems, pressure and humidity controls: in
short, as the professorial manager was to say, everything necessary to
create an Earth atmosphere inside capsule and spacesuit. He was
waiting for me at the entrance. First of all, he said with the air of
pronouncing who knows what sentence, I should know who Cliff Garrett
was: a great man. Cliff Garrett and nobody else had founded Garrett, a
pioneer factory, one of the most important industries concerned with
aeronautics and space; it was thanks to Garrett and nobody else that so
far no astronaut launched by the United States had died. Having
cleared that up, he prepared me for the sight of Garrett's latest miracle:
the system that converts sweat and urine into pure drinking water.
Naturally he wouldn't waste time explaining to me how it worked. I
wouldn't have understood the first thing and he could tell in half a
second whether a visitor understood something about technology or

not. He would sooner just get me to answer a few questions. He pointed his finger at me.

"Of what does the fuel for space flights consist?"

"Oxygen and liquid hydrogen."

"What is the drawback of this fuel?"

"It's very heavy."

"What is the number-one problem for a spacecraft?"

"Not to be too heavy."

"Why does a spacecraft carry no water on board?"

"Because water is heavy and can be made from the fuel."

"What happens when the Apollo spacecraft is traveling without fuel, by force of inertia?"

"They're without water."

"Well then, how do we get water to drink?"

"By sweating and peeing."

"Precisely. This complicated system serves precisely for this: to filter, distill, purify and refrigerate sweat and urine so that they become purest water: very much purer and more hygienic than the water we drink at home. Anyway, what is it after all, the water we drink? It's water from the sky, water from the sea, dirty water cleaned by nature. Actually, nature only does what we're doing at Garrett."

"Plagiarism."

"What was that you said?"

"I was saying that such economy is most praiseworthy, sir. If I am not mistaken, this is the first time in the history of the United States of America that nothing is being wasted. You must excuse me, but what— in short, what do you do with what's left?"

"What do you mean, what's left?"

"Well . . . in short . . . yes, exactly, the shit, sir. These three men aren't only drinking. They're eating too. I know they eat vegetables, meat, spaghetti, and . . . they make shit."

The manager was arrogant but, on the whole, polite. And perhaps shy too, in front of women. He blushed violently and looked at me in dismay. I had to tell him I don't know how many times that there was nothing wrong in what I had asked: we all go to the toilet, my God, and such realities accentuated if anything the desperate nature of the flight. Come on, out with it, courage—was the rest also filtered, distilled, purified and refrigerated, turned into something edible? With difficulty the manager swallowed, sighed, confessed.

"No. We've thought about it. We've tried it. But the thing seems to be impossible, at least for the moment. And the problem is a serious one: there's a hygienic corner in the Apollo capsule, obviously, but what can be done with the waste matter? To waste fuel on burning it would be madness: every drop of fuel is already necessary. To throw it out into space is technically difficult: you know that anything ejected from a flying object continues to fly at the same speed as the object itself. To get rid of it, in short, we would have to accelerate, and that would be a further waste of fuel. So what can be done with it?"

"Yes, what can be done?"

"Some suggest abolishing it by using a liquid diet that doesn't atrophy the intestine. They're conducting experiments in a San Francisco prison and the volunteers are in perfect health. But there is a drawback: they never stop chewing. They chew anything they can find, and when they can't find anything else they bite their clothes and their shoes. The astronauts have greater willpower, true, but what if they couldn't resist? What if they started to chew their spacesuits? It would be the end, better to give them a solid diet. But what can be done with the waste matter?"

"Yes, what can be done?"

"Well, what they do now is bring it back to Earth."

"Bring it back?"

"Yes. So that it can be analyzed. . . . They put it in little packages and seal them up and then they put the little packages in the drawers they took their food out of. And they keep them there till they get back."

"For days? For weeks?"

"Sure."

"Gosh. And what about when they go to the Moon?"

"Well, some people say: Let's leave it on the Moon. I may be wrong, but I think that to leave it on the Moon would be very rude and ill-bred. The Moon isn't a bathroom. Besides, that would present the danger of contaminating the Moon. And one of the questions that concern Garrett is precisely that—not to contaminate the Moon."

"Not to contaminate the Moon?"

"Naturally. Follow me, please."

———————

To go into the Cleaning Room you have to don plastic overalls, plastic shoes and plastic gloves and then pass through a corridor that sprinkles you with jets of air and sucks up the most invisible bit of hair, the smallest grain of dust. There is great silence inside, and white ghosts work in this silence, their bodies encased in plastic coveralls, their feet in plastic shoes, their hands in plastic gloves, their hair gathered into plastic bonnets, the women identical with the men, the young identical with the old, one next to the other, one behind the other: the Cleaners. The Cleaners clean with special substances the various parts of the instruments that make up the spacecraft and, when they have cleaned them, send them into another room to be sterilized so that every microbe, every form of contagion should disappear together with the most fantastic of the worries that afflict the men of the space age: the contamination of the Moon and the other planets. The man who worries about not contaminating the Moon has an Italian name: he is called Orsini. He was born in Florence, where he took his degree in biology many years ago. Now he is around sixty, lines furrow his face like scars.

"Contaminate the Moon, Professor?"

"It is possible. Suppose that, however unbelievably, the Moon is a museum full of traces of life, that it preserves intact something that has survived for millions of years. Something that moves, that breathes, a lichen, a seed, a spore—didn't we find bacteria in flakes of salt a hundred and eighty million years old? Well: what happens when a spacecraft lands on the Moon, bringing with it billions of micro-organisms that live happily with us? The exterior of the craft is sterilized by the heat that scorches it when it breaks through the atmosphere, but the interior is not; so it is contaminated. Hence the sterilization of every instrument, the feeble effort not to infect the Moon or the other planets."

"Feeble effort, Professor?"

"Worse than feeble, useless perhaps. Because, you see, sterilizing the instruments is child's play, but sterilizing the man is impossible: quite apart from anything else, the poisons man carries with him are indispensable to his health. And so he gets out, with his thousand poisons, and his first breath is already mortal contagion for other forms of life. We sterilize and sterilize, but God forbid that the Moon has life on it, because if it has we'd destroy it for sure."

"And if the Moon contaminates us, Professor?"

"That's also possible. We sterilize the machines and spacesuits when they go, but we don't sterilize them when they come back. So all the poisons, the micro-organisms that preserve possible life on Mars, on Venus, and—who knows?—on the Moon might be fatal to the Earth, might destroy it. The danger is clearly reciprocal."

I thought of you, Father, with a feeling of guilt and a little shame. Bradbury's prayer seemed so far away at that moment, buried by your mute reproof. If you had been with me I would have asked your pardon. Or your help. But you weren't there, people are never there just when you need them most; you spend days, months, whole years with someone to whom you have nothing to say, and the very moment you have something to say, maybe: forgive me, help, he isn't there and you're alone. And so I continued my visit, I went into the assembly buildings, where the luckiest workers in the world are working, the Garrett workers, and it felt as though I were collaborating in some absurd crime, some absurd senseless suicide. Garrett machines are all automatic. The workers sat in comfortable chairs, motionless, staring at all that commotion of levers and pistons and steel, and their arms hung inert like the sleeves of a shirt hung out to dry. I saw their faces in profile dejected, the freedom to live dead. . . . I was dying too, Father, little by little. I too was being drawn, little by little, into that herd of automatons. It had only taken a very few days for me to become inured, corrupted: at five o'clock, when the others finished work, I would become suddenly sleepy and unable to shake myself out of that obedient sloth. Like them, I would yearn for a drink and the idleness of mind and body watching TV, that wretched little god that brings the world into your house like a postman, and the dinner hour becomes an empty promise. NASA, the governing body in control of the space race, arranged my appointments and put a helicopter at my disposal. Going by helicopter rather than automobile had become an everyday matter for me by now, and I felt betrayed when I sometimes had to walk a short distance down a runway to reach it; I felt insulted if the helicopter engine wasn't already running when I arrived. The swish of those rotating propellers that at first had seemed to me like a great guillotine by now sounded familiar to my ears: I would casually land in Santa Monica off Pico Boulevard. NASA's Western Operations Office was in Santa Monica, on Pico Boulevard, and the Public Affairs office was run by two ex-marines, Stan Miller and Bob Button. As the helicopter landed, Stan and Bob would come to meet me and take me for a drink in the bar across the street. We would sit exhausted, as if we had made who knows what effort instead of having the machines do all the work for us. To record my interviews there was the tape-recorder, to copy any sheet of paper there was the photostat, to move there were wheels. But we would sit exhausted, saying nothing, like old men sitting around the fireside in winter eating chestnuts, and it was an effort to get up and go home or back to the hotel. It was Bob who generally took me back to my hotel. Anyway it was Bob that particular evening.

The evening was sad and sweet, one of those evenings that make you love the Earth. The automobile slid smoothly between the palm trees of Wilshire Boulevard and the breeze blew caressingly through the windows on your eyes and your hair. Suddenly I turned toward Bob and, confident of his complicity, perhaps because of his shy little face and his Charlie Chaplin mustache, rather English-looking, I admitted my uncertainty to him.

"Tell me, Bob: do you really think it's right to be going to the Moon?"

"What?" Bob exclaimed, stunned.

"Yes. Why the devil should we go to the Moon?"

"And why the devil shouldn't we?" Bob sounded very offended.

"I don't know. That dehydrated food. That water extracted from urine. That fear of contaminating the Moon and being contaminated by it ourselves . . . I don't know."

"I thought you liked the idea," Bob observed. He sounded even more offended.

"I did like it, I do like it: but I've seen things today that confuse me. You know, like kids who go eagerly up to a valve to see how it works and it gives them an electric shock."

"The other day," Bob said conciliatingly, "I read an essay by Arthur Clarke. It said that throughout the world's history most of human energy has been employed in moving things from one place to another. In short, no sooner is something standing still than man moves it. If he's standing still himself, then he moves himself. Moving is ingrained in us, and so is moving faster and faster. For thousands of years, according to Clarke, we moved ourselves at two or three miles an hour: the speed of a man walking. For hundreds of years we moved at ten miles an hour: the speed of a horse and carriage. Now we move at twenty-five thousand miles an hour: the speed of Saturn. But to move at that speed the Earth is no longer enough for us, it's too small. We don't have enough room, get me? You fall out. So to move we have to go to other planets, starting with the Moon."

"As a conclusion, that strikes me as pretty absurd."

"It strikes me as being logical."

"As far as I'm concerned, it's not enough being logical if it's useless."

"Useless! The first plane of the Wright brothers was called useless too. They said nobody would ever use it. And I use it every evening."

"Do you live so far off, Bob?"

"Not at all! Only half an hour away!"

"Then why do you go by plane every evening?"

"I just do. Because I like it. For no reason."

"For no reason?"

"For no reason. To get myself from one point to another. To get there quickly."

And then I thought of the story you used to tell me when I was a child, Father. And I told it to Bob. That is, not the whole story: just the ending. At the end, remember, there's this man who might be wicked or might just be stupid and he's running around a tree. Faster and faster. Until he goes so fast that he runs into himself. And breaks his nose.

Bob took offense and left me without a helicopter that day.

I remember very clearly my despair, Father. The despair of someone who finds himself unexpectedly without electric light and has to use candles.

"Bob, you must be mad. And how am I supposed to get there?"

"By taxi. By bicycle. On foot. But don't run. You might break your nose."

"A taxi all that way: are you joking?"

"By taxi it takes an hour, an hour and a half, ninety minutes. What are ninety minutes compared with eternity? What's the point of all this haste, more and more haste, until you don't know where to stop?"

I went by taxi, Father. And no vehicle has ever seemed so slow to me as that one, as it sped along the road to Redondo Beach for an hour and ten minutes. All my life I had lived without a helicopter, but now I'd had one and I couldn't do without it, the car already seemed very slow and inconvenient. I thought I would never get there, I grew bored, I felt I had gone back to Grandfather's day when to go from Florence to Mercatale—barely twenty miles—you left by carriage at dawn and arrived in the afternoon. Much longer and I'd have started running around a tree, faster and faster until I ran into myself and broke my nose. You know that story of Bradbury's called *They Were Brown with Golden Eyes?* The story about the pioneers who emigrate to Mars and, having exhausted their stock of food, Earth food, start eating what grows on Mars. When they landed they were white-skinned and their eyes were blue or black or brown. After eating that food they become brown-skinned with golden eyes. Only one of them still has blue eyes: the one who, like myself, is always seized with doubts, always hesitates, one moment he will and the next moment he won't, and to save himself he decides to mend his rocket and return to Earth. But gradually the urge to mend his rocket wears off, gradually he takes to eating the same food as everyone else, and one morning he gets up, looks at himself in the mirror, and his skin is brown and his eyes are golden, and he's become a Martian like the others.

7.

First of all, it wasn't a hotel. It was a motel. That is to say, a hotel for a man and his car. Or rather for a car and its driver.

"But I don't have a car," I said. "So I don't need a motel. I don't understand why they booked me into a motel."

"All the hotels are motels here," growled a man who resembled Jack Ruby. He scornfully tossed me the first room key that came to hand.

"O.K. Can you send my bags to my room, please?"

"If you want your bags in your room, I'll tell you what you can do. You can pick them up and carry them there yourself," he growled.

"O.K. May I have a cup of tea before I go to bed?"

"If you want tea, I'll tell you what you can do. You put your money in the machine and you drink it," he growled.

"O.K.," I said and picked up the key. And quickly leaped backward—for a moment I'd thought he was going to shoot me. But what he was holding out was a pen.

"Eight ninety-five for the night. No breakfast, no service. Sign here."

What do you do at one in the morning, after traveling for four hours, with all those hostile eyes staring at you and if you go out there's only the night and the desert? So, Father, what do you do? You sign and say nothing. Then you pick up your bags and hurry to lock yourself in your room. There, at least, you feel safe. Safe, did I say? I was joking, Father. To start with, motel rooms are right on the road; like shops. Anyone passing can get in and finish you off. Or, if you're lucky, just kidnap you. If you're very lucky, just rob you. Secondly, the wall that looks onto the road isn't a wall, it's glass. They swear it's unbreakable, but I've seen plenty of broken ones. Thirdly, between that glass and your state of nerves there is only a curtain. If you forget to draw the curtain, anybody can see you getting undressed and washed. The bath and the shower, in fact, are in the bathroom, the washbasin is in the bedroom. Did I say bedroom? I was joking, Father. It's an

automatic cell that holds a TV, a chair, a little table, a divan, and dozens
of buttons but you don't know what they're for. To switch off the light?
No, to switch another one on. To turn off the radio? No, to raise the
volume. To lower the air-conditioning? No, to increase it. There are
matches everywhere, and handouts that console you with descriptions of
the enormous development of these motels, and some scraps of material
printed: "Want your shoes cleaned? Help yourself." All right, but
where's the bed? Hopeful, you look along the walls and the ceiling and
are about to give up and lie down fully dressed on the divan when
somebody knocks at your door.

"Who is it?"

"The bed."

Cautiously you draw aside the curtain. A black face is looking at
you over a waiter's jacket.

"You're bringing me the bed?"

"Open up."

You open and he comes in. He presses a button. The divan
immediately grows larger and wider, and voilà: there's the bed.

"Oh, thank you! Very kind of you, thank you!"

"Tip, please."

"I beg your pardon?"

"I said tip. T-I-P. Tip." His pink palm is outstretched toward you.

"Oh, of course! Of course!" You give him half a dollar.

"That all?" The palm is still there, holding your half-dollar like a
tray.

"O.K." You give him another half-dollar.

"Night." He pockets the dollar, without thanks, and goes away.
You drop exhausted into bed and go straight to sleep.

It must be three in the morning when something fearful happens.
The bed that looked like a bed is no longer a bed, but a live monster that
humps up and down and around, shakes you, tosses you, in your sleep
you've evidently pressed a button: the massage button? It's started to
massage you. While it was massaging you you evidently pressed
another button: the sleep button? It stops shaking you and now it will
start talking, and say come on there, go to sleep, why did you get up?
You're tired, come on there, go to sleep. So you cry out, mad with
fright, and your fingers reach out to press the buttons, the warm-air
button, the cold-air button, the radio button, the TV button, the massage
button, the buttons' button, until all the buttons break and the radio goes
off, the TV goes off, the warm air goes off, the cold air goes off, the bed

goes back to being a bed that lies still and doesn't talk. Thank you, my God. At the same moment, breathless and sweating, you realize that you've been shouting out loud, and you listen in embarrassment, and you get up and tiptoe to the curtain, very slowly draw it aside, thinking that your noise must have summoned the whole city and they'll all be standing there. But when you peer through your embarrassment into the darkness you can see nobody. There's nobody on the pavement. There's nobody anywhere. You're alone. Alone with your buttons.

That was the night I telephoned you, Father. By then I wasn't sleepy any more and in Italy it had been day for many hours. I asked the telephone operator if I would have to wait long and she said: One moment, then the receiver went *tu-tu* and my ears were filled with sweet balm—Mother's voice crying: "Ciao, where are you?"

"In Texas, Mother. Where the astronauts are."

"Oh, the poor boys! Oh, the poor little things! Have you seen them?"

"Not yet. I just got here, Mother. I'm in a motel."

"Oh, you make me jealous! Tell me, is it beautiful over there?"

"Very beautiful, Mother. Stupendous."

"Goodness knows what they must be like, the woods and the prairies."

"Beautiful woods, beautiful prairies."

"And the cowboys? Have you seen the cowboys?"

"Sure. Lots of cowboys."

"Tell me, what are they like?"

"Like in films. With spurs on their boots . . . and broad-brimmed hats . . . and they always go on horseback . . ."

"Oh, you make me jealous! All those horses. You know how I love horses."

"Yes, I know. There's heaps of horses down here."

"And the cows? Is it true there are lots of cows?"

"Quite true. Pastures full of cows."

Then I spoke to you, and you'd been out shooting birds, you'd had a very good time and you couldn't care less about Texas.

"The thrushes are flocking over the hills. Pity you aren't here. Every shot brings them down in clusters."

"Where, by the cherry tree?"

"Especially by the cherry tree. They drop onto the dry branches. It keeps my hands warm, shooting. It's cold up at the hut. What's it like over there?"

"Here it's hot, Father. Hot as hell. I've broken the button for the air-conditioning. Ciao, Pa!

How I envied you, Father, as I waited for the dawn. Up at the shooting hut the dawn was a bluish bowl with a ball of gold in the middle. The ball of gold would rise higher and higher, bringing the day with it, and the air would be fragrant with grass, and the leaves would rustle like a caress from the wind. With our guns resting in the slits we would stare at the sky, the branches sharp against the bluish sky, and we would speak in whispers. "If it comes from the left, I'll take it. If it comes from the right, you take it. If they come in a flock, we'll fire together. One, two, and fire on three." "O.K., Pa." At the hut, dawn would be a bundle of taut nerves, watchful eyes, listening ears. Suddenly the decoys in the cages would start flapping their wings and then singing their snare to their companions, and you would whisper: "Ready, they're coming." I would quickly grasp the gun, set the sights, and fluttering darts would flash past and settle on the top of the cherry tree. "One, two . . . shoot!" The darts would fall like ripe bunches of grapes: a little thud of feathers. And then, my heart filled with unexpected guilt, already useless repentance, I would open the gun, take out the spent smoking cartridge, reload in silence, and the waiting for the next flock would be a tender cool shuddering, a serene boredom, a woodland whispering. Dawn at the hut was beautiful. But here it was a gray light through the curtain, a still gray shadow on the pavement, a frown on my forehead: who's that, what does he want? The horses and the cows and pastures and cowboys existed only in my imagination: I'd told my mother a lot of fibs.

I went out. Through the open curtains the motel rooms were vomiting unmade beds, crumpled pillows, heaped up towels, the obscenity of a brothel. They were empty and yet obscene. Seeing them without meaning to, out of the corner of my eye, I could imagine their intimacy, the unpleasant odors that fill bedrooms in the morning. As for Houston, it was a tomb of concrete and an asphalt road that led to NASA's Manned Spacecraft Center, an edifice of soldiers in civilian clothes that you could get out of only with a pass pinned to your jacket. To get the pass you had to answer a thousand questions, repeat for the umpteenth time who you were and what you wanted, defend yourself against traps and cunning. My Censor ran the Public Relations office, his name was Paul Haney, a name you may have heard, he is also called the Voice of the Astronauts because it is he who speaks for them, answers for them, during the space flights it is he who tells what happens, in his slow monotonous voice with no surprise, they can die and his voice has no surprise. He is a big man with a big indifference, whatever happens, and you never understand whether he is serious or whether he is joking, maybe he is not serious and he's not joking, and I never did understand up to what point he was serious and when he was joking that day, whether he regarded me as a threat or a game.

"But you've never been to Russia, have you?"

"No, not yet."

"Odd. Why not?"

"For one reason or another the visa didn't come through."

"You asked for one, then."

"Yes, of course, I asked for one."

"And why did you ask for one?"

"To go to Russia."

"And why were you going to Russia?"

"To write some articles."

"What kind of articles?"

"Articles."

"Favorable or not?"

"How would I know? I didn't go."

"Oh, yes, you didn't go."

"No, I didn't go."

"Shame, eh?"

"Yes, a shame."

"Especially being a party member . . ."

"A party member? What party?"

"The party."

"Look, I'm not a member of any party."

"Truly?"

"Truly."

"A lot of people are, in Italy."

"And I'm not."

"How come? Pardon my asking, I'm just curious."

"I don't fancy any of them."

"But you have your own ideas."

"I'm certainly not a reactionary. Much less a fascist."

"Oh! Ah! Eh! Look, it doesn't make any difference to us. We welcome everybody."

"Then why did you ask me?"

"No reason. I mean, you could be a Russian, a member of the

party, and you could come and see the astronauts and get inside here just the same."

"I know—but I'm not a Russian. And I'm not a communist."

"O.K. Is the pass ready? Will you give her the pass?"

"Thank you. And now what do I do?"

"We'll give you an escort and you can have a look around."

"And the astronauts? May I know whom I'll see?"

"Not yet."

"I understand. Good day." And I went off with my escort and later wrote in my notebook: "The meeting with the men who will go to the Moon was in the city called Houston, in the south of the state called Texas, between the 30th parallel and the 95th meridian of our planet, where they live, amid acacia woods, waiting for the Great Journey. The aerotaxi took me there at midnight. The Moon was full and barely 240,000 miles above. Ridiculous, indeed absurd, to think that fifty Earth years ago, when Houston was just a village and cows grazed in herds everywhere, cowboys with their guitars sang sad love songs to the nearby satellite. Cows and cowboys became extinct in the Plastic Age, together with other forms of life such as horses, flies and trees. There are no trees here in what might be considered the most important lunar base on the terrestrial globe. The woods where the astronauts live are the only woods for miles around, and even they remain only so that the men can absorb the maximum amount of chlorophyll before the Departure. Beyond, the Earth is a flat expanse of upturned soil where useless flowers tell of prehistoric times. There are traces of prehistory in the old town too, where the skyscrapers have doors and windows, buildings are indicated by name and people walk around without helmets, blind to the danger of meteorites. But it won't last long. In the new Houston, in fact, the buildings are indicated by number (Number One Building, Number Two, etc.) and every construction looks as cities of the future will look, which is to say a huge cube or a huge parallelepiped without doors or windows, the former being invisible, the second superfluous. Pavements here have been abolished: it is many decades since the old method of getting about on your legs and feet has been banished, anyone without a car is not a real man. The owners of the cars always wear a helmet and carry a plastic pass with their photograph, name, address, telephone number and the name of the firm for which they work. (Everybody works for a firm, nobody works for himself and not to work would be inconceivable.) This is necessary not only because everyone looks the same beneath a helmet and nobody can recognize anybody, but because each man must be watched and reported on, if necessary reprimanded and rejected, by the local government, which is called NASA. Entrance to the city of the future is prohibited, without the plastic pass. And what's also prohibited is the melancholy and fear and regret that all this causes." Even today, Father, it still seems to me the most precise thing to be said about the city placed between the 30th parallel and the 95th meridian of our planet, called Houston, Texas.

My escort was a girl whom I shall call Katherine.

Employed for four years at NASA, Katherine reflected that world as a clean lake mirrors clouds, and the fear, the regret, the sadness burned her eyes like long-held-back tears. She couldn't give it up, evidently, but even so she hated it, with a wicked hate full of love. "Put on this dirty thing," she said as she tenderly donned her helmet. "Look how revolting," she said as she proudly pointed out a house. And every space object, every allusion to the future, loosened her tongue in a torrent of enthusiasm and disgust, defenses and offenses. Then, before the houses of the astronauts, she fell silent, confining herself to pointing them out. At one time she used to work for them, and perhaps one of them, not indifferent to a pretty face, had made involuntarily a hole in her heart: the wound was still visible. When you asked her what kind of men these astronauts were, she answered through her teeth: "Romeos."

"Well, that's nice, isn't it?"

"I don't see anything nice about it."

"Come off it, Katherine. They're young and healthy. It's natural that they should like women. Should they like men?!?"

Katherine sighed deeply and took me back to the office. The office was run by a severe and touchy gentleman, Howard Gibbons, who at first sight makes you exclaim: "Heavens! He's lost his helmet!" Without his helmet his head was bald or, rather, naked, and you felt you wanted to get one for him quickly, like a wig for someone who's been scalped. Moreover, everyone in there looked as if they'd lost their helmets: the only ones who looked as if they felt fine with only their hair were a couple of fellows sitting in a corner, and it turned out that they were Swedes who were just passing. They were called Stig Nordfeldt and Bjorn Larsson, the former a journalist and the latter a photographer, Katherine explained. She took me over to them and they sensed that I too had been born without a helmet; we were instantly united in the fellowship of the shipwrecked. Stig and Bjorn were staying in the same motel as I was. Although they hadn't broken a single button and didn't actually detest the place as violently as I did, you know those Swedes, staying there made them feel extremely ill at ease: we consoled each other by turns and from that day on we were always together, the most anarchic trio that NASA had ever tolerated. On the one hand Stig, very tall and thin and absent-minded, a Swedish version of James Stewart; on the other hand Bjorn, jolly and athletic, with his spectacles and his Leica; in the middle myself, so small and angry—can you see us, Father? We paraded a Europe that for these people was something in the remote past, something from the Niocene Era.

"Absolutely not: we cannot tell you which astronauts you'll be seeing."

"But we have to know: to prepare ourselves."

"Impossible."

"Katherine! Mr. Gibbons!"

"Sorry, it's regulations."

At that time there were thirty American astronauts. We felt it was important to know in advance which of the thirty would fall to us, but from their military viewpoint this was quite unimportant and stupid, and all we could get was a probability: they would select them from among the group consisting of the first Seven. And so we waited, discontented and impatient, like children holding an Easter egg and wondering what novelty is inside, and all our remote past was boiling with curiosity about their future. Undoubtedly the astronauts represent the most fascinating, the most human, the easiest aspect of the expedition to the Moon, and anxiously our questions rebounded: What kind of men were these men destined to land on the Moon, on other planets? Very different from ourselves? What would they seem like, these men who are at once guinea pigs, pilots, explorers, engineers, scientists, martyrs, gods and heroes, whose bodies can withstand unspeakable tortures and whose minds can withstand the adulation of the world? In 1958, when NASA was looking for volunteers for the new career, a general exclaimed: "What we need is a group of normal supermen." Was he serious? And if he was serious, were they supermen or not? "It's obvious that courage isn't enough," Stig was saying. "You could have all the courage in the world and still not have the kind of nervous system necessary for flying through space. In other words, you could be a hero in war and good for nothing on the Moon or on Mars. They must have something even stronger than courage—coolness, I don't know, the ability to react to situations outside the normal, nerves of steel." And Bjorn: "Obviously they must have nerves of steel: all of them were chosen from among the test pilots, don't forget, all of them were men with the qualities of courage, coolness, immediate reflexes, all accustomed to fly in danger, to make sudden decisions calmly . . ." And Stig: "All right Bjorn. You might have all the coolness in the world and a body that can't withstand hardships: you need muscles and organs to match all that coolness, exceptional health. Did you read about the tests they were submitted to in 1958? Comparable with the tortures imposed on witches and heretics by the Holy Inquisition, I would say. They would place them on the centrifuge which turned them round faster and faster and when the force of gravity became twenty times normal, when their capillaries were bursting and they felt as if their teeth were leaping out of their mouths, the wheel would be stopped in a few turns. Or they would shut them inside heat-pulse ovens, no less than a hundred and forty degrees Fahrenheit, keep them there for about two hours, then take them out and fling them boiling hot into ice, burying their feet in it for ten minutes . . ." And Bjorn: "O.K. But even that isn't enough. You might be as healthy as an Olympic athlete, as cool as a test pilot, and still be as ignorant as a hen: you need profound preparation, careful study, a good amount of intelligence to manage such an enterprise. And more: you might know as much as ten astrophysicists or mathematicians or geologists or doctors put together and yet not have the moral stature, the maturity, to face certain experiences . . ." "For heaven's sake! But really you are describing a branch of supermen, inhuman beings!" "Supermen or prefabricated men—why not? Prefabricated in some laboratory, like bottles of Coca-Cola . . . One thing I'd really like to know is whether they aren't as alike as bottles of Coca-Cola . . ." And so we went on and on. For hours, Father, we spoke of them and everything contributed to feed that subject, our long impatience like children who tear off lizards' tails in order to see how lizards look without tails, accurately, coldly, as if they were laboratory specimens, biology experiments, instead of living creatures. Besides, wasn't it partly the fault of this hallucinating Houston, this Haney, this Gibbons, this Katherine, that we were denied any clue to their humanity that would allow us to consider them living creatures rather than laboratory specimens, biology experiments? Number One Building, Number Two Building, Number Three Building: sorry, it's regulations. Plastic passes, helmets, press buttons: sorry, it's regulations. Melancholy, terror, regret: sorry, it's regulations. But then I met her, standing by that spacecraft . . . and it's curious how things happen with such logic, Father. The logic that you call fate, that Mother calls providence, that others call chance.

Stig and Bjorn had gone to interview someone and, to keep me quiet, to relieve my boredom, Gibbons had asked if I'd like to see a replica of the Mercury spacecraft, the one used in the first human space flights, remember? So I had let myself be led into some building or other to see this Mercury spacecraft, a funnel that allows no more room to whoever squeezes into it than a nutshell does to a nut, I had even let myself be shut up inside it, bent in that position I told you about, back supine, legs at right angles, and there I had stayed for a few minutes, more terrified than when they'd shut me inside the Apollo spacecraft, baffled, obsessed by the same old questions; and I longed to get out.

As soon as the hatch opened I shot forth like a scalded cat and "Uncomfortable, isn't it?" said a woman's voice. A pleasant voice, so you instinctively looked not so much for the woman as for the mouth from which such a voice had come: and the mouth was huge, painted the reddest of reds, full of white teeth to make that red stand out. But after the mouth you immediately sought her eyes, which were also huge, of a blue even more blazing than the red, the blue of cornflowers in summer, and with something in them that canceled out all the passes, helmets, people like Katherine or Howard Gibbons, regulations. Should we call it humanity, that something? After the eyes you looked at a mole on her left cheek, this too so huge that it seemed artificial, like one of those velvet beauty spots that at one time were used out of coquetry, lastly at the black bob of hair that adhered to her forehead, her temples, her cheeks in a lot of funny bangs that recalled Mother when she was young and beautiful and used to do her hair that way. This, I think, was why I took to her immediately. And then because of the way she stood with her shoulders squared, her sturdy body erect on her sturdy legs, another way in which she recalled Mother when Mother was young and beautiful and able to square her shoulders and thus went her way into a world that was alien to her and cruel, but in which she trustingly believed, so gentle and yet so tough. The dress was white. On the tips of the collar she wore two badges on which something was written, but I didn't take any notice of them although I had been wondering who she was and why she was there.

"Yes, uncomfortable."

"The boys say so too."

"What boys?"

"The astronauts, the fellows."

"Oh! Is that what they call them?"

"It's what I call them."

"I'm to see them this morning, the fellows."

"I know."

"You know?"

"Here you get to know everything."

She burst out laughing, as you do when you feel like having a chat about nothing in particular, you were just passing, you spotted someone you'd heard about and you felt like having a little chat with them. She leaned back against the capsule as if it were a perfectly familiar object intended for one to lean against.

"You'll find it an interesting experience. The fellows represent the most positive aspect of the whole business. Without them the whole business would be drearier, duller, colder. Good boys, you know that? Plenty of heart, plenty of brain, not—how can one put it?— not . . ."

"Not laboratory specimens, biology experiments."

Another burst of laughter, from between two streaks of red.

"That's it. It's odd how many people think of them that way before they get to know them. Maybe because they think they must be quite different from themselves."

"Are they?"

She offered me a cigarette, lit it for me and then lit her own without shifting from her unusual backrest. She grew thoughtful.

"Well . . . If a couple of characters are walking down the street and one of them's an astronaut, you sure don't turn around to look at him. With a few exceptions, I'd say. But if you talk to him, even just for a few minutes, you'd certainly stop for a second look. They have something, yes, that something that men have for whom death is a toy to play with, or who have seen something you haven't seen. The ones who have been up, especially. They have something, a sort of wild look, I would say, as if they had fallen in love with a mystery up there, sort of as if they haven't got their feet back on the ground, as if they regret having come back to us. . . ."

Again I wondered who she could be and what she was doing there.

"Yes, especially the ones who've been up. Don't pay any attention to people who tell you they have such a wild look because of tension, of exhaustion, of joy at having made it. It's got nothing to do with these things. It's rage at having come back to Earth. As if up there they're not only freed from weight, from the force of gravity, but from desires, affections, passions, ambitions, from the body. Do you know that for months John and Wally and Scott went around looking at the sky? You could speak to them and they didn't answer, you could touch them on the shoulder and they didn't notice: their only contact with the world was a dazed, absent, happy smile. They smiled at everything and everybody, and they were always tripping over things. They kept tripping over things because they never had their eyes on the ground."

"You seem to know them well," I exclaimed.

"Sure I know them well!" she said.

"What did you say your name was?" I persisted.

"I didn't say," she replied, amused. "My name's O'Hara. Dee O'Hara. I am the astronauts' nurse."

I'd heard about her, I must tell you. I'd even read a booklet about her. For a long time she had made news in America and everybody knew who she was, Dolores O'Hara, Dee to her friends, born on August 9, 1935, at Nampa, Idaho, by profession aerospace nurse, the only aerospace nurse in existence. From Idaho, the booklet said, she had very soon gone to Oregon with her mother, father and brother. Her father, a lumberman, had been crushed to death by an avalanche of tree trunks when she was seventeen, and from then on she had always earned her own living working as a nurse, first in the hospital in Providence, Oregon, and then in the Air Force Nursing Corps, where she held the rank of second lieutenant. As a second lieutenant she used to live and work at Patrick Air Force Base, a stone's throw from Cape Canaveral, and here she had been selected from God knows how many thousands of envious colleagues. She was twenty-four years old at the time and she didn't even know the meaning of the words *astronaut* and *spacecraft*—nor did anyone else, for that matter, it was 1959 and Project Mercury wasn't even under way. To her great amazement, they had selected her. They had immediately made use of her as a personality, sending her around to give lectures, show herself, wherever she arrived there were journalists waiting for her, bouquets of flowers, cameras, but in spite of it all she had managed very well until she became more or less indispensable, a kind of institution, you might say. And, for the astronauts, a sister, a friend—it was she who watched over their health during training, the period of retirement that precedes the Great Day, she who controlled their blood pressure, their digestion, their moods, who prayed for them every time they went forth in their spacesuits on their way to the launch pad, the only woman in a world strictly forbidden to women, a world of men who do not know how to pray, and what a challenge! Can you imagine Mother, for example, in such a world? Mother when she was young and beautiful and used to color her lips the reddest of reds and comb her hair in a lot of funny bangs? Can you imagine, for example, all the possible envies, enmities, treacherous traps? It wasn't by accident that people now talked a good deal less about her, as if they were maybe tired of paying her homage, thanking her for having spent in NASA's service the greenest years of her life. At God knows what cost: around those blue eyes the skin was beginning imperceptibly to become wrinkled with a thousand swallowed disappointments, a loneliness, bitter and never admitted. Unlike all the others I was meeting, you see, Dee O'Hara wasn't married. She wasn't even divorced, engaged or whatever, and although this was a choice for which she showed no regret, but rather pride, and this made me like her even more, still it takes courage to remain single in a country that regards single people as outlaws. I couldn't help comparing her with Mother in this respect too. You see, I don't believe Mother would have been able to meet you if her best years had been taken up with checking the blood pressure, digestion, moods of the astronauts. And, you see, I don't believe Mother would have been happy not having met you.

"Ah! The astronauts' nurse." And I looked at the badges on her collar: nursing insignia, I now observed.

She smiled.

"I've heard about you."

She pulled an odd face, as if she were indifferent or rather displeased to hear that people were still talking about her. She took up where she had been interrupted and her whole body, her whole willpower, repulsed my questions, personal curiosities. Nuns, I don't know if you've ever noticed it, and women who live alone often have this guarded modesty, this jealous self-concealment.

"As I was saying, they keep on tripping over things, as if their eyes were still up there, and they begin to raise their eyes to the sky the morning they go up. You should see them the morning they go up. They want to walk as usual, they try but they can't manage it and they go much faster. They run, I would say, they don't want to but they do: as if they were afraid of being late for an appointment, or of losing everything, and they've already lifted off from the Earth, they're already up there in the sky while they're saying So long. So long, never goodbye: of course. And you feel like . . ."

"Crying?"

"Yes, but not because you're sad, because you're happy. With them, for them. Crying, but not tears of fear, you know, tears of satisfaction, of joy. It's their day, and they've waited so long for this day and . . . have you ever seen a launching?"

"Not yet. Except on TV or in the movies."

"Oh, TV and the movies take all the magic away. You have to see a launching at the Cape, in the silence of waiting, such a profound silence that you even hear a far passing car or a whistle or a breath, and the fellows go up in the elevator to their spacecraft, are shut inside it: all of a sudden so alone. Everybody is around them and yet they are all of a sudden so alone. And while you're thinking that they're so alone, gloriously alone, happily alone, the gantry separates, you hear count-down getting lower and lower and your heart is bursting with joy. You hear that word *lift-off*, you see the rocket rising and somehow it's you who are lifting it, pushing it with your joy, with your hands, with your eyes looking, looking, until you can't see it any longer but your eyes keep on looking just the same, happy because you know the fellows are happy. And this makes it all worth it, the jealousies, the angers, the humiliations, the bitterness, and you don't think of anything else."

"Not even that they might die?"

"No, because you know you mustn't think about it, you know you must suppress any such thought, you must drive it out of your mind: or else they feel it. They're so perceptive, they feel it. Although they are ready to die, we are not ready to see them die."

Then she moved away from the spacecraft, led me out of the great shed, walking along a path where, needless to say, nobody else was walking, and don't you think this is extraordinary too? Instead of going on wheels, she went on her own feet. And those long big feet, Father, took me further away from you who without saying anything, indeed miles and miles away from me as you were, had taken me back home during those days. Number One Building, Number Two Building, Number Three Building—sorry, it's regulations. Plastic passes, helmets, press buttons—sorry, it's regulations. She too lived within the regulations and yet . . .

She smiled. "You look puzzled."

"I was wondering what I'll feel like when I meet them," I lied.

"I used to wonder too before I met them that day at Cape Canaveral. In those days Cape Kennedy was Cape Canaveral. I

opened the door of Hangar S, the home base of the Mercury flights, and
there they were, all seven of them: Al Shepard, Deke Slayton, Wally
Schirra, John Glenn, Gus Grissom, Gordon Cooper, Scott Carpenter,
there were no others in those days. "Oh!" I stammered and shut the
door again. I'm not shy, I never have been, but behind that door was
the cream of the cream of America, you see what I mean, and I felt so
shy. Then "Dee! Come here, Dee!" Deke Slayton called. I'd already
met Deke Slayton. I shyly opened the door again and went in. I went
toward them, shook hands with them and suddenly my shyness
vanished. I heard my voice saying: Can I get you a Coca-Cola?
Because, well, because they were so young, so happy. You see, they
had the same aura of mysterious enviable happiness that pregnant
women have."

"Pregnant women?"

"Yes, I know it's funny to compare these champions of virility with
pregnant women, but that's what I thought: that they had the same aura
of mysterious enviable happiness as pregnant women. Have you ever
really looked at a pregnant woman?"

"Yes."

"Have you observed one with attention?"

"I have. They have a special kind of smile. And the way they
hold out their hand is special, and so is their voice when they say good
evening. They hold such a secret, such a promise, ahead of them lies
such a difficult glorious undertaking, this life that is growing and growing
inside their belly even if it can't be seen, that they feel rich. They feel
precious, ready for anything, you understand, and nothing frightens
them, nothing worries them, not even the fact that they might die, that
their child might die . . ."

"Exactly like that. And this makes them young even if they're old,
happy even if they're unhappy. Just looking at them gives you such
warmth and respect that you feel you have to do something for them, get
them something, anything, a Coca-Cola. Maybe that sounds funny."

"No, it doesn't."

"I mean, we risk sounding ridiculous when we put certain things
into words: maybe we shouldn't. But it's what I think, and when the
Great Day comes, when they're shut up inside that spacecraft that's
made like a womb, when it's shot up into the sky, brought forth in the
sky, I can't help thinking of the birth of a child. Maybe because I've
helped so many children to be born. You know, I was an OB nurse
before I was the astronauts' nurse."

"An OB what?"

"OB nurse. Something like a midwife."

A midwife: what do you say to that, Father? Doesn't it make you shudder, Father, doesn't it honestly shock you, the idea that this woman accustomed to helping babies to be born now helps these grown-up men to be born again in space? Doesn't it stir a little hope for this future that we cannot escape, doesn't it strike you as a symbolic sign from providence or fate? After the baby has spent his appointed 266-or-so days in the tranquillity of his mother's womb he is abruptly shoved out by a 100-pound propulsive force . . . Because of one thing I'm certain: it doesn't make you laugh, Father, it just doesn't make you laugh.

"You aren't laughing, honest?" Dee asked, astonished.

"No, I'm not laughing."

"Everyone laughs when I tell them. They laugh like crazy. The fellows laughed a lot too. An OB nurse? they used to laugh. What's an OB nurse going to do with us?"

"I'm not laughing, Dee."

"I wonder why."

"It's just an old idea of mine, Dee."

"What idea?"

"I'll tell you some other time, Dee." And I didn't tell her another thing, Father. I didn't say that the example might go further, that there is something sexual in the entire fact of going up in space. Even the joining of two spacecraft resembles a moment of physical love: remember when Stafford and Cernan wanted to enter the virgin capsule of Agena? Don't laugh, Father. I know it doesn't make you laugh.

"I'll tell you some other time, Dee."

Stig and Bjorn were approaching, looking as if they had some news. Then they were beside us and I made the introductions, but I didn't say that before she became the astronauts' nurse Dee had been an OB nurse because I was afraid they'd start laughing and I didn't want them to start laughing.

"Stig, Bjorn, this is Dee O'Hara, the astronauts' nurse."

"Oh!" said Stig.

"Oh!" said Bjorn.

They were very impressed and they bowed, asked her I don't remember what, and only after a while passed on their news to me.

"The Chief is giving us himself and four other ones. To be divided in equal parts and with fairness."

"Agreed. Who's the Chief?"

"Deke Slayton," Dee explained. "The one who's never been up. God knows he wants to go. You'll like him."

"I've liked you too," I said.

"Oh! I'm only a nurse," she said. And she smiled her two streaks of red, with a fluttering of cornflowers. Just like Mother when she says oh, I'm just a mother. Mother when she was young and beautiful, when she was able to square her shoulders, her sturdy body erect on her sturdy legs, and thus went her way into a world that was alien to her but in which she believed in spite of a thousand swallowed bitternesses, in spite of the envies, the enmities, the treacherous traps, Mother whom you always find again when you look for a clue, a clue to humanity. Now I was ready to meet these living creatures. No longer biology experiments, laboratory specimens, Father, but living creatures.

"Only a nurse? I wouldn't say that. Anyway so long, Dee, and many thanks."

"So long, I hope we'll meet again: I'd like to hear this old idea of yours that stops you from laughing at what I say."

"We surely will. Chance is sometimes generous."

"Oh!" she said. "I don't believe in chance. There's no such thing as chance. If the Suns and the planets rotated by chance, every hour, every minute would be the end of a world."

And then she went. And it was as if one hundred persons went with my regret. We'll hardly ever speak of women in this book, Father. Traveling into the future, I found so few of them and, with another exception perhaps, never any interesting ones. Women are almost totally excluded from the space venture and if you look at them, if you question them, you understand why: they don't care in the least about what lies ahead of us. They're neither for nor against, they stand motionlessly by like the Garrett workers: the march of man in the cosmos is for them reduced to a conquest of new domestic appliances, automatic cooking pots, automatic washing machines, home comforts. Nothing more. Out of their wombs will emerge the son who will go to his death on Mars, on Alpha Centauri, God knows where: and their sole contribution is their properly functioning ovaries. Yes, I know that when the right moment comes they will follow their husbands, leave with them to settle those remote worlds, etcetera etcetera amen. I know. They already did so in America when beside their husbands they shot Indians. But when the moment comes we'll realize that, apart from a woman astronomer here, a woman geologist there, they won't be doing a thing to deserve such a privilege. Like all great enterprises, decisions, the discovery of new continents, new medicines, the revolutions, the wars, the Moon remains a man's job. A man's responsibility. Nevertheless there are a few things I wouldn't have understood or accepted if Dee O'Hara hadn't been there. Dee O'Hara, a simple nurse. Only a nurse.

When the Easter egg was broken it was midday. I was getting Glenn, Shepard and the Chief. Stig was getting the Chief and two new ones. Separate interviews, naturally. And we weren't to expect too much time for chattering: the normal length of a conversation was between fifteen and thirty minutes. A door was opened immediately and I went into an office, bare, furnished only with a table and three or four chairs, some little models of rockets and planes. Among the little models of rockets and planes stood a man I had never seen, not even in a photograph. He was tall and strong, attractive; the tweed jacket was enough to show he hated ties. This, I remember, was the first thing that struck me. The second thing was his rugged hard manly face, the face of a soldier used to being exposed to wind and rain without batting an eye, or of an actor who always plays incorruptible heroes in war films. The third thing was his eyes: very bright and blue, at the same time full of irony and sadness. Slowly he raised his well-kept hand and shook mine. Then, without moving those eyes, he said, "Good morning. My name is Deke Slayton."

I knew that voice: it was a voice from home. Just like yours, Father—low, vibrant, very beautiful.

8.

So here was Donald K. Slayton, Deke to his friends, chief of the astronauts and victim of the most atrocious misfortune that can happen to anyone in that job. You know, Father? They had chosen him because he was the best of the group: according to his own comrades, the one who was coolest and best prepared. It was only seven weeks before his launching when the Air Force doctors told him he wouldn't be going: his heart was not perfect. He was suffering from idiopathic atrial fibrillation: the violent acceleration, the pressure six times greater than normal, might cause cerebral anemia or worse. "Ridiculous. I came through the tests perfectly well. I'm in much better shape than I was then. I feel fine and nothing can happen to me," Slayton replied with composure. "Absurd. His heart defect was noted at the end of August 1959. It's a minor defect that doesn't even register during flight. Deke already had it when he was working as a test pilot," his comrades were to protest. But the Air Force doctors were to insist, no, no, no, and then began the most desperate battle that a man can undergo when he sees his dream slipping from his grasp. And from doctor to doctor, taking every test again, the centrifuge, the heat-pulse oven, his feet in the ice, the tortures that none of them would want to repeat and that they would give who knows what to forget, Slayton tried to prove that the defect was harmless, insignificant, that it happened only once in a couple of weeks, sometimes not for a month, and then not always, only if he'd been running for three or four miles, who wouldn't be a bit out of breath if they'd run for three or four miles without stopping, they had to believe him, for God's sake, they had to believe him, it made as much difference as having one green eye and one blue eye, didn't the NASA cardiologists say as much?

They certainly did: "It is a matter of a disturbance that is not at all serious, difficult to detect even when it reaches its most acute stage, dangerous only to anyone suffering from hypochondria. But he is quite the opposite of a hypochondriac: he is distinguished by exceptional control." However, they said other things too, while the argument spread into the newspapers: "No, he shouldn't go up. If he dies, what will the world think of us?" "No, we mustn't send him. If he dies, it'll set everyone against the space race." Very few observed: "Why should NASA need so many OK's: didn't NASA pick him to be an astronaut?" Yes, they'd picked him: but Slayton the Air Force major depended on the Air Force doctors and his place was taken by Glenn just the same. After Glenn his place was taken by Carpenter. After Carpenter his place was taken by Schirra. After Schirra his place was taken by Cooper. And every time he was there—to see them go, to congratulate them, to follow their flight on Earth, in the control room, on the TV screens, to answer ruthless questions from reporters. "Major, how do you feel to see them go up?" the press would ask. "I feel like you would feel," he would answer. "Damned disappointed, damned hurt. Damned determined to make them change their minds." To get out of the clutches of the Air Force cardiologists, he had asked to go back into civvies, to become a NASA employee and nothing else. But the reply from the generals never came, and when finally it did come, the Mercury project was already over; if he wanted to go, he would have to wait for the Gemini project: "In the Gemini project, you know, there will be two astronauts and the spacecraft costs millions. If anything happens to you, at least the other can save the spacecraft." That, Father, is the drama of Slayton, the astronaut who would risk his life twice when going into space. And this, Father, was the man who stood there among the little models of rockets and planes, who looked at me with eyes at the same time so bright and so blue, full of irony and sadness, defenseless timidity, the disarming simplicity of country folk. Of Norwegian origin, Slayton was born in Sparta, Wisconsin, a green state of forests and torrents, his father and mother are still country folk living on the farm handed down from the great-grandfather. He was eighteen when he went to the war, a volunteer, and found himself piloting B25 bombers over Italy, Japan, Okinawa. He was twenty-three when he was discharged and entered the University of Minnesota and in two years earned what others take four years to get: a degree in aeronautical engineering. Of the Lutheran religion, I am told, he spends his time hiding his feelings or pretending he doesn't have any. His replies are usually brief, people make him feel ill at ease, one speaks to him and feels at once that he would give a lot to be a thousand miles away, among the stars or in his forests, lost in a stubborn lack of trust. The harder I tried to be friendly, to tell him with my eyes that no, I wasn't looking at him as one looks at an animal in the zoo, I was looking at him as at another human being, the more he shut himself away—obstinately. It felt as if I had before me one of those hedgehogs that follow you as long as you take no notice of them, but shrink and become a ball of prickles when you touch them. His arms folded on the table, his neck sunk into his shoulders, he was smiling a smile that was more a bending of the lips, a spine bristling in defense, his whole face motionless, his nose, his mouth, his cheeks sculpted by blows from an ax. He seemed less like a man than the statue of a man, a fine wooden bust, that some bizarre fate had for some reason endowed with two eyes, and the eyes told all: the past bitterness, the indifference to celebrity, the passion for the sky, the headstrong faith of his fathers who one day had left the fiords, the calm waters of home, and had sailed across the great sea until they arrived at the land called Wisconsin. For the rest, he was silent; what was worse, he invited silence. Courteously, not with arrogance. And—do you believe me?—I truly do not know how I managed to risk the first question.

"As a matter of fact, it must be hard for you, Major, to stay there watching the others going up. Not being able to convince them that you could have done it all right, that they were wrong . . ."

"It hasn't been very agreeable, no. It has been very disagreeable, yes."

"Forgive me for bringing it up, Major."

"Everybody brings it up. But what else can I say? There you are, with one foot on Earth and the other in the capsule. You've been waiting four years for this moment. And then they tell you to get out, your heart isn't good enough. What do you do about it? You aren't a doctor. You can't prove to them that they're wrong. You stay there, thinking how wrong they are. And you can't do a thing about it. Not a thing."

"How did it happen, then, that—"

"It happened that some were convinced, others weren't. So they began arguing about it. Trying to reach some kind of agreement. They couldn't, and they said it was better not to run any risk. You know how conservative people are. Fearful. The least doubt is enough. And they decide not to run the risk. I feel fine, I tell them. Damned fine. The thing's imperceptible, just a murmur. When it's at its worst I can hardly feel it. If I had to say what it was, I wouldn't know what to call it. It doesn't have the slightest effect."

"It might have some effect during the flight, Major. The violent acceleration, the pressure six times greater than normal, the effort . . ."

"No. Nothing of the kind. It's a very minor defect. I've said so before and I'll say so again. Like having one green eye and one blue. Only the ultra-conservatives, the ultra-prudent, talk like you. And since they're afraid they can't say yes, go, with complete confidence, they prefer to say no, don't go. The world is full of people who say no. It always seems to be so difficult to say yes. For fear of damaging your reputation. Not yourself. Your reputation. One no and your reputation is safe. Anyway, as long as you stay on Earth, nothing can happen to prove they're wrong. But if you go up and something happens . . . aha! Then their reputations are ruined, all right."

The statue moved, became a man again, dejected, with bowed head. Now I couldn't see his eyes. I could see only his forehead and his hair. His hair was cut very short and stood on end like the bristles of a brush.

"You see . . . I have never been lucky. I mean, I've never been the kind that gets the breaks. Whatever I've got I've had to work for. Yet I was so sure I'd be the first. I was wrong, obviously."

"Don't take it to heart, Major. Everyone knows that you'll be the next to go up. They even say you'll be the one to lead the expedition to the Moon. Now you're in civvies in every sense of the word, you can do what you want."

"Hm. Yes. This time it really looks like I'll be going. Yes. I can't wait to go."

"In that steel nutshell, Major? Listen: this morning—"

"Steel or paper, what does it matter? So long as it flies. Anything that flies, I'll use it. I'd use an umbrella if an umbrella could fly. I've been flying for twenty years. I was nineteen when I was a bomber pilot flying over Italy. Work it out and you'll find that makes twenty years."

"Wait, wait . . . Italy?"

And suddenly the awkwardness vanished. Believe me, Father. Like a blow, like a slap, it all came back to me—the wail of the sirens, the buzzing of those cicadas which weren't cicadas but airplanes, ten planes, twenty, a hundred, one after another, the whole sky filled with planes, pitiless, close, closer and closer, and lower, more and more distinct, remember, Father, by then you could pick the lettering out quite clearly, the glass cockpits, the men in the cockpits, and they wore helmets, like motorcyclists, and everybody was hurrying away, like ants, and I was hurrying too, like an ant, alone, all alone that day, I was hurrying away on my bicycle, there was a saucepan tied on to my bicycle, the saucepan was full of soup, soup to take to you in prison, the fascists had put you in prison, I had tied the saucepan to the handlebars to take the soup to you, the cicadas were above me and I couldn't untie the saucepan, and I was pedaling, pedaling, pedaling, and the saucepan knocked against the handlebars like a pendulum, toc-toc, toc-toc, toc-toc, and with each knock a little soup slopped out, staining my legs, my dress, my shoulders, the people were shouting, calling each other, crying, a bomb fell, then another, then another, one explosion, then another, then another explosion, the people were shouting, calling each other, crying, the soup was staining my legs, my dress, my shoulders, the saucepan was going toc-toc, toc-toc, toc-toc, safety lay across the bridge, there were no railroad lines on the other side of the bridge, Lord I beg you, let me reach the bridge, just the bridge, the bridge was so far off, so very far off, and another bomb was coming down, close this time, very close, bits of stone were flying about, the street was a cloud of dust, and I was pedaling on through the cloud, desperate, ever more desperate, ever more alone, ever more helpless, the bridge was twenty yards away, fifteen, ten yards, thank you Lord, I've made it, and the last bomb was dropping, an exploding volcano, a gaping hell, a blinding light, a roar, a cyclopic blow, a monstrous slap, and then I was rolling on the ground, among the broken mortar, in the smoke, and the bicycle was on top of me, the empty saucepan that was still going toc-toc, my foot was hurting bad, a horse was lying on its back beside an upturned wagon, its long teeth clamped together, its hoofs raised to a sky of dust, as if asking for help and . . .

"Wait, wait. Italy?! And where were you bombing, Major?"

"Here and there, everywhere. Naples. Tuscany. Florence, I remember. In October of '43."

"Florence? In October of '43?"

"Yes. That cursed railroad."

"That cursed railroad." And I think, it's very likely, I got gooseflesh. It may be stupid, but I always get gooseflesh when I think of that day, Father.

"Why? . . . Where were you?"

"Below you. Right below, Major." And I think, it's very likely, my eyes grew wet. It may be stupid, but my eyes always grow wet when I think of that day, Father.

"No! Oh, no! We missed . . . we missed a lot of targets, I remember. And . . ."

"God forbid. I only twisted my foot, Major, just a slight injury. It was just our house that was destroyed, Major. But it was right by the railroad, right next to it. You couldn't avoid it, Major."

"I'm sorry. I'm very sorry. It was my job."

"It was the war, Major."

It was the war, and they were our friends, those men in the cicadas. You used to say so, Father, and I used to repeat obediently that they were our friends. But I was a child and I couldn't understand why they were bombing us if they were our friends: and I used to hate them. Hating them I used to wonder what they looked like and now I know, Father: they looked like a nineteen-year-old Deke Slayton, a decent person.

"A cigarette, Major? Oh, yes. I was forgetting that astronauts don't smoke."

"I'll take one. I shouldn't, we shouldn't. But I'll take one."

And he clutched it as you clutch a rope when you've been swimming a long time and you're tired. Then, the rope in his hand, he started looking for some matches. He looked everywhere, in all the pockets of his jacket and his trousers, and with each movement you could almost hear his joints going creak, creak: until you couldn't hear any more creaking and there was a man whose cigarette I was lighting.

"Thanks. Oh, thanks. You're leading me astray. It's always you girls who lead us boys astray. What were we talking about?"

"About the steel nutshell, Major. The one you'll go up in. I went inside the Apollo spacecraft a few days ago: frankly, I couldn't get out quickly enough. A bit uncomfortable, apart from anything else."

"Oh, no, there's plenty of room. All you need. Truly. I can't see the difference between shutting yourself up in a plane and shutting yourself up in a spacecraft. Flying in a spacecraft just means that you fly faster and higher, just means changing from one method to another method. Today you think spacecraft are a nightmare, in thirty years you'll think of them as a normal means of transportation in which people like me will carry people who are going to spend their holidays on other planets. And . . ."

And remember, Father? When the city changed masters and the Americans came, my foot was still hurting. I hadn't taken proper care of it during those months, what did a mere broken foot matter, and on some days I would limp a little, hopping along, and with every hop my eyes would seek out the eyes of the new soldiers as if to ask them: Was it you? The soldiers looked at this little girl who looked at them as if asking for something and they would give her a bar of chocolate or bread or cake, and pull her plaits, and . . .

"Major, I realize that in twenty years or even sooner the astronaut's job will be a job like any other; like being a jet pilot, for example. But for the moment it isn't, and that steel nutshell strikes me as a trap: a very dangerous trap that goes a bit too far away from the Earth. In fact, when you're inside it you need oxygen."

"And don't we need it when we go underwater? A lot of people like living underwater and to do so they equip themselves with oxygen, diving suits and other such stuff. We're no more made to live underwater than we are to live up in the air, or beyond the air. Even so, we go underwater, and up and beyond the air, and from the moment it becomes possible to do so it is no longer unnatural. If we thought of the risks involved in doing things, we'd never leave home. And even if we stayed at home, we wouldn't move because even at home we could get hurt. How many people get electrocuted in their bathrooms or break their legs falling downstairs or cut off a finger slicing salami? But if we stopped to think about this we'd have to stay there, never moving, sitting forever on the bottom step, like terrified larvae thinking of only one thing: the various ways of dying. Huddled up, silent, tensely hoping that the chandelier won't drop on our head, that the roof won't fall in, that lightning won't strike through the window. But what kind of a life would that be? It would be a death. A living death. Listen: anyone who's afraid to die isn't worthy of life, that's my opinion. And . . ."

And remember, Father? they would pull her plaits and I would be ashamed of accepting the bar of chocolate, Mother used to say that decent little girls didn't accept chocolate from anybody, least of all from soldiers, but I would also be ashamed of refusing it, Mother used to say you had to be polite when someone offered you a gift. So I would stand there with the chocolate in my hand, red-faced, confused, staring at the soldier as he went away and was never the one who'd hurt my foot. When you're looking for somebody, you know when you've found him, don't you think so, Father? Something deep inside you stirs and . . .

"Yes, what you say is fine, Major. You're probably right, too. But the fact remains that I feel afraid. You see, Major, centuries separate us. You are born now and I several centuries ago."

"Oh, no. It's just that my job isn't your job, that's all. Other people's jobs always seem difficult: because we don't understand them. For example, I find it fantastic that you'll be able to turn our talk into written pages. You find it fantastic that I can shut myself up in a spacecraft and go up. That's the only difference there is: and it doesn't mean that I belong to the future and you to the past. We both belong to the same century, and then don't think you're the only one who gets these ideas. America's full of people who think of my job as something exceptional, and they're afraid of it. But they're not really afraid: they're diffident, doubtful. People are always diffident or doubtful when they're faced with things they don't understand, things they can't do themselves."

"Knowing how to do a thing isn't enough, Major. As well as knowing how to do it, you need something else: the courage."

"Now I'll tell you what it is, this famous courage. Take an example. If you have to enter a car race, you get yourself a good racing driver . . . No, that won't do. Got it . . . you make me think, I've got it now. If you have to have a difficult operation, you get yourself a good surgeon. Yes, this'll do, this'll show what I mean: because I'd be scared to death of performing a surgical operation. And why would I be scared to death? Because I don't know the first thing about surgery, for me it's a completely alien job. You can imagine how I'd shake if they pushed me into an operating room and said look: that girl has to have a heart operation. My God! I'd be overcome with panic, I'd fall down in a dead faint. I'd say, first I drop bombs on her, now I'm going to kill her by chopping her to pieces with a scalpel. Help! But a surgeon wouldn't be scared because he'd know how to use the scalpel, how to fix your heart. Now take a surgeon who isn't even a pilot: throw him into a spacecraft, seal him in hermetically, light a great blaze under his tail and send him up. He'd be scared to death, obviously. And why? Because he doesn't know anything about what's happening to him. I don't get scared because I know what's happening. I know every smallest part of that spacecraft, in the same way the surgeon knows every smallest part of your heart, your veins, your arteries. I've been using it for years, that spacecraft, I talk to it, I understand it, I'm fond of it. And so we come back to what we said before: we're always afraid of things we don't know and don't understand. And . . ."

And remember, Father? The new soldiers were fat, with friendly big faces and always laughing. They went on laughing even when they were drunk and other soldiers with helmets marked with the letters MP loaded them into olive-green trucks: taking them, I suppose, to prison. It really didn't seem as if they were fighting a war, they seemed to be on holiday, and they seemed as if they would never die or kill either. It seemed impossible to me that men like these could drop bombs to kill horses and break children's feet. They were all in the infantry. You used to say that the occupation forces have nothing to do with the planes. And so, little by little I became resigned to not finding him, the one who'd hurt my foot. Then my foot got well and I forgot about it.

"But listen, Major, are you quite sure you'll get to the Moon?"

"Quite sure. Of course."

He looked at me with stupefaction, as if I'd said: are you quite sure you have a nose?

"And are you sure of getting back again, Major? Getting back without the help of the thousands of people who control your departure from the Earth, follow you minute by minute, direct you . . ."

This time he looked at me as if I'd asked: are you really sure you can get out of this chair?

"Certainly. You must get this into your head: if we didn't think we could make it, we wouldn't go. None of us wants to make that damn trip without returning and there's no question of any damn ticket that isn't round-trip." He shook his head. "I don't understand. A lot of people think of this journey as a journey made to land on the Mare Nubium or the Mare Imbrium or whatever they call those plains, and to say here we are, and then come down to Earth again as happy as someone with a weight off his mind. Say, baby, did you see that? We knew we could do it and we did it. Come on, let's go and have a drink on it. Pretty idiotic, don't you think? Our journey is a scientific journey and it's got to give us more knowledge of a universe about which we know hardly anything."

"Hardly anything. Not even what kind of landscape will meet your eyes. Good Lord, aren't you even a bit worried about that?"

"No. I'm not worried."

"I don't believe it, I don't believe it! We know that the horizon is much more restricted on the Moon: the Moon is so much smaller than the Earth. Since it's more restricted, it's near. Since it's near, it seems like the brink of a nearby precipice, and beyond it is the sky. A great black sky, with the Earth looming hugely as if it were about to crush the Moon . . . Doesn't this mean anything to you!"

"It means a very fine photograph, a really interesting photograph. Think of sitting on the Moon and looking at the Earth. It must be better than sitting on the Earth and looking at the Moon."

"All right. And how about if you can't bear it, this sensation of looking at the Earth from the Moon?"

"Why shouldn't I be able to bear it? Because nobody's felt it before? Because nobody's seen the Earth from the Moon before? Somebody has to be the first. Others will see the same thing later on."

If this were a novel instead of the story of a journey, I'd have some fun writing about a type like this, don't you think, Father? I'd make him into a really improbable character. Even when I tell you this or that bit of conversation, I sometimes stop and wonder: did he really talk like this or was I dreaming? He really talked like this: I didn't dream a thing. Nor the fact that he kept it up for over an hour, he whose voice dries up after three or four sentences. Nor the fact that Bjorn and Stig frequently put in an impatient jealous appearance: their interview with MacDivitt had been over for some time and now it was their turn to meet Slayton. Nor the fact that he was a bit too perfect to be alive. I admit that a doubt crossed my mind, a suspicion that he was not a man but an imitation of a man: which is to say, a robot. Yes, on that I had my doubts, I admit it, Father. And also the temptation to say to him: "If you aren't a robot, hit me." But something in those eyes told me he really would—"Silly girl, take this!" And because I attach great value to my teeth, I refrained. Besides, you'll realize quite well that he's no robot, this Slayton. You'll meet him often, further on, and you'll realize it more and more: there's something in him that you rarely find in people of physical courage—and that's what's known as moral courage. The two things don't often go together, do they, Father? I mean, a man might defy ten machine guns singlehanded, or go to the Moon and start calmly taking pictures of the Earth, and yet the slightest misfortune, the least little problem turns him into a coward. Remember that friend of yours who resisted tortures, they gave him a medal for it, and then ten years later when he met one of his torturers at the theater he didn't have the courage, the moral courage, to refuse to shake his hand. Tell me, you exclaimed, have you forgiven him? Not for anything, he answered. Did you do it out of embarrassment? Are you joking? he answered. Then why did you do it, why? You know, he says, now he's got a lot of power, he's director of a factory and I'm planning to do business with them. . . . The older I get, Father, the more I admit how right you were when you said it takes more courage not to shake hands with a rich beggar than to let them tear out your nails when death is only a step away.

"And how do you spend your day, Major? In short, what does it consist of, this astronaut's job? Waiting to go to the Moon?"

"We work, like slaves we work: I haven't been to a movie for nearly two years. Here in Houston, for example, we each have our own office: we have to be in the office at eight every morning. At quarter past eight we have to go to the meeting, which is a damn meeting for discussing who'll do one thing and who'll do something else. Who'll go to watch the launching of a new rocket, I don't know, who'll go to try out a new spacesuit, I don't know. After the meeting comes school, we study like kids. Physics, astrophysics, astronomy, biology, geology, that kind of stuff. After school there's training, the centrifuge to keep us in practice and so on. Anyone who thinks we're doing nothing or spending our time flying is making a big mistake. Flying is only a small part of our work, the tail end of it. The rest is technology, technology, technology. Roger?"

"Who is Roger?"

"Roger's O.K."

"Roger is nice?"

"Roger *means* O.K." Not a smile. "We're more engineers than pilots, as I said, more students than astronauts. And we're hardly ever in Houston: we spend most of our time traveling. Cape Kennedy, Washington, San Antonio, St. Louis and New Mexico, California, Arizona, New York. To watch a rocket under construction, to examine the geological structure of a desert zone, to learn how to manage in the jungle or in a very hot lava region, to get our orders from government men. We're never still, never, never. Out of the three hundred and sixty-five days in the year, I spend at least two hundred away from home. My wife's always complaining that she can't go on running the home by herself."

"I realize it, Major. And I'm wondering: how do you think of the Russian astronauts—as colleagues or adversaries?"

"How should I think of them? As another group of men doing the same hell of a job I am, that's how I think of them. As colleagues, I think of them, even if they are in competition with me. The Russian astronauts . . . what do you suppose they're like? They're like us. I've never met them, but Shepard and Glenn have met Titov and, if I'm not wrong, they said he seems a damn decent guy. Understanding comes of itself when you do the same job, and nationality doesn't make much difference. That's what I think."

"Even so, you're still rivals."

He shrugged his shoulders.

"Bah! . . . The Russians have a different attitude. When they pick their astronauts they don't follow the criterion of selecting pilots. They don't care at all whether they're good pilots. They prefer to send up subjects for physiological rather than technical research, passengers rather than engineers." He shrugged again. "Everyone has his own method and his own good reasons for using that method. We would never have selected the people the Russians have selected. We've always thought the success of a space flight depends on the man inside the capsule. It's very difficult to construct completely automatic machines: machines have a tendency to blow their fuses, to take matters into their own hands, machines can't do without men. And so the man might as well be somebody who understands about it." He gave a dazzling white smile. "Theoretically we could also send up the first passerby. You, for example. But what would be the point? You'd be able to tell me a good story, but not to give me technical information. And that's what I need, and nothing else."

"Quite right. But what a pity! In spite of my hesitations, my excessive fears, I'd go up there to the Moon."

"You'll go. You'll go, believe me. I'll take you myself when flights to the Moon are just routine and astronauts are like taxi drivers."

"We won't be in time, Major. We'll be too old."

"Not at all. I don't think I'll be too old when I take others up. Because I don't think it'll be a long time from now. We'll go and come back, and go and come back again, because that's what the future holds for us."

The second reel of tape was nearly finished. Bjorn and Stig, enraged, were getting ready to break down the door and demand their interview. Howard Gibbons entered and whispered into my ear that Shepard had already asked twice whether or not I wanted to see him, Glenn had asked the same thing and the Colonel had no time to waste, so I made up my mind.

"Yes, of course," I answered Gibbons.

"What?" asked Slayton.

"He says I'm taking advantage of your patience, Major."

"Nonsense."

"Oh, no! It's true." I stood up. I was trying to find something nice to say to him. "It's true. But in return you have convinced me, Major. We'll go and we'll come back and—"

"That's it! Attagirl!" And he was like a happy child who's been trying for days and days to fly a kite: the kite keeps falling, then suddenly it starts to climb and goes up and up. Standing up stiffly, almost standing to attention, he looked at me as if I were the kite. Instead I looked at him, Father, and thought what a small place the world is, and how ridiculous: this man who will go to the Moon is the same one who twenty years ago nearly made me die of fright. At that time I hated him, I hoped he would crash with his bombs. Now I liked him and felt I was his friend.

I held out my hand to shake his. "But be careful, Major, when you go up. Now that I know you, I shall be very anxious."

"You don't have to be anxious. I'll come down again. To go up again and then down and then up, as long as my damn heart holds out."

Then he stretched out his arm and gave me a hearty clap on the shoulders which made me stagger slightly—his way of grumbling thanks or showing he was touched. As they do in Sparta, Wisconsin, and in our country districts. As you do, Father. A long way away, in the dawn a few years hence, a kite climbed and vanished into the sky. The sky was blue and soon it would not be blue but black. The kite disappeared into the darkness, a spark of light flickering on and off, and I switched off the TV. You know that story by Bradbury called *The Rocket Man?* The rocket man has a strange job; he constantly travels from Earth to other planets. He's never on the Earth, never at home. When he comes back for a short break he leaves again, saying: "See you in six months, two years. I have to go to Jupiter." Or to Mars. Or Neptune. Or Venus. His wife sighs, his little boy just says: "Father, be careful, Father. Be careful when you go up." The rocket man claps his son on the shoulders and says: "Don't be anxious, my boy. Because I'll come down again. To go up again and down again." The boy staggers and thinks what would happen if his father died on Jupiter, or Mars, or Neptune, or Venus. He couldn't bear to look at those planets on nights when they were visible. "Well. It wasn't Mars," he tells. "It wasn't Venus. My father's spacecraft fell into the Sun. Ever since then my mother and I sleep by day. We have breakfast at midnight, lunch at three in the morning and dinner before the first light of dawn. We only go out in the daytime if it's raining and the Sun is obscured. We can no longer look at the Sun."

I made my way toward the office of Al Shepard.

9.

The first, he had been the first: on that dawn of May 5, 1961. A short flight, only fifteen minutes, at a modest height, only 115 miles, and yet—the first, you know, to enter that cone-shaped capsule, to lie there while the great flames roared, to feel himself thrust into space, and you're like a guinea pig, an experimental rat, a motionless speck of humanity without any idea what will happen. None of your colleagues has ever tried it, you're the one who's going to try it for them. That dawn, on the *Lake Champlain,* one of the ships sent into the Pacific to recover the capsule, the engines were still, the whole crew stood motionless, and in heavy silence the chaplain spoke into the loudspeaker the following prayer: "Dear Lord who hears us, now that a precious life is about to be flung into the heavens, we are filled with fear, we are afraid of imminent danger. Dear Lord who hears us, we thank Thee for giving us men ready to sacrifice their existence to open up for us the doors of space. May he succeed without losing his life. May success crown his endeavors to explore the paths of knowledge, not only that we may expand into the universe but that it may be a peaceful universe where we live with each other and with Thee. Amen."

It was a gray dawn, in spite of its being late spring, cold, heavy with threat. For three days Florida had been shaken by a violent storm, thunder and lightning that tore the air as in winter, lightning that struck down the trees. On the beach the people waited shivering in their raincoats and ponchos, exhausted by lack of sleep. The previous evening had also been spent waiting, but at 7:25 the radio had announced that the launching had been canceled for that night because of bad weather conditions. Those hours in the rain had served only to reveal that the chosen man was Shepard; up to the last moment NASA had kept the secret, saying only that it might be Shepard, Grissom or Glenn. Shepard was awakened by Dr. Douglas, the astronauts' physician, at one o'clock exactly: "Come on, Al. They're filling the tanks." Having gone to bed at ten, he had slept for barely three hours, but he promptly opened his eyes and answered: "I'm ready. Is John awake?" John Glenn, back-up pilot, the one who would take his place if he was unable to go at the last minute. For months they had been training together for that flight, in the last two weeks they hadn't left each other for a minute, the evening before they had gone catching crabs along the beach, and for those three hours they had been sleeping in the same room. The room was one of the rooms kept for astronauts the night before a flight, in Hangar S, not far from the launch area.

"John's awake. We're all awake. Did you sleep well?" asked Dr. Douglas.

"Very well. No dreams," answered Shepard. "I only woke up once, about midnight. I went to the window to see if it was still raining or if the stars were out. The stars were out and I went back to sleep." Whistling, he went into the bathroom and had a shower. Then he came out and said he'd like some breakfast. He seemed, said Dr. Douglas, like a man getting up to go hunting.

Breakfast came immediately: rare steak, scrambled eggs, ham, orange juice, in equal portions for Shepard, Dr. Douglas and Glenn. Dr. Douglas and Glenn didn't have much appetite, but Shepard ate everything, including the steak. Rare steak had been a standard breakfast item for the past fifteen days. When breakfast was over, Glenn went out to check the spacecraft, and Grissom, who was to repeat Shepard's flight a year later, came in. Accompanied by Grissom and Dr. Douglas, Shepard underwent the medical examinations. The examinations took over two hours and showed Shepard to be in good shape: he had only a slight shoulder sunburn from spending too long in the sun at the swimming pool and a black toenail on his left foot which Grissom had accidentally trodden on. His heart action was good, his pulse was seventy-five to the minute, his nervous system excellent. "He realized the dangers he was about to face, but showed no fear," said the psychiatrist who spent nearly an hour with him. "Never seen a man so calm. I tried to get him to talk about other things than the flight, about his family, for example, to see whether this would make him anxious, but I didn't succeed. All his mind, every nerve, was concentrated on the flight: nothing else interested him. Even while on his way to the suit room he was already a part of the spacecraft."

Dressing him took a long time, Father. "I don't quite know why," says Dr. Douglas, "but it reminded me of the dressing of the matador before the corrida. An astronaut and a matador have nothing in common, but once I was in Spain and I was present at the dressing of a matador and the atmosphere was the same: a solemn anxiety, a religious silence, a lot of people around him. And over everything a vague smell of death." The doctors attached the sensors first, the battery-run instruments that would transmit to Earth information regarding his physiological condition during the flight. Three sensors on his chest to record heart and arteries, one sensor on his stomach to record his temperature and one attached to his nostrils to record his respiration. Then Shepard put on the ankle-length underpants, the socks, and was ready to put on the suit—a job for the specialist Joe Schmitt. After the suit they fitted him into his helmet, put on his gloves, his boots, and encased him in oxygen to maintain the proper pressure. In that strange silver sheath he truly looked like a matador, or a science-fiction creature. They had to use the microphones to talk to him.

"How do you feel, Al?" Dr. Douglas asked through the microphone.

The reply seemed to come from very far off.

"I have butterflies in my stomach, Bill."

"Happy butterflies, Al?"

"Very happy, Bill."

Then Joe Schmitt deflated the suit, which he would reinflate just before launching. Shepard took off his helmet and with Grissom and Glenn moved toward the exit from Hangar S. Shepard was gay, joking with his two comrades. For months, you know, his favorite TV comedian had been Bill Dana, who had invented the character of a frightened astronaut, José Jimenez. And now his two comrades were teasing him.

"José, what will you do during this epic flight?" Grissom was asking.

"I'll sure cry a lot," Shepard moaned.

"José, have you anything to say to the people of the United States?" asked Glenn.

"People of the United States," Shepard wailed, "don't send me up, not me!" Then he looked at the rocket as if he wanted to impress it on his memory forever. "Beautiful, eh? So tall and slender. It looks as if it's waiting too. Pity it'll get lost. I was getting fond of it."

White plumes of smoke were drifting up from below the rocket, slowly and gently enfolding it. The sky was dark, a sliver of a moon peeped out from between dark clouds. Shepard, Grissom, Glenn and Dr. Douglas went up together in the elevator that ascends to the spacecraft. At the top the technicians inflated the suit again, Shepard lowered the visor of his helmet and lowered himself into the capsule, settling himself in the supine position. Dr. Douglas handed him a box and Shepard burst out laughing inside his helmet. It was a box of colored pencils; on his space flights José Jimenez always takes a box of colored pencils because instead of controlling the instruments he spends his time drawing little houses and women; once when José Jimenez forgot his colored pencils and wouldn't go, von Braun's double had to run and buy some pencils and bring them to him.

"Thanks," said Shepard as he handed them back to Dr. Douglas. "This time José's going to be busy. Take good care of them for me."

Dr. Douglas put them into the pocket of his white coat, visibly moved. So was Grissom, who couldn't manage, remember, to utter the expression of good wishes that test pilots say to each other before takeoff: "Go and blow up." So was Glenn, who could only point to a slip of paper among the instruments in a place nobody could see. The paper read: "Ball games forbidden in this area." Glenn had put it there during check-up. Shepard laughed again and handed it to Glenn: "The TV might put it on the screen." Then Shepard shook hands with everybody and was ready. Someone shut the spacecraft hatch. It was just after five and the sliver of moon was paling, the sun was rising. The elevator took them all down again, the service structure was removed slowly, leaving the rocket unsupported: smooth, fragile, straight as a pencil with a well-sharpened point, slate-colored.

"José? Do you read me, José?" said a low calm voice.

"I read you loud and clear, Deke," said Shepard.

"Don't cry too much, José," said Slayton.

"All right," said Shepard.

Wearing headphones, his gaze fixed on the red and green lights that indicated go or no, Slayton was to remain in direct contact with Shepard from this moment to the end of the flight. Sitting next to him in the control center were Grissom and Glenn. Schirra and Carpenter were at Patrick Air Base, ready to go up in their jets and follow the recovery of the spacecraft from the air. Cooper was in the blockhouse, very close to the rocket, studying the atmospheric conditions. Now all jealousies, all envy, all past quarrels were forgotten and they were six brothers united in following, helping, protecting the seventh who is leaving to face his moment of truth. A moment of truth that takes four hours to come, Father: the time taken up by delays and postponements. Four hours are a lot when you're shut in a steel nutshell that's swaying and vibrating ninety feet above the ground and you don't know what's happening because no one has tried it before, you're melting with the heat, nervousness constricts your throat, impatience wrings your heart. Deke, what's up? It's because visibility isn't good, the Control Center couldn't follow the first stage of the flight because of the clouds, it'll clear in half an hour. O.K., half an hour has passed, Deke, what's up now? It's a valve that's overheated, Al, we'll have to change it, how do you feel? I feel fine, Deke, will you ring Louise and tell her I'm fine? O.K., Al. How long will it take to change the valve, Deke? Thirty or forty minutes, Al. O.K., Deke. Ten minutes, twenty minutes, thirty minutes, forty minutes, fifty minutes, sixty, seventy, eighty, eighty-one, eighty-two, eighty-three, eighty-four, eighty-five, eighty-six minutes to change the valve, well, are we ready, Deke? Yes, Al, starting countdown again. Deke, countdown has stopped again, what's up now, Deke? It's the technicians who want to check an electronic computer on account of the trajectory, Al. Well, it's done now, this time we're all set, far from it, they've stopped again, what is it now, Deke? It's the fuel pressure that's too high, keep calm, Al. I'm calmer than you are, by God, why don't you sort things out and light this candle, for God's sake?

It was 9:23 when they started countdown again. The sun had dried up the last drop of rain.

"Are we ready, Deke?"

"Ready, Al."

"Freedom Seven calling. Fuel is go . . ."

"Oxygen is go."

"One point two G. Cabin at fourteen psi."

"Go! Go! Go! Go! Go! Go!"

"Final count, start!"

"Ten . . . nine . . . eight . . . seven . . . six . . . five . . . four . . . three . . . two . . . one . . . zero . . . lift-off!"

"Ignition. Lift-off!"

"You're on your way, José," said Slayton's low calm voice.

A very short trip. Started at 8:34 and already over at 9:50. At ten o'clock Freedom Seven was already floating in the sea at the prearranged recovery point and a Marine helicopter was already hovering above it, ready to haul up Alan Shepard. But it was the first trip of the Seven. And nobody would ever forget it. Nor would he ever forget it, that was the rub. It was then, I am told, that it began—his awareness of being taller than the others (four inches more than Grissom, two inches more than Schirra, one inch more than Cooper, half an inch more than Glenn, Slayton and Carpenter), his habit of holding his shoulders a little too far back, of holding out his chest a little too much, of raising his nose a little too high to catch the scent of glory. It was then, I am told, that he began to show a touchiness, a hardness that one day led an exasperated colleague to exclaim: "Come off it, who do you think you are? You didn't change your skin, you know, when you went up! You're just the same as you were before you went up in that thing!" And then began, I suspect, a certain irritation or lack of friendliness that many showed toward him: journalists, publicity men, people in his own world. They would say, "Alan is an extraordinary pilot and a most intelligent man. It wouldn't be unreasonable to consider him a sort of intellectual: you know, the type who reads *The New York Times* every day, who knows everything about Vietnam and the Congo and can't rest until he understands a thing. He's very sharp, always wants to know the whys and wherefores. But he has his faults: above all else, a very hot temper that often gets him into arguments, a habit of criticizing everything and everybody, and, lastly, that mania for always wanting to be the first. If he isn't the first, he gets irascible, jealous, unhappy."

I'm not sure whether this is true or not: my impressions of the man are conflicting, Father. At times I like him, at times I don't. After the following interview I saw him on other occasions and he never seemed the same man: now friendly and now standoffish, now full of confidence and now shy. But there may be some truth in these remarks: it isn't easy being the first. This was shown by Gagarin, whom they described as a very timid boy, ill at ease in company, yet after the flight he seems to have turned into Moses, criticizing everything and everybody, allowing himself to condemn Evtushenko as if he were Tolstoy or Dostoevsky rather than a cosmonaut. Many others had shown it before him, Olympic champions, heroes: celebrity is a sickness that always leaves a trace, you'd have to be a saint not to get burned by it. And of this Alan Shepard can be absolved. He has never acted the saint. He likes women, money, racing cars, applause. And, as far as one can tell, he likes to laugh, a virtue not particularly common among the saints. Shepard was born and grew up in New Hampshire, a state they call the smallest but the wittiest of America. Son of a retired colonel who is now an insurance agent, he grew up in a middle-class background and lacked for nothing; his only idiosyncrasy was to bicycle to the airport and run errands for the pilots so that they would occasionally take him on a flight. Here it was that he fell in love with flying. Later he attended the Pinkerton Academy in Derry, then went on to the Naval Academy. What else? He married Louise and now has two daughters.

He also has a farm with eight hundred cows and fifty-eight horses, which interest him as much as the Moon and the stars. I personally suspect that he's not really that keen on the Moon and the stars, but considers them merely instrumental to his ambition.

This crossed my mind, I still wonder why, as soon as I entered his office and saw him, finally: a large mouth with protruding lips, a white flash of pointed teeth made for snapping shut, round eyes, hungry and so large that they seem to come out of their orbs to snatch better what is to be snatched. The whole was surrounded by the halo of an extremely large forehead and ears as wide and powerful as a radar bowl. Tall and slim, he emanated a virility at once subtle and aggressive, but somehow you found it difficult to go up to him and shake him by the hand. So I wondered if he reminded me of someone: someone, for instance, with whom I hadn't got on well. He reminded me of nobody—that mouth, those teeth, those eyes were unique. I wondered if it was he who somehow was repulsing me with self-importance or vainglory, but he wasn't repulsing me at all. On the contrary, he was holding out his right hand invitingly and smiling at me with so much warmth that I could have fried an egg in it; and he, however, would have eaten it together with my hand, my arm and all the rest of me. He was like, Father, yes, he was like that carnivorous plant I saw in the London Botanical Gardens that time you wouldn't come because you'd have to fly there. Nor did one sense the danger when one went up to the plant and its little leaves vibrated as if they wanted to caress you, calling to your finger. So you put your finger on the leaves and the little leaves tried to take the finger off and eat it as if it were a fly. The man was shrewd, you had to attack him directly.

"It appears that you have a complex, Commander. The complex of having been the first."

The hungry eyes flashed. The knobby well-kept hands trembled almost imperceptibly with irritation. His voice grated.

"As far as I know, no, I don't have that complex. I have, shall we say, a sense of victory. That flight was a personal victory for me, a challenge to the others. It was also a stroke of luck, I'll admit. Grissom was less fortunate than I was. He was only second."

"You were second too: Juri Gagarin had already made an orbital flight when you went up for those fifteen minutes. Did you feel jealous when Gagarin went up?"

Again his eyes flashed.

"Of course I was jealous, I'm still jealous. But the fact remains that I had the satisfaction of being the first American. And of having flown alone. Especially, alone. In the Gemini project there are two, in the Apollo project three. I was in time to fly alone and I was the first. Naturally I wasn't expecting to be the first. I knew I deserved to, but I wasn't expecting it. When they told me I stood there staring at the floor for at least twenty seconds in surprise. Then I looked up and they were all looking at me. Each of the Seven would have liked to be the first, each of the Seven had been hoping for two years, and now the moment had come, after two years, and there was no longer that possibility for any of them, only for me. . . ."

There was one disagreeable feature of that carnivorous plant in the Botanical Gardens in London. I'll tell you: not the fact that it swallowed flies or tried to suck off your finger as much as the way it raised its head after sucking in the fly—as if waiting for applause. Was it possible that this was the man who had liked José Jimenez? Could Jimenez be his alter ego, his confession?

"Now what are you going to ask?" He smiled. He seemed to have guessed.

"I was thinking about José Jimenez." And I looked him straight in the eye. But his eyes swallowed up mine.

"Ah! José Jimenez."

"I was wondering why you liked him. I was saying to myself that there are times when a joke is like a confession, a liberation from a burden."

"No, it was just for fun. There was this TV program and I was crazy about it. It was so close to the way we see things when we're in a good mood. Great man, Jimenez. For example, he appears in his spacesuit and the reporter asks him: 'How does it feel?' 'Well, it's uncomfortable,' says Jimenez, 'truly uncomfortable.' 'And what's that?' the reporter asks, pointing to his broken helmet. 'It's a broken helmet,' answers Jimenez. 'And are you going to use it?' asks the reporter. 'I hope not,' replies Jimenez. 'And how will you spend all those hours in space?' asks the reporter. 'I'll sure cry a lot,' says Jimenez. 'Fine,' says the reporter. 'As you are chief astronaut of the Interplanetary Forces of the U.S.A. and as you are about to leave, you'll surely have a message to give the people of America.' And Jimenez: 'Yes, I have.' 'Go ahead,' says the reporter. And Jimenez: 'People of the United States, don't do this to me! Don't send me up, not me!' In short, I liked him so much I recorded it on tape, then I took the tape to Cape Canaveral and during the Ranger launching, at a moment when they'd had to stop countdown because something was wrong, I put the tape on at full volume there in the Central Control Room. Sometimes we like to have a little fun too. It releases the tension."

"Or the fear, Commander?"

He shook his head, patiently, indulgently.

"I wouldn't call it fear. If anything, it's fear that things won't go well and you'll look bad. In other words, concern for the success of the flight. And then I was excited, of course I was excited, and when you're very excited the adrenalin affects your nervous system, your heart beats faster, your pulse rate doubles, you become short of breath. Let me give you an example: if you're speeding along the winding road to Amalfi in a Ferrari—I go crazy for Ferraris, I go crazy for any kind of car . . ."

But there was one interesting thing about that carnivorous plant, which was that it ate everything: ants, flies, grubs, and at one point I saw it swallow a wasp. The wasp fought for its life with angry desperation, sucking back at the plant, making holes in it, making headway through the leaves with beating wings, but the carnivorous plant withstood its efforts and won. The carnivorous plant always wins, whatever it's eating or doing. He was winning against me, too, Father.

"One can't remain a perpetual astronaut. Do you think about it?"

"Of course I think about it. I think about it a great deal, but I don't make myself sick over it. I'll make a success of some other job. I'm a man of many interests."

The fly, the wasp, the ants, the gnats, the grubs. It swallowed absolutely everything and digested everything. And it didn't even need to be watered: the caretaker told me he couldn't remember ever watering it. Oh, yes, Commander.

"And what are these interests?"

"First of all, the bank. I'm the vice-president of Baytown National Bank of Houston, I'm part owner. That takes up a lot of my time. Twice a month I have to attend the meetings of the Executive Committee; the rest of my work I have to manage by telephone, but it's worth it. Then there's the ranch, raising horses and cattle. I only have eight hundred head of cattle at present. Only fifty-four horses: all race horses, though. About twenty have been bred for the quarter-mile, but a dozen can also run the half-mile, and there's one that's outright fantastic: he can trot, he can gallop, he can do anything. He's worth at least fifteen thousand dollars, but I won't sell him. I sell the others, though: mostly for upwards of three thousand dollars. Of course, there are always some at two thousand dollars or a thousand: very high-class, though, these too. Strong legs, iron fetlocks, excellent teeth. Do you want to buy one?"

"No, no, Commander. Where would I keep a horse?"

"I'll give him to you for only a thousand dollars."

"No, no, really."

"You can be sure he's worth three thousand. Come on, it's a bargain."

"I've no doubt, Commander. But seriously: where would I keep a horse? In a suitcase?"

"You send him home, don't talk nonsense. How much do you suppose it'd cost to send him?"

"As far as that goes, it'd cost quite a bit. But that's not the question: it's that then I'd have to ride him, look after him, and I'm always traveling. Truly, Commander, I'd be happy to buy the horse, but I couldn't keep him."

"Then buy a cow. You need a cow in the country. Haven't you even got a cow in the country?"

"No, but I've got two pigs."

"Pigs! Pigs! A fine cow, that's what you need. I'll let you have her for only five hundred dollars."

A bit longer and he'd have sold me one. He'd have sold me the horse too, some shares in the bank, and he'd have cleaned me out. I was looking at him in surprised amusement and I couldn't understand how he could combine his cattle-raising activities with his banking activities, his banking activities with his profession of astronaut, stars with horses, the Moon with banknotes, the double-breasted gray suit of vice-president with the cowboy blue jeans, the cowboy blue jeans with the space-suit, the spacesuit with the double-breasted gray suit. I could see only that everything was food to satisfy his very earthly hunger which had nothing in common with the hunger that should lead a man to fly in the cosmos.

"Five hundred dollars isn't much, I know. The trouble is I don't have the money you have, Commander. You're quite rich, Commander."

"Not rich, not yet. But one day I'll be very rich."

"Through your horses? Through the cattle?"

"More through the bank."

"Forgive me if I seem indiscreet. But how did you manage to buy half a bank? After all, an astronaut's salary isn't so high."

"No, but we have this contract with *Life,* and the thing about money is knowing how to invest it. All you need is to be ambitious."

"And you are. God knows you are. But where do you want to get, Commander?"

"Wait and see."

"Are you referring to the stars, or the bank, or the cattle?"

"All of it."

"But without the stars there wouldn't be the bank, without the bank there wouldn't be the cattle. So we could put it like this, this Genesis of an ambitious man: first there were the stars, and from the stars to the bank, and from the bank came the cattle."

This time the round blue eyes flashed in anger. His voice rasped more than ever.

"You are a very romantic woman," he said.

"Very," I told him.

"Too much so," he said.

"We can never be romantic enough," I said, "when we look at the stars."

"Oh? You must be joking," he said. "There's nothing romantic about going to the stars, believe me. At bottom it's another commercial enterprise."

A commercial enterprise. And if he were right, Father? And if my dreams, my hopes, my entire research were wrong, and you had spoken the truth when you said "men will always have the same problems on the Moon or on the Earth, they will be always sick and wicked, on the Moon or on the Earth," then wasn't it also true that he was not being romantic? Wasn't he mixing the stars with the cattle, with the bank, seeing them as equal manifestations of intelligence? I raised my eyes, I met his eyes. They looked at me with a hidden smile. No more a carnivorous plant, now all a man, he seemed to understand my doubts, my potential disillusion, and for a second I liked him so. But then, Father, I got up in anger and I said to myself that no, he couldn't be right. We need to be romantic, being heroes is not enough. And I thought dammit, we should never look too closely at heroes. Heroes, La Rochefoucauld used to say, are like paintings: to appreciate them, you have to look at them from a distance. Which is true for most of them. But does it diminish them after all? Is it perhaps shameful to be human? And was it not a great discovery that far from being robots, automatons, these men were human? It was. A consolation too, after all.

I made my way to Glenn's office.

10.

That day when I left Shepard's office to go to see John Glenn he wasn't a "used astronaut," an "unsuccessful politician," a tired sick disappointed man who says, "People don't often have to start again at forty-three." He was a man full of health, enthusiasm, glory, and the future was his. He couldn't imagine that the future would collapse on top of him one morning at the end of a winter. He had gone into the bathroom to shave and the cabinet was there, hanging on a strong hook. Inside were the soap, the brush and the rest. He opened it and the hook gave, the world fell on his head. He fell too, struck on the temple and the ear. He fell between the wall and the bath, with that body he had so trained, cared for, protected, while a trickle of blood took away all his dreams. The champion who had orbited the Earth three times, challenged disasters and meteors, overcome the most hallucinating dangers—the entry into space, the weightlessness, the re-entry into the atmosphere with the capsule becoming a ball of fire—cut short by a bathroom cabinet because a hook gave. Many laughed about it, Father. There appeared all kinds of cartoons of Glenn breaking his head in the bathroom. The funniest was one of him dressed as an astronaut, with the soap in his right hand and a toothbrush in his left; facing him was a general waving the American flag and saying: "I am entrusting you with a very dangerous mission, Colonel." I didn't laugh about it. I thought rather of that atrocious Persian tale entitled "Appointment at Samarkand." In the king's garden Death appears to a slave. "Tomorrow," she tells him, "I am coming for you . . ." The slave runs to the king and asks for his fastest horse so that he can flee far away to Samarkand. Next day when he reaches Samarkand, Death is there waiting for him. "It's not right," yells the slave, "it's not fair." "Why?" replies Death. "You fled without letting me finish what I was saying. I went into the garden to say: tomorrow I am coming for you in Samarkand."

When the hook gave, he was no longer thinking of space flights, it is true. Abandoning his career as an astronaut, he aimed to run for Senator from Ohio as candidate for the Democratic Party. He had always liked politics. Besides, he had everything to appeal to the voters: a likable face, a famous name, a hero's reputation. And also the eloquence of an orator who can sway the masses, and an obsession with setting a good example to the young. "John always acts as if he were being watched by an army of Boy Scouts or children," Alan Shepard used to say, "even when he's scratching his nose or peeing." His private life was blameless, the life of a saint who doesn't drink, doesn't smoke, doesn't swear, dammit, and isn't lazy, isn't conceited, isn't unfaithful to his wife—virtues he has never lost. It is the general opinion that from the day he was born he has loved only one woman, Anne Castor, the woman he married: when needs be, it is said, he is also very chaste. While training for Project Mercury at Langley Air Force Base in Virginia, he told Anne to stay in Washington and not come to see him. The others had their families with them; he lived in his office and slept on a camp bed. He slept on it for eight months: even boxers training for a championship fight can't manage as much. A devout Presbyterian, a Sunday never passes without his going to church, and before his accident he was prone to deliver sermons: "Observe the universe, brothers. Think of the millions and millions of stars that circle around without ever colliding. Think of the order that governs the solar systems, the planets. Think of the perfection of an orbit . . ." You know, Father, I shouldn't even say a saint. I should say a Boy Scout. The most perfect fantastic Boy Scout in a nation of Boy Scouts.

To such a man, politics did not seem an art or a profession but a duty. And so one day he resigned from NASA, plunged into his new adventure with the innocence of a Boy Scout who loves his country as he loves his mother, and only a scornful observer could say that one begins to wonder whether for him the sky was not some kind of electoral instrument, whether when he looked at the stars he didn't see reflected the Earth and the White House. Most people said: "Glenn is the best thing that has happened to America in recent years, the trouble is you don't believe anyone can be as good as he seems." He was sustained, above all else, by a very clear mind, a well-tested discipline, an untiring vigor. There was no doubt that he would at least reach the Senate. But the hook gave and all that remained of his political dream was the sum of $9,473 to be paid to the Zanesville printers who had printed his campaign material. And he paid it all out of his own pocket, and nothing now remained of his dream of going to the Moon. Taken to the aerospace medical clinic of San Antonio, Texas, he was immobile for two months: he couldn't move his head by so much as an inch with-

out the world becoming a ship on a storm-tossed sea and nausea grip-
ping him by the stomach. Then he got up, but any sudden movement
put him on the brink of an abyss, the journey from one chair to another
became longer than the journey to Venus or to Mars. "O God!" he
kept repeating. "I only ask this: that I may walk a little in a room that
isn't a merry-go-round." The blow from the cabinet had damaged his
inner ear, the delicate structure that controls our sense of balance. He
had been able to tolerate the centrifuge up to 20 G, but now could no
longer keep his balance or stand up straight. "Recovery is proving
longer and more difficult than we expected," said the physicians, and
somebody put forward the hypothesis that his space flight two years
before might have something to do with his illness—hadn't something
like this happened to Titov? The hypothesis was not confirmed, for some
mysterious reason NASA took refuge behind a Soviet reserve, and
months later, when this book took me back to America, I was to find an
ill-concealed embarrassment whenever I mentioned Glenn. To direct
questions NASA replied only that he would get better, and, in fact, he is
better: but all that is left to him is the memory of a golden dawn when
he went up to the top of the tower, into the capsule. That miraculous
flight, that fairy-tale experience. It was nighttime in Perth, Australia,
when he was preparing to re-enter the atmosphere and so the people of
Perth switched on all the lights; every house, every office, every street,
every factory streamed with light; white sheets and silver plates had been
placed everywhere to reflect the lights, to help him in his descent. It
looked as if a star had come down from the sky, and through his capsule
porthole he saw the star, wondered in surprise what it could be and
called Gordon Cooper: "Roger, Roger calling, I can see a great light on
the Australian coast, but I don't understand what it can be," and Cooper
answered, "It's Perth, it's Perth, Australia. They've put their lights on
for you, to make your re-entry easier," and he said: "Thanks, thank
them Gordon, thank the people of Perth." I hesitated for a long time,
Father, before including in these memoirs my meeting with Glenn, now
on the Board of Directors of Royal Crown Cola. He belongs more to
the past than to the future, now, and it seemed as if I were going beyond
the scope of this book. Then one day, while I was thinking of a story to
tell my little sister, Father, the sad story of Glenn came to mind. And I
thought that when she will travel to Mars and to Venus as now I travel
to America, she might like to know what we said when I met him. So
here it is. And let's go back to the moment when I was waiting in his
office.

Glenn arrived almost immediately: a whirlwind of freckles and strong white teeth smiling the most contagious and happiest smile I had ever seen; a pair of sparkling green eyes, whether shrewd or innocent I couldn't tell. He was wearing an unpressed dark brown suit and an absurd little bow tie below his round face that appeared the rounder on account of his close-cropped head, which was also covered with carrot-colored freckles. Tall, bulky, not really handsome yet handsome, he reminded me of those well-fed GI's who used to throw us chocolate or chewing gum during the war; and his great open hand bespoke the prodigality of one who has just thrown chocolate or gum. To balance this he had a firm handshake, the handshake of a man who is sure of himself. So I couldn't understand why he often colored in a blush that burned his ears and swelled a bluish vein at his temples. It is true that he would laugh when he blushed. A gurgling laughter that shook his little tie, his shoulders, and you know whom it reminded me of, Father? Your friend Ohio: the sergeant who used to come to our house during the Allied occupation and whose name was so difficult that to save time we called him Ohio because he had been born there.

To start with, Ohio had the same nose: a round snub nose that turned up slightly at the tip. And he had a close-cropped head, so close-cropped that I used to ask, remember: "Father, how old is Ohio? He's lost all his hair." Then he used to blush for nothing: a blush that burned his ears and swelled a bluish vein at his temples. And he too used to laugh when he blushed. Ohio was with the tanks but he used to go around in a jeep, and you'd met him, remember, when you'd crashed into his jeep on your bicycle. Whose fault it was I don't know. Ohio would say it was all your fault, you naturally would say it was all his fault. Anyhow you made your peace and out of this peace was born a great friendship that would culminate every evening at seven when Ohio would come with a great loaf of white bread and innocently eat up what little meat and vegetables we had. Mother didn't like this too much and she used to grumble: "Listen, all the Americans are giving food to people, but this one gobbles ours all up in exchange for a bit of bread." But I know that you liked him a lot, and with your sweeping gestures, with drawings, or by invoking my aid as interpreter, you would lead Ohio on to relate dreadfully boring war stories that lasted through as many as four candles. At the fourth candle Ohio would look at his watch and go back to his barracks: and this went on until the day Ohio went with the tanks to Bologna. The farewell, which filled Mother with jubilation, upset you both enormously. Standing by the table you clapped each other hard on the shoulders and your shadows on the wall looked like two mad enormous butterflies. Then Ohio blushed and removing his watch from his wrist he held it out to you saying solemnly: "Souvenir of Ohio." "Oh God!" Mother exclaimed. "Now he'll give him our turnip!" Our turnip was Grandfather's pocket watch, as big as a turnip, made of copper, fastened to a long copper chain. Mother used to say it was a very beautiful watch, that you couldn't find any like it nowadays because it was also decorated all over with little enameled flowers. "Will you give him our turnip?" she repeated. But at the same moment you snatched up the turnip and held it out to Ohio saying: "Souvenir of Florence." Then Ohio left with his turnip, and a terrible argument broke out between you and Mother during which you said: "Shut up, the turnip was mine and I'll do what I like with it"; she said: "All right, in this house we give away our shoes to act like the rich." You didn't speak to each other for at least two days, remember, and every time you mentioned Ohio the quarrel broke out again, fiercely, until Ohio's watch broke and she, politely, never spoke of it again. But the day I was leaving for America for the first time Mother whispered into my ear: "If only you could find that wretched Ohio. If you could get back Grandfather's turnip. Pay him for it, of course." Ever since, every time I go to America and see someone who looks like Ohio, I feel like asking him: "Excuse me, but are you any relation of Ohio? You know, the one who has Grandfather's turnip?" Glenn certainly looked like Ohio and I'd have asked him gladly whether Ohio was his cousin or his uncle: but something about so much affability discouraged that kind of confidence. Sitting in an armchair, his legs crossed and his arms folded, he was looking at me as much as to say: don't let's start with the turnip because I haven't got it; on the other hand, I'm in a great hurry, I'm expecting certain calls from Washington. Silently asking Mother's forgiveness, I began.

"Colonel, there's a question I often ask myself: if astronauts are really heroes, supermen . . ."

First blush.

"Hero, superman, nonsense! I feel absolutely normal myself, absolutely ordinary. And consequently I really cannot understand what people see in me that's interesting. Like when they ask me: how does it feel, John Glenn, to be a star? I truly don't feel like a star. Yet it seems inevitable that they should think of me as a star, a superman, a hero."

A pause, a very slightly satisfied pause.

"The fact is that people are always fascinated by anything new,

new work, new explorations, especially if one risks losing his life by them. Risk always rouses their imagination. And, for good or ill, space flights are risky."

Another satisfied pause.

"And then there's the fact of having to face the mysterious, the unknown, of experiencing what no one has ever experienced. I mean, when you're the first, or one of the first, to put a piece of chocolate down in mid-air and see that it doesn't fall but remains where you put it, in mid-air, you wind up being looked at as if *you* were the piece of chocolate."

"Something you are very aware of, I know. I can't remember who it was who said that even when you're shaving you behave as if you were setting a good example to a Boy Scout."

Second blush.

"Don't let's exaggerate. I'm aware, yes, of the responsibility that comes with being famous. Isn't it a responsibility? Think of the youngsters who think I really am a hero, the children, the Boy Scouts. We have to show them that space flights don't constitute the sole interest of society in the future, that we need and shall need young people in politics, in law, in teaching: not only in astronautics. So I go around telling them this. And then I give a lot of time to religious groups . . ."

"You are very religious, I know."

"Yes, very."

"I have always wondered whether astronauts were."

"Why shouldn't they be?"

"True. And were you before you went into space, Colonel?"

"Yes, certainly. I don't really think I've become any more religious since flying beyond the atmosphere. Yet . . . yes . . . maybe . . . definitely I am more religious now." He rested his elbow on the arm of the chair, put his hand to his forehead. "I must explain what I mean. Of course I wasn't expecting to find God out there in space or to have some particular religious experience just because I was in the void; faith in God is the same wherever you go: on Earth, underwater, into space. Yet the more I see in these space flights, the more I study and learn, the more I become convinced that our religion is probably valid. In other words, I don't believe that by increasing our knowledge we'll become able to substitute ourselves for God. On the contrary. The things we're studying are so incomprehensible and vast, so mysterious, they pose such problems to our ignorance and so add to the mystery, that they lead me to this conclusion: there must be a kind of creation in the cosmos, an order."

I thought of Bradbury, Father.

"For many others, Colonel, it is different. For many others space flights pose terrible questions to the religion in which we were born. For many others they lead to doubt, to loss of faith."

He raised his head sharply, as if I had stung him.

"What leads to doubt? Let's hear what it is."

"Colonel, think of the claims of Genesis. I am speaking from the theological point of view, naturally."

"What does Genesis say? Come on, I want to ask *you* some questions for a change. How does Genesis lead to doubt?"

"In Genesis it says God created the Earth in six days and on the sixth day he created man and made him in His own image and after His likeness."

"Oh! Oh, well. I thought you were referring to something else. To seeing God in space or things of that kind."

"I have never pictured God with a beard and white robes, Colonel. Except when I was a child."

"Well. Whether the Bible is reliable or not, word for word, has nothing to do with the discovery of other planets. It raises, if anything, the old conflict between science and religion, not between space flights and religion. Or am I wrong?"

"Forgive me, Colonel, but if you ask me, I'd say you were wrong— and how. Science in general has never proved that there is life on other planets. But space flights can—and how. And the day you meet unimaginable creatures on another planet—let's call them 'beings-of-unknown-appearance'—how will you explain the Genesis story, Colonel, sir?"

"The Bible doesn't deny life on other worlds. Indeed, I'll tell you that I'd be very much surprised not to find what you call 'beings-of-unknown-appearance' on other planets. We'll find them—perhaps in the form of beings or worms, although you can be certain that one day, among the millions and millions of celestial bodies, we'll find man too. But I can imagine creatures that don't develop with our cycle of water and carbon, creatures that feed on rocks, for example, and have no blood or tissues or organs: and the Bible says nothing to deny this. It doesn't deny that God might have created them too in His own image and after His likeness. It doesn't deny the possibility of loving them as true Christians."

"And what if it were necessary to kill them, to exterminate them, these worms or rock brothers who have no blood or tissues or organs . . . would you find that painful, Colonel?"

Again he leaned his elbow on the arm of the chair. Again he raised his hand to his forehead. Bradbury was so far away, Father.

"No. I don't think so. It would be sad; it grieves me even to think about it. But I could do it. I'm a man who doesn't want to see anybody die, not even in war. But some expeditions will be like going to war, and the essence of war is death. And then, excuse me, but what makes you think we might have to exterminate the 'beings-of-unknown-appearance' on other planets?"

"Because they might be hostile to us. They might be far from happy to see us come, Colonel."

"I'm optimistic: they might be completely friendly. They might also be good, pleased to see us, and we might not have to exterminate them at all. Of course . . . of course I would be suspicious when I saw them, ready to defend myself . . . I don't know . . . Certainly, if some exist in our own solar system . . . My God . . . they surely exist in other solar systems, but we won't be going to other solar systems in your lifetime or in mine. At best this will be a hundred, two hundred years from now, and a hundred or two hundred years are not many, I know, but enough to leave me with painful questions."

"Then, Colonel, one old worn-out question. They've put it to von Braun . . . If you could take five books to the Moon, which would you take?"

A flash of eyes, a third blush.

"Books? To the Moon? I don't think we'll need books on the Moon. When they get there they'll . . . we'll have too much to do, too much to look at and think about, to allow ourselves the luxury of reading books. Forgive me, but it's like asking: what books will you bring this evening if you come to dinner with me? When you're dining with someone you have other things to do than read a book in front of his face. You'll need your book afterwards, or the next day."

"Very clever. Very brilliant, Colonel."

"Very kind, very charming."

He displayed his contagious smile. I avoided it.

"Let me put the question another way, Colonel. If some other person, wishing to influence the future, decided to burn all the books on Earth, which would you save? Tell me five, three."

"I knew you were getting to this. You're real malicious."

That smile again.

"Well, Colonel?"

"Three   books . . . three   books . . . let's   see . . . three books . . ." He flung out his arms, a sad and sorry sight. "I don't know. Oh, I don't know."

"But what do you read, Colonel?"

And again that smile. I never knew anyone who knew how to use his teeth as well as John Glenn. His lips parted, his teeth were revealed, beautiful, white, clean, and voilà! He fired. But I was looking at his tie.

"I read a lot of books about politics, current events, technical books. I read a lot of books about history, exploring, science. No science fiction. I read the newspapers a lot. Very carefully. I don't read novels or poetry or things like that."

"True, Colonel. It seems that certain things are of no use these days. The useful has taken the place of the beautiful, technology the place of art. To what use can you put an ode by Sappho or a Ghirlandaio painting, going to the Moon?"

"Don't be so pessimistic, don't think that people like me don't know what Shakespeare said, don't think that the lunar landscape blinds us to the sight of a fine cathedral or a fine painting. I love the past as much as you do, and the past serves me as a guide to the future. You aren't supposing, are you, that we have gasoline instead of blood and an electronic computer instead of a brain? We're men, not machines. Your question is aimed at something else, I know: aimed at showing that progress can become damaging and that consequently we don't have the right to push on too far: to the Moon, to Venus, to Mars. But I say no, the question can't be put in these terms. Pushing on to the Moon, to Venus, to Mars isn't a question of right: it's a duty. The duty gives us the right to make this effort and go. Go . . . even if Russia didn't exist, even if Russia weren't racing with us, we ought to be doing what we are doing. That's what I think and what I will always say, to anyone and anywhere, whether I go on being an astronaut or not. That's why I will always keep on harping, to everyone and everywhere, that we must go to the Moon, to Venus, to Mars, whatever the cost. Up to today it has cost us little: only work and money. So many men went, so many came back. But it won't always be like this, I know, we know. Some of us will die, maybe a whole crew will die: but remember, it's worth it all the same. And because it's worth it, we will accept our losses and continue with those who remain. Many pilots have died in the history of aviation, but that hasn't stopped aviation. Many mountaineers have died climbing mountains, but that hasn't altered the courage of anyone who climbs mountains. Many ships have sunk since we've been sailing the seas, but that hasn't stopped ships from sailing the seas. Yes, we must go up there, we must. And one day those who are against it will look back and be pleased at what we've done."

He spoke with passion and at the same time glanced at his watch. I can't understand how one can be passionate at the same time one watches the time, but that's what he did. And he had hardly finished speaking when a great hustle and bustle broke out. Someone came in and said that Washington was on the line. Then someone else came in and said they'd put the call from Washington through to the office on the right. Then someone else came in and said they'd put the call from Washington through to the office on the left. Then all three together said the call from Washington had been transferred to the Colonel's office, the Colonel must come quickly. And the Colonel grew very red, leaped to his feet, held out his hand to me, said: "Goodbye, it's been a pleasure, a real pleasure" and disappeared: just like the whirlwind he had been when he came in.

I spent the rest of the day by myself. Stig and Bjorn had been invited home by their escort and I had no wish to be with other people. I had something to eat and ran and locked myself in the automatic cell that was my room. The button for the air-conditioning had been fixed. It was very cold in the room. The cold increased my loneliness. It's terrible to feel alone in a place that's cold, you know, Father? It's like being the only fish in the sea, the only bird in the sky, the only fly on earth. You look around and you can't see anybody. You listen and you can hear nothing. You stretch out your hand and you touch no one. Only that buzzing cold—and the television seems a gift from God. I put on the television, but there was one sentence that was either beautiful or horrific, I couldn't decide, which kept echoing in my memory: "Although you can be certain that one day, among the millions and millions of celestial bodies, we'll find man too." So the cold, the loneliness, everything, didn't end here: it went on somewhere else too, Father. Like a curse, a guilt. And far away, millions of miles away, there was a woman similar to myself who was watching television and feeling like the only fish in the sea, the only bird in the sky, and she was looking around and couldn't see anybody, and . . . That night I had a bad dream. I dreamed that I was reaching another solar system with Glenn and drawing close to a planet where everything was identical to this planet: the men, the women, the old people, the children, the white, the yellow, the Negroes, their fear, their unhappiness, their hate, and then the houses, the motels, the streets, everything. Each one of us was existing again, as if reflected in a mirror, with his sorrows, his difficulties, his fears. And each one of us was doing again what he does here, without hope. The city we had approached was called Houston, in the south of a state called Texas, between the 30th parallel and the 95th meridian of this twin planet. In the room next to mine there was a character like an FBI man who was writing "guilty, guilty, guilty" and then, desperate, I ran to Glenn, saying: "Colonel, tell him I haven't done anything wrong. Tell him, please." Glenn went on laughing, laughing, with his beautiful white happy teeth, then he mockingly dangled Grandfather's turnip.

I I.

"I'm not spending Sunday in Houston even if I'm dead," said Bjorn, flinging his Leica onto the bed.

"Nor I even if I'm alive," answered Stig laconically. Then he began poking about among the little bottles of perfume and nail polish, with the slightly childish curiosity men always have when they're in a woman's room. My room was next to theirs, so I always had them under my feet.

"We've seen these damn astronauts, we've talked to them, I've taken pictures of them down to their shoes. What else do we want?" said Bjorn.

"To go back to Sweden," answered Stig. He stretched out in an armchair, pulled his cap down over his eyes, a bored James Stewart.

From the freeway that passed the motel came the obsessive, incessant sound of cars. The air was a stink of evaporated gas. Evenings, a blanket of boredom.

"I've had enough of this city, if you can call it a city," bellowed Bjorn.

"When the Mama Troll puts her little Trolls to bed and hangs them up by their tails, Mama Troll sings to her little Trolls, ay ay ay buff!" warbled Stig from beneath his cap.

"And I want to go to San Diego," Bjorn finished. Then he grabbed me by the arm. "Come with me."

"I have to go to Florida, to Cape Kennedy."

"Oh! We've already been to Cape Kennedy. There's nothing to see at Cape Kennedy. Two steel towers and a beach. Why do you have to go to Cape Kennedy?"

"To understand about Glenn, about Slayton, about Shepard."

"Christ! Haven't you understood them yet?"

"No. I haven't understood them yet."

"Maybe there's nothing to understand," Stig said from beneath his cap.

"I'm convinced there's a great deal to understand. A great deal," I said almost to myself. "For example, why—"

"Will you stop forever talking about them?" yelled Bjorn. "I'm sick of you and your astronauts. I take pictures of astronauts, dream about astronauts, drink astronauts. From now on the first one to mention the word astronaut pays a fine. A ten-dollar fine."

"Right. I have a proposition to make," said Stig, standing up on his interminable legs. "San Antonio is a four-hour drive. It's a pretty spot and the food's good. Let's leave Houston and spend Sunday in San Antonio. Then we two can go to San Diego and you can go to Florida."

"Hooray!" shouted Bjorn.

So we went to San Antonio.

The morning was green and gay. Along the freeway cows were grazing and we saw little wooden houses, the sort that are painted white, with sugarloaf roofs and verandas with little columns, rocking chairs on the verandas for summer lazing. Bjorn was driving, happily; I was sitting next to him, relaxed; and Stig was stretched out in the back, asleep, his cap over his eyes. Halfway we came to a hut with buffalo horns and a sign: INDIAN MUSEUM. The owner was an old Cherokee and he sold the most absurd objects, from poisoned arrows to feathered headdresses, from war hatchets to human scalps. He asked if we'd like to buy a scalp, a real scalp with real hair from a woman's head, his grandfather had given it to him and he'd let us have it for only thirty dollars, and Bjorn bought it even though it was a pretty disgusting-looking thing—a clump of black dusty hair on a bit of mummified skin. In San Antonio we ate with healthy appetites and San Antonio was the end of a nightmare. There were actually trees, carts drawn by old horses, myriads of flies, pigeons that met us with a flapping of wings, and a vague smell of dirt. In such a setting the Moon became once more what it had always been, a white light in the darkness, and everything looked beautiful to us, the river, the streets, the governor's palace, the district they call La Villita, we even thought the Alamo was beautiful, the little fort where Davy Crockett died with the two hundred besieged by General Santa Anna's three thousand. We didn't notice it had all been rebuilt. By now we were saturated with the space age, full of hostility toward the future, we were loving every trace of dust. And, isn't it strange, Father, it was the same dust that revived my interest in tomorrow.

We were visiting the missions, I remember, which are the fortresses built by the Spanish monks in the eighteenth century against attacks by the Indians, against the hazards of nature: like barracks surrounding a church. We were in the Mission San José, walking among the worn stones, when a thought struck me dumb: those walls lost in the great prairie, those cells thousands of miles from Andalusia and Castile, were the settlements of their day on the Moon of their day. Yes, Father, they were the armored shelters of the Slaytons, the Titovs, the Shepards, the Gagarins of two hundred years ago, and the settlements they would build on the Moon would be like these missions of the Spanish monks: made of plastic maybe, or steel or who knows what alloy, uglier maybe, more pagan, more humble, but more or less the same. The Slaytons, the Titovs, the Shepards, the Gagarins will reach the Moon, and at the beginning they'll be alone as the monks were: full of faith, suspicion, hope. They will reach the Moon, and millions of miles away from home they will build their little forts and fling open their doors to those who follow them, to pioneers accustomed to great cold and great heat, heedless of danger, tough, like themselves. And these pioneers will fill the little forts, will perfect them, will grow old in them and die in them, and then others will come out of the sky, others less heedless of danger maybe, less tough, less accustomed to great cold and great heat, but now reassured by experience and now ready to go forth, to render the desolate valleys desolate no more. Little by little, they will bring it the life that five hundred years before it did not have, and our faults and our virtues, and in ever more frequent and greater waves new people will land, the crowds of prudent mediocre weak ones, of those who have nothing to lose but nothing to conquer either, ordinary people who won't dare unless others dare first, and they'll settle there for always: until Earth is forgotten and it seems normal to be there, by now Moonmen on the Moon like today's Americans in America, and their sons will look at the first settlements as I am looking this Sunday at the Mission San José. Immediately opposite the Mission there was an agglomeration of red modern buildings like a village within a city. I asked Stig what it was. He replied that it was the place where they selected the candidates who wanted to be astronauts. It was the School of Aerospace Medicine. He had visited it and advised me to visit it before going to Florida. "I will," I told him. "Yes, I really think I will." Bjorn started yelling with horror.

We said goodbye, promising to meet again in New York. The two of them went on their way to San Diego by plane and I stayed in San Antonio. Stig had given me the name of Major Turbutton, who is in charge of public relations at the School of Aerospace Medicine. Major Turbutton came to collect me immediately. A friendly fat giant of a man, squeezed into a uniform, he promised to show me everything I wanted to see: centrifuges, simulators, psychiatrists, physiologists. He opened his eyes wide in surprise when I told him I wanted to go into a centrifuge and to undergo the tests that are obligatory for the men who want to go to the Moon.

I 2.

The psychologist who since 1959 has been paid to measure the intelligence of those who want to go to the Moon stared at me with cold eyes set in the coldest face I had ever seen. Without taking his eyes off me, he handed me a sheet of paper on which was written *Wais Record Form* and told me to fill in my name and surname, my date of birth, my age, in case it could not be deduced from my date of birth, sex, civil status, spinster married widow divorced, nationality, the color of my skin, my employment, my educational qualifications, the date. Finally he was ready to examine me and decide whether I was intelligent or idiotic, and, if by any chance I was intelligent, to what degree. The minimum permissible degree of intelligence, he told me, was 80. If I got 100 I was of normal intelligence, if 110 I was of more than normal intelligence, if 120 I was very intelligent, 130 I was extremely intelligent, 140 really extraordinarily intelligent. If I got 150 my brain would burst. Naturally, he added, the questions took into account not only intelligence as a faculty of understanding but also intelligence as a faculty of associating, imagining, deducing, and the intelligence that derives from culture. I would be at a disadvantage inasmuch as the questions were framed with a view to an American culture and education: but, seeing as I knew America, I'd be able to manage all right. So I was ready? Yes? Then go: starting with the list headed *Information.*

"How many stars are there on the American flag?"
"Fifty."
"What shape is a ball?"
"Round."
"What is a thermometer used for?"
"For measuring temperature."
"What is rubber made from?"
"From the resin of rubber trees."
"Give me the names of at least three American Presidents."
"Kennedy, Eisenhower, Roosevelt . . ."
"Who was Longfellow?"

"An American poet."

"How many weeks are there in a year?"

"Hum . . . four times twelve . . ."

He gave me a strict look.

"Fifty-two. Where is Panama?"

"In Central America."

"Where is Brazil?"

"In South America."

"What is the average height of American women?"

"I don't know."

He gave me a strict look.

"Five feet eight. What is the capital of Italy?"

"Rome!"

"Where is the Vatican?"

"In Italy!"

"Where is Paris?"

"France!"

"Who was Hamlet?"

"A prince of Denmark."

"Who was Yeats?"

"An Irish poet."

"How many American Senators are there?"

"I don't know."

He gave me a strict look, but he didn't tell me how many there were. Perhaps he didn't know either.

"Who wrote the *Iliad?*"

"Homer."

"Who wrote *Faust?*"

"Goethe."

"What is the *Koran?*"

"The sacred book of the Moslems."

"What are the channels along which blood flows in the human body?"

"The arteries, the veins, the capillaries."

"What is ethnology?"

"The study of human races."

"What does apocryphal mean?"

"Not authentic, false, counterfeit. Generally referring to documents."

He gave me a look of respect: that last one, he said, was something hardly anybody knew. I thanked him and refrained from saying that his test was idiotic and any child could have answered three-quarters of it. He pulled a long face and then picked up another list on which was written *Analogies*. This time I was to tell him within a second what were the analogies between the things he was reciting. The reply had to be the one given in the book. This test, he said, was particularly important for anyone who wanted to go to other planets.

"Orange, banana."

"They're both fruits."

He consulted his book: "Correct. Coat, dress."

"They're both garments."

He consulted his book: "Correct. Dog, lion."

"They're both animals."

He consulted his book: "Correct. North, west."

"They're both cardinal points."

He consulted his book: "Correct. Air, water."

"They're both terrestrial elements."

He consulted his book: "Wrong."

"Why is that wrong?"

"Because it is. Wood, alcohol."

"They both burn."

He consulted his book: "Wrong."

"Why is that wrong?"

"Because it is. Praise, punishment."

"Both forms of judgment."

He consulted his book: "Wrong."

"Why is that wrong?"

"Because it is. Tree, butterfly."

"Both living creatures."

He consulted his book: "Wrong. You were wrong on the most important questions. There is no similarity between air and water, wood and alcohol, praise and punishment, a tree and a butterfly. What can a tree and a butterfly have in common?" I could go on telling you about it for a year, Doctor: we'd never understand each other. Maybe you don't know trees, perhaps you've never listened to them breathing, never seen them making love: you don't know that they breathe and make love like butterflies. There's a cypress in the garden of my house in the country, a very tall magnificent cypress, and he loves and is loved by a very tall magnificent female cypress on the other side of the road. At night they talk to each other, throw each other their light seeds, which then drop into the bushes with the grass, and in spring you always find two or three little cypresses that are their children: born from those nights of love. It sometimes happens that a little cypress dies, struck down by wicked or careless people, and then my cypress stirs, calls to his lady cypress and starts making love to her again, exchanging seeds with her again, undeterred, and when winter comes . . . I could go on telling you about it for a year, Doctor: we'd never understand each other.

Then the doctor picked up the third list of questions, on which was written *Comprehension*. This consisted exclusively of questions relating to social behavior and I had to answer with complete sincerity.

"What would you do if in the street you found a stamped letter that had not been mailed?"

"I might pick it up and put it in my handbag."

"And then?"

"Then it would get left there. Even my own stamped letters get left there. I always forget to mail them."

He consulted the book, shook his head in disgust. The book said: "I would pick it up and mail it."

"What would you do if you were in a movie theatre and it caught fire?"

"Get out."

"Get out?"

"Yes, get out."

He consulted the book, shook his head in disgust. The book said: "I would get up quietly, without attracting attention so as not to alarm people, and look for a policeman and tell him to call the fire department."

"Why should we pay taxes?"

"We shouldn't have to pay taxes at all."

"Don't you pay taxes!"

"Of course I pay them—if I don't, they fine me. But every cent I pay is a curse on whoever makes me pay it and I hope the curse works."

He consulted the book, shook his head in disgust. The book said: "Taxes must be paid because this is the first duty of a good citizen."

"Why should we always avoid bad company?"

"Who avoids it?"

"What did you say?"

"I said, who avoids it?"

"You mean, you frequent bad company?"

"Certainly. It's the most interesting."

He shook his head in disgust. The book said: "Bad company should be avoided lest we become bad ourselves."

"Why should children be protected by child-protection laws?"

"So they won't become astronauts!" I joked. And that put an end to it. The doctor shut the book, coldly informed me that the test had gone very badly, that I had in me an excessive tendency to be facetious and take up anti-social attitudes, that this indicated a very low rate of intelligence, then he showed me a blank sheet of paper, asked me what it was. Prudently I answered that it was a blank sheet of paper, nothing more. He exclaimed with satisfaction: "Very good, exactly," and brought out the usual ink blots, asked me what I could see in them. I told him I could see a pelvic bone, a mouse, my grandfather's pipe, the pearl earring I lost in Paris, a .22-caliber bullet, an anenome and a hen. He seemed rather disconcerted, but he made no comment and showed me a photograph of a fair-haired little boy playing the violin with a bored air who looked like von Braun at ten years of age. He asked me to make up a story about the boy. I told him it wasn't a case of inventing a thing, but simply of reporting. This was von Braun at the age of ten when his mother, the Baroness Emmy von Braun, tried to make him play the violin in the castle of Wirsitz and he used to play wrong notes until the Baroness would say that's enough, for mercy's sake, that's enough, and send him out into the park, where he would set fire to the roses, practicing for the destruction of London with the V2. The doctor, who desperately admired von Braun, snatched the photograph out of my hand, hissed that my intelligence was below average, so far below that it could hardly be considered intelligence at all. He would give me 30 and even that was too much. At all events, he was glad to tell me that the astronauts averaged 130, many of them got as much as 135 or even 140, one of the second group had 144, only two had as little as 123, which was the normal average for pilots. The astronauts were men of superior intelligence, people always insisted on their physical superiority but he insisted on their mental superiority. Was there anything else I wanted to know? Nothing else. Could he go, then? He could go. And he did go while I thought that he was less stupid than I was, after all.

In fact, their system of measuring feeling and brain power isn't stupid, Father. My totally unscientific, anti-social, disrespectful nature had been shown as clearly as the great unlikelihood of my going to

Mars. And the tests I had taken formed only a minute part of the examination that lasts for at least eight hours, sometimes for several days, and always brings out the truth. You can't get away from the Exam: however crafty, intelligent or controlled or however much of a liar you are, the Exam always shows you for what you are. This is the most pitiless, cruel test you have to put up with: more pitiless and cruel than the physical tortures to which you are submitted when they are studying your body. What with interrogations, written and oral tests, electroencephalograms, your soul is turned inside out like a sock, scrutinized like a germ under a microscope, washed like dirty linen, profaned, laid bare, until, stripped of every secret, it lies naked as a bare body before the executioners. Read this, Father. This is the interview I had, after my test, with one of the physicians who select the astronauts at the School of Aerospace Medicine in San Antonio.

"I can tell you this: when NASA began looking for astronauts, we spent a long time discussing the psychological requisites necessary for an astronaut, and the result of our discussion was that we ought to look for them among the priests. Young healthy priests, qualified in engineering, in chemistry, in medicine, in geology. We told this to NASA. All of them answered that they didn't want priests, they wanted pilots. We replied: Then priest-pilots. They didn't take us seriously, NASA evidently thought we just liked speaking in paradoxes, joking. But when people ask us what an astronaut should be like, we still say he should be a priest. A young healthy priest, qualified in engineering, in chemistry, in medicine, in geology, and able to pilot a plane competently. Do I make myself clear?"

"You make yourself very clear, Doctor. The Mission San José was built by monks."

"It's not only for sexual and emotional reasons, although you may be sure that these are very important; in fact, it isn't possible for an astronaut to be calm if he doesn't get along with his wife or if he's in love with another woman. At most he can allow himself casual encounters, short fleeting adventures: but heaven forbid, heaven forbid that he should let his own affections become involved, heaven forbid that he should give in to passion. There will always come the moment when his attention will be distracted, the moment when his reflexes will be slowed up: like a trapeze artist who miscalculates his distance and his timing and so he misses the trapeze and falls. A priest doesn't have these problems. Priests are what we need. Priests. And consider this: a team must have someone in command, someone who is more qualified to give orders than the others. No astronaut is more qualified than any other to give orders, none of them knows more than the others, they all have the same training, they all have the same worth and, having chosen who is to be in command, the others can say why him and not me? You don't draw lots among generals for a general, only priests are able to do this. In the conclave for electing the Pope every cardinal might become Pope, yet when the Pope is elected all the cardinals bend to kiss his hand. For them humility and obedience are conditions of living, but for lay people they are a burdensome duty. And then the astronauts don't choose their commander themselves, it's NASA that imposes its own choice. Do you think it's reasonable to risk a mutiny on the Moon or on Mars? The argument will never finish. NASA prefers hard guys: that's still another point on which we disagree. We've reached the conclusion that the best types are extroverts. When they are put in a position without authority, they are more disposed to obey; given authority, they have a greater likelihood of being obeyed. In fact, they are warmer, more persuasive, more friendly. And isn't a good priest always warm, persuasive, friendly?"

The doctor's face was pale and wan, he was wearing his official uniform as if he didn't like it. His point of view was strictly scientific. As we talked he took me around the school and showed me the simulators, which are iron boxes, some as small as a train compartment, some as big as a room or a two-room apartment, and inside are only a couch, a table and a television camera. The doors are as heavy as the doors of a bank vault: once you're shut inside, the world becomes a memory of what might have been a dream. On the other hand, you know they're watching you: the television is screening you every moment, as you yawn, as you scratch yourself, as you attend to your private needs. For you the walls are made of steel, oxyhydrogen flames couldn't burn through them; for the others they are made of glass. You feel spied upon, followed; at the same time you hope you're being spied upon, watched, because you're afraid they'll forget you. God! How many times in this book, Father, have you come across the word "afraid," again and again?

"Look, I spent two days in this one," he said.

The simulator he was referring to was a transparent cube, sealed with a lid and full of water. It serves for experiments on psychological and physical reactions in the floating state, the only way of giving even a vague idea of weightlessness.

"And what did you do, Doctor?"

"Nothing. I floated. I breathed with oxygen cylinders."

"I can imagine that. But what I mean is did you think?"

"No. To start with, I thought a little, then I stopped thinking altogether. Not that I felt ill or anything like that. I simply couldn't think, that was all: incredible how idleness of body leads to idleness of mind. After two days I'd turned into an idiot. That's the reason why, during a flight, astronauts are always kept busy. They don't have a moment's idleness."

"That's all very well when it's a matter of going to the Moon, Doctor. But what about the journeys to Venus and Mars? How will it be possible to keep them occupied for a whole year, two years?"

"We've thought about that and the best solution seemed to us to alternate periods of exhausting activity with periods of artificial sleep. For example, a month of work and a month of sleep. Or six months' work and six months' sleep. A spacecraft is much smaller than a submarine: boredom has to be avoided at all costs. So does excessive use of the imagination. That can also be dangerous when you're idling."

The last simulator was a box of unbreakable glass: the decompression chamber. It was used to demonstrate the effects of the lack of atmosphere caused by a sudden drop in pressure. Inside it was a glass full of water.

"Now I'll show you what would happen if an astronaut tore his spacesuit on the Moon," he said. "The pressure inside the chamber at the present moment is the same as on Earth. Right?"

"Right, Doctor."

"Now I'll suddenly lower it to zero. That is to say, I'll suddenly establish a lack of pressure similar to that on the Moon. You follow me?"

"I follow you, Doctor."

He set in motion an instrument that emitted a strange buzzing noise. And what I saw was over in the twinkling of an eye, less. The water shot out of the glass in splinters of frozen crystal and stuck to the walls, the ceiling.

"Did you understand?"

"No, Doctor."

He was momentarily dismayed.

"Of course you'd understand better if there'd been a mouse or a dog instead of the water. But . . ."

The animal-protection society in America forbids the use of mice and dogs in lethal experiments, I am told. Nobody is troubled if at San Antonio dozens of men undergo tortures like the tortures of the Inquisition, but there's a general outcry if an animal is submitted to the same tortures. Guinea pigs are hidden away in the School of Aerospace Medicine just as the newspapers that sang the praises of liberty were hidden away in Europe during the German occupation.

"I'm not a member of the Society for the Prevention of Cruelty to Animals, Doctor."

The doctor hesitated.

"Uhm . . . Considering that the experiment will be done in any case . . . You won't scream, will you?"

"No, Doctor. I won't scream. At worst I might feel bad."

"I feel bad too. Every time."

He took off his cap, scratched his head, put on his cap again, called to a student.

"Get the mouse."

The student went to get the mouse. It was a clean white mouse with two red and frightened eyes. It looked no bigger than an egg in the student's hand.

"Put it in," the doctor said.

The student opened the hatch in the decompression chamber and put it in. The splinters of ice had turned into water again and in the middle was a puddle. The mouse avoided the puddle. I began to feel sick.

You know, I haven't got anything against mice. A lot of people are afraid of mice, but I don't understand that fear when they're so small, as that one was. Our house in the country is full of mice and you say they eat the books, drink the olive oil, devour the salami, and every Saturday evening you come home with a new trap. Monday morning, before you go back to town, you collect the traps, there's always one mouse caught, and call the cats. A disagreeable ceremony, especially with those basketwork traps that have a hole in the middle so that the mouse is still alive inside. Mother says I'm inconsistent. Isn't it worse to shoot a bird that sings, she says, than to set a trap for a mouse? A bird that bothers nobody and a mouse that does? Mother is right, I know, but when you're out shooting, the birds aren't birds any more: they're targets, you shoot at them from a good distance, you don't have to look them in the eye, and when you collect them they're dead already. But the mice are still alive in the trap, they look at you, that's what it is, and that's the one thing I don't understand about you, how once during the war you were ill for six days after the execution of that traitor.

"Make a note of the time, the day, and so forth," said the doctor to the student. The mouse raised its small head attentively, two saddened eyes. It knew quite well they were going to kill it.

Because mice are intelligent, as you know. If you ask me, they're more intelligent than dogs or horses—especially the small ones. Do you remember the day we came across those two tiny ones climbing up the steps to the back kitchen? We stayed there watching them for ten minutes. The steps to the back kitchen are very steep and the mice couldn't have been very old because they were dragging themselves along like young puppies and when they tried to make the big leap they would fall down again, with their little feet in the air. Then one of them leaned against the side of the step as if he were standing upright, and the other clambered up on him and onto the step. When he was up he sat on the edge with his tail dangling, his back to his companion. His companion clung to the tail with his little feet as if it were a rope, and let himself be pulled up by the other one. Do you remember? They were so intelligent, so endearing, that even you couldn't raise a finger to kill them, indeed you said that they really deserved to live, those two. The maid killed them, shouting: "Mice! Oh God, mice!" and raining blows on them with her broom.

"Decompression," the doctor said.

Everyone stood still, including the mouse. The strange buzzing sound started, the mouse was looking at me. I lowered my head.

When I looked up again the mouse was no longer there. There was only a huge white ball. As big, say, as a carnival balloon. Except that they are red or green or purple, and this was white. They are smooth, and this had little nails in four places, and a minute pair of whiskers in the middle. And above the whiskers, full of horror and accusation, were his eyes.

"He didn't suffer, you know," the doctor said. "He didn't have time."

It truly seemed as if he were talking of the execution of a man.

"That's good," I answered.

"However, this is what happens to an astronaut on the Moon if he tears his spacesuit."

"I understand, Doctor."

"Not quite so quickly, perhaps. In the space of a minute. I don't know if I'm being clear: first the blood would start to boil, then the skin would rise, then—"

"Yes, yes, I understand, Doctor."

"It's not nice to talk about, is it?"

"No. But we must. And for how long would his mind remain clear, Doctor?"

"Thirty seconds, maybe longer."

"So he would have time to realize he was dying?"

"Plenty of time."

"But not time to save himself, Doctor?"

"Perhaps. If the hole was very small, and if he was no more than five or six yards from the spacecraft, if his companion was ready to let him in, if he was in time to shut him inside the spacecraft, if the spacecraft was well equipped . . . But for the moment our space-craft are very small. The LEM has barely enough room for the two astronauts and the controls."

"I understand, Doctor."

"Well . . . let's get out of here. There are a lot of other things to see."

And so we went out, with that white ball bouncing before my eyes, that comment hammering at my ears and I didn't know who'd said it to me, maybe nobody had said it to me, maybe it was I who was thinking it at that moment: "If you ask me, an astronaut is automatically a hero. For the simple reason that he is an astronaut."

I saw many other things that day, but I want to tell you about the algae, Father, the algae from which another physician, Dr. Fyfe, thinks he can get oxygen for the astronauts during long space journeys. The algae had small round leaves the size of a pea, of a handsome bright green. Dr. Fyfe gathered them from ponds, then put them in tubs of water, in which they multiplied at a fantastic speed. In six or seven days, for example, two little leaves would become a tub full of algae.

"The process is clear," Dr. Fyfe said. "The plants absorb carbon dioxide and replace it with oxygen. And then, if necessary, they're also fit for eating."

I smiled. "Providing they don't reproduce too much."

"Why?"

"Just a thought. It's given me an idea for a science-fiction story. Maybe I'll write it."

"What story?"

"Well . . . the story of a handful of algae that doesn't want to get eaten. So it grows and grows, reproduces, reproduces, until it bursts out of its tub and invades the spaceship and eats the men."

"Not bad," said Dr. Fyfe. "But I have a better story than that and it isn't science fiction either, it's a story that will come true."

"What's that, Doctor?"

"Well, then. You know that Venus is completely covered with clouds that prevent our knowing what is beneath? There's a great probability that it's a planet similar to Earth, younger than Earth, overheated by a very high temperature. The temperature remains very high because the pall of cloud prevents the boiling vapors from escaping: think of a pan of boiling water, hermetically sealed with a lid. You follow me?"

"I follow you, Doctor."

"Good. We have reason to believe that those clouds contain water —in short, a percentage of oxygen and hydrogen. Well. This alga has one characteristic: it will grow at any temperature, providing it has water. We've tried drying it and then throwing it into very hot water or very cold water, and it grows just the same. What we have in mind is a possibility on which Russian scientists and American scientists are in agreement: to circumnavigate Venus throwing handfuls of algae into the clouds. If it's as we believe, the algae will go on reproducing themselves until they've made a great hole in the clouds, which will be like taking the lid off the saucepan. The boiling vapor which is preventing life on Venus will escape through the hole and Venus will cool down and in the course of thousands, millions and millions of years, will develop a climate similar to our own. This is almost certainly how life began on Earth."

God, Father! God! Who threw the algae onto Earth? Where did they come from, the algae that took the lid off the pan of boiling water called Earth?

13.

I awoke sweating with anxiety: today they were going to put me in the centrifuge. Me, who can't even stand watching a merry-go-round or manage two turns in a waltz without being overcome with nausea, or being in an elevator with its unexpected lurching, sudden halts, and when I have to go up to a forty-third floor I feel as if I'm fainting and once I'm up there I don't have the courage to come down again. I who use every pretext to put off that overturning of the stomach, that plug that stops up my eyes, my throat—I had asked to be put in the centrifuge. But why? What had I been thinking of? Who had asked me, suggested it, advised me to? Do you have to die in order to write about death? I should die, that would be all. I should have a cerebral hemorrhage, or my head would burst, at the very least I'd be blinded for life. Yet there was no getting out of it now. To carry this fine gesture through to its end I had even left my hotel and moved to Brooks Air Force Base, where Major Turbutton had given me an apartment in the officers' quarters, women's section. I should first have to undergo a quantity of medical examinations: electrocardiogram, measurement of blood pressure, X-rays. Even for a harmless little ride, which is how Dr. Fyfe regarded an experiment at 3 or 4 G, my body must be in excellent condition. Desperately I hoped that my body would turn out to be a wreck, that my heart might be on the verge of an attack. I staggered into the kitchen to make myself some coffee. Coffee gives courage, Mother always maintains.

It was a really modern kitchen, a space kitchen. When you put the glass container on a thin spring coil, without so much as pressing a button, let alone lighting a flame, the water heated: if the quantity of water was correct, the weight of the container lowered the spring coil, boiling point was reached in ten seconds, a black dust called coffee tumbled from an automatic device and then everything went by itself. I lost a good fifteen minutes trying to find the correct quantity of water, but eventually I succeeded and drank the coffee. It didn't do any good. I needed brandy. In the kitchen there was brandy also, in fact, a quantity of liqueurs. But every bottle was fixed to the metal shelf by a magnetic process and to demagnetize it you had to put a half-dollar in a slot. I looked for one. I didn't have one. The extraordinary thing in America is that all doors open when you put a coin in the slot but it must be the right coin and you never have the right coin. To make a telephone call, for example, you need two nickels or a dime: I never have nickels or dimes. To get cigarettes out of a machine you need a quarter, a nickel and a dime: I never have them. To go to the john you need a dime and nothing else, and this, I must say, is the most dreadful thing: you have to try it to know how dreadful. There you stand, in front of that damn door that locks you out of the cleanest lavatory in the world, and all you want to do is pee, and you can't because you haven't got a dime. If you ask me, the whole tragedy of our future lies in this kind of thing. However, to get back to my brandy, I had to go out to the drugstore, change a dollar, ask for a half-dollar, put the coin in the slot, before I could get a drink. The brandy didn't help, except to make my head spin. Half a dollar's worth of brandy at eight in the morning, you understand.

The medical examination took nearly two hours and established that I was a champion of good health. Enviable lungs, strong stomach, a heart that was functioning like a new Swiss watch. My blood pressure was low, but that was an advantage. But look, Doctor, I broke a leg six years ago. That doesn't matter, that doesn't count. But look, I've a piece of bone missing here behind the ear—I had a mastoid operation. That doesn't matter, that doesn't count. But look, I sometimes get vertigo. That doesn't matter either. But look, my center of gravity is out of alignment, my balance is pretty faulty. That doesn't matter. But look, I can't even stand elevators, or waltzing, or merry-go-rounds. The centrifuge has nothing in common with elevators, waltzing or merry-go-rounds, you could make your application to be an astronaut, all you need is a pilot's license, let's go. I couldn't get out of it now. There were no more excuses. The centrifuge was waiting for me, inexorable as the judgment of God. I had never seen a centrifuge. I couldn't even imagine how it worked. All I knew, roughly speaking, was that it's a kind of spinning top: a huge wheel. Seeing it from the control room was worse than receiving a blow on the head.

It was in a round room. In the middle was a motor, to which an arm of steel was fixed horizontally, like the pole on an olive press to which donkeys are tied for crushing olives. The arm was about twenty feet long and ended in a capsule like the sidecar on a motorcycle. It was entirely enclosed and big enough to contain a man lying down. The room was white and the centrifuge blue, the very contrast of colors was somehow threatening, dramatic. The doctor was the one of the algae.

"Beautiful, eh?" said Dr. Fyfe.

I didn't answer.

"As you see, this is the control room. The centrifuge is operated from here. The walls are glass only so that we can see the centrifuge, everything else is done by television or electronics. This computer is connected to the sensors which are attached to the man in the centrifuge and they provide simultaneous information on everything that's happening to him. If the ascending or descending graphs warn us that something is wrong, we stop the experiment immediately."

"Thank goodness for that."

"This, on the other hand, is the television screen that permits us to observe the subject while the centrifuge spins round: the camera is focused directly on him. Nothing of what is going on, or that he wants to communicate, can escape us. If, for example, he cannot stand it and is suffering too much, he raises a hand and we stop the motor."

"Thank goodness for that."

"Are you afraid?"

"Me? . . . No, no . . ."

"I'll give you three to four G. If you stand it, up to five. No more."

"Thank you very much."

"More or less this speed."

He raised a lever, the metal arm began to spin round: at first slowly, then faster, then really fast. I gulped.

"It's not much, as you see."

"No, no . . ."

He lowered the lever, the arm lost speed, stopped.

"Shall we go down, then?"

"Of course! . . . Let's go down."

There was a small ladder leading from the control room to the rotunda of the centrifuge. Seen from above, it looked very long, but actually it was very short, you were down in a flash, in that rotunda, beneath that blue-painted thing, in front of the capsule that was shaped like a shell, a shell to hold your prostrate body, your legs here, your back here, your head here, your head to be placed on a rest shaped exactly like the headrest of a dentist's chair. A lighted bulb hung from the ceiling of the capsule.

There had been a lighted bulb in the operating theater that day too,

Father. And I was lying tied to the table and I was staring at the light bulb. Around me were all those eyes, you could see only the eyes because of the gauze masks that covered their faces, and a voice was saying yes, maybe she'll live. But I was wanting to live, I wanted to live without that maybe, and I was staring at the light bulb . . .

"Can you manage to climb in by yourself?" asked Dr. Fyfe.

"Yes, of course."

"If you feel bad, remember to raise your hand."

"Yes, of course."

. . . I was staring at the light bulb and I felt a great pain. But it wasn't the pain that bothered me—as you know, one is able to stand physical pain—it was the thought of dying. Because dying for a reason is all right, dying for someone you love, for example, dying for an idea you believe in, dying for a curiosity—walking on the Moon for example, but dying because a part of you has gone wrong or because you climb onto a merry-go-round is too idiotic.

"Get in, then," said Dr. Fyfe.

"No!" I yelled.

And I really yelled, without shame: can you believe me? I couldn't have cared less about looking foolish, cowardly. I couldn't have cared less about the eyes that were staring at me ironically from the control room up there. I couldn't have cared less about making a fool of myself, the hell with looking like a fool, the hell with Venus, Mars, the Moon, I wasn't going to climb up into that thing, I wasn't going to spin around in it, I'd never know what it felt like, too bad, I'd stay on this Earth forever, too bad: I turned my back on it and ran. This time the ladder seemed very long, like one of those dreams in which you want to escape but your legs are made of lead and the last rung means safety.

"I'm sorry, Dr. Fyfe."

"There's nothing to be sorry about. It often happens."

"I couldn't, I really couldn't."

"Many can't. One of our pupils broke his leg to avoid going into it."

"But I wanted to go in it, Doctor, I wanted to."

"He wanted to too. They're all volunteers."

"But it's nasty to discover one's a coward."

"It isn't cowardice, it's the instinct of self-preservation. If you're falling out of a window, it isn't cowardly to try to hang on to something. If you feel you're drowning, it isn't cowardly to call for help."

He was a truly kind man, this Dr. Fyfe. I really don't know how he could be one of those who tortured the astronauts, stripping bare their souls, stealing all their secrets, forbidding them to fall in love. Something like you, Father, you who were sick for six days because you witnessed the execution of that traitor and yet you are able to throw mice to the cats.

"You're very generous, Dr. Fyfe."

"I'll tell you what we'll do: we'll send someone else into it. O.K.?"

"That—"

"Where's Sergeant Jackson?" asked Dr. Fyfe.

"He's playing ball, Doctor. It's his recreation hour."

"Call him."

"But he's playing ball, Doctor!" I implored.

"So what?" said the doctor.

Sergeant Jackson came almost immediately. He was a boy of twenty-two with very fair hair and blue blue eyes, a plump and likable face. He was wearing a pale blue track suit and didn't look annoyed. Only a little resigned.

"Good morning, Sergeant."

"Good morning, ma'am."

He held out a hand covered with dirt and excused himself for being all covered with dirt, they hadn't given him time to wash his hands, but he'd wash them now.

"It is I who must ask you to excuse me, Sergeant."

"Not at all, ma'am. It's a pleasure."

"I ran away, Sergeant, did you know?"

"I ran away too the first time, ma'am."

"But nobody went instead of you, Sergeant."

"No . . . I can't say that they did." He smiled. "They caught me again and stuck me inside."

"How high can you go, Sergeant?" asked Dr. Fyfe.

"I can manage up to twelve all right, Doctor," answered the Sergeant.

"Shall we try fourteen or fifteen?" asked Dr. Fyfe.

"Yessir, if you want."

He washed his hands, went down the ladder, climbed into the capsule, where they attached the sensors over his heart, at his ankles, at his temples, fixed a rubber gum shield inside his lips, like the ones boxers wear. Then they shut the hatch of the capsule and he was alone, facing the TV camera. Motionless in front of the screen, I was looking in his eyes and he was looking in mine. In a way it was the same as it had been with the mouse. But in him there was no terror, only waiting. Waiting and patience. Perplexed, I wondered why he had chosen this job, why so many young men of his age, in America and in Russia, chose this job. Nobody obliges them to do it. When they volunteer there are those who do all they can to discourage them from it, they can resign at any moment, and yet they stay there, like the mice, offering their fine healthy bodies to scientific curiosity, to cynicism, to machines that toss them around as if they were machines. And maybe they don't even have any hope of going to the Moon, to other planets, because at best they've only got a technical-school diploma and they don't even think of taking a degree.

"Dr. Fyfe, how long will it last?"

"A little longer than we'd have given you. Three or four minutes."

Silence fell in the control room.

"Are you ready, Sergeant?"

"I'm ready, Doctor."

"If anything's wrong, raise your hand, Sergeant."

"Of course, Doctor."

"Four minutes, fifteen G," said Dr. Fyfe. And he raised the lever.

A bell rang.

The great arm began to rotate. Slowly at first, then faster. Faster and faster, very fast.

Five G. Six G. Seven G.

The Sergeant's face was tensed as when one makes a great effort, the veins in his neck were swollen, and his teeth seemed to be squeezing a long wail from his clenched mouth.

Eight G. Nine G. Ten G. The speed was becoming fantastic, accelerating more and more, and now the swelling had mounted to his face, which looked distorted, yet contorted, as if a terrible wind were buffeting it: his skin was running back over his ears like wrinkled mud and there were two dents where his cheeks should have been, like dents in a deflated ball. His eyes looked huge, as if about to come out of their sockets.

Eleven G. Twelve G. Thirteen G. By now you couldn't pick out the steel arm, you could only see a blue ring, and the Sergeant's face was a shapeless mask in which you could barely distinguish even the nose— only the teeth could be seen clearly, protruding so far that they looked as if they were going to shoot out, one by one, like a necklace with a broken thread losing its beads. His eyes were glazed, looking at me blindly.

"Doctor, stop it, please."

"Why? He's standing it."

"But he's suffering, can't you see?"

"He's suffering, but he's standing it."

Fourteen G. Fifteen G. Forgive me, Sergeant Jackson. You were playing your ballgame, perfectly happy, and it's my fault they've put you in there. It's your job, I know, you chose it and they pay you for it, but I'd rather you were outside playing ball. You're only twenty-two, Sergeant, twenty-two is very young to lose your teeth. Enough, Sergeant. Raise your hand, Sergeant. If you don't raise your hand this'll go on until they kill you: for them your body is like a mouse's body, an engine to be tested, a machine to be perfected, they live in the conviction that everything is possible and you can even drop dead, they won't bat an eyelid. Anyway if you drop dead they'll just take another and start all over again. Raise your hand, Sergeant, maybe that wind prevents you from raising it and forces it back, maybe you feel too ill even to move your fingers, make a little effort, Sergeant. Raise your hand, Sergeant.

"He'll make it, he'll make it!" someone said.

"I say no," said Dr. Fyfe.

"He hasn't asked us to stop," said the same voice.

"I'm asking you to," said Dr. Fyfe.

The electronic computer was indicating something.

"Shut down. Stop!" said Dr. Fyfe.

The blue ring became once more an arm of steel that was rotating fast, then less fast, still less fast, then almost slowly, then slowly, until it came to a standstill. Everyone rushed down the ladder. Dr. Fyfe himself opened the hatch.

They didn't take him out immediately, they administered first aid inside, and twenty minutes passed before Dr. Fyfe came to find me.

"Do you want to see him?"

"No, Dr. Fyfe."

"Why not?"

"Because I don't, Dr. Fyfe."

"I think it would be nice of you to see him."

"And I don't think he'll want to see me."

"On the contrary, it'll please him very much. It's far pleasanter to open your eyes to a woman, after a faint. And we don't often see women here. Fix your hair."

I fixed my hair and also powdered my nose. Sergeant Jackson was coming around. His face was scarlet, his eyes were bloodshot, his nails blue as if they'd been hit, one by one, with a hammer. But he was coming around. He gave me a happy innocent smile.

"How do you feel, Sergeant?"

"Not bad, ma'am."

"Your nails are blue."

"We went a bit too high that time."

"Forgive me, Sergeant."

"But it's my job, ma'am."

"Forgive me all the same, Sergeant."

"There's nothing to forgive, ma'am."

"Thank you, Sergeant. Thank you very much, Sergeant."

"Thank you, ma'am. Thank you for coming."

"Goodbye, Sergeant."

"Goodbye, ma'am."

He shook my hand with those fingers with their blue nails and I left. Later someone told me that he'd been taken to the infirmary on account of a slight indisposition.

That same evening I left San Antonio. I didn't want to stay there any more and I'd already caused enough trouble: one murdered mouse and a sergeant in the infirmary. The pigeons fluttering among the trees no longer meant anything to me and the Alamo was only a ruin I'd already seen in the movies, where one could buy picture postcards, Davy Crockett caps, horrible hunting knives and huge vulgar hundred-dollar bills (counterfeit, of course) on which was written: "This certificate tells you that warm hospitality is the treasure of the Magnificent State of Texas." Major Turbutton accompanied me to the airport and gave me as a memento a very uncomfortable cowboy hat: the one I gave you, Father. He also gave me a great bundle of cyclostyled papers that I threw away immediately and a copy of the speech made by Kennedy at the Brooks Air Force Base on November 21, 1963: twenty-four hours before he was assassinated in Dallas, capital city of the Magnificent State of Texas, center of its warm hospitality.

"I have come to Texas," Kennedy had said, "to salute an outstanding group of pioneers, the men who man the Brooks Air Force Base School of Aerospace Medicine and the Aerospace Medical Center in San Antonio. . . . We have a long way to go. Many weeks and months and years of long tedious work lie ahead. There will be setbacks and frustrations, disappointments. There will be, as there always are, pressures in this country to do less in this area as in so many others, and temptations to do something else that is perhaps easier. But the research here must go on. This space effort must go on. The conquest of space must and will go ahead. That much we know. That much we can say with confidence and conviction. . . . Frank O'Connor, the Irish writer, tells in one of his books how, as a boy, he and his friends would make their way across the countryside and when they came to an orchard wall that seemed too high and too doubtful to try and too difficult to permit their voyage to continue, they took off their hats and tossed them over the wall: and then they had no choice but to follow them. . . ."

When my plane took off I pressed my face to the window and tried to pick out the Mission San José, the military hospital where Sergeant Jackson lay with his indisposition. Who knows if Sergeant Jackson had ever read or heard that speech of Kennedy's? He too had thrown his hat over the wall but when he went to get it back he had fallen down and hurt himself. I on the other hand had thrown my hat over and for fear of getting my knees scraped I hadn't even bothered to go and get it back. The difference between real pioneers and those who dream of becoming pioneers is just that, I reflected in some humiliation. It was a direct flight to Orlando, Florida, to the place that had been arousing my curiosity for years: that point on our planet from which rockets leave for the Moon, and which they once called Cape Canaveral and now call Cape Kennedy. After the man who paid with his life for his habit of throwing his hat over the wall and then going to pick it up.

14.

Your letter reached me at NASA in Cocoa Beach, the small residential town between Cape Kennedy and Patrick Air Force Base. I opened it as if it contained a bit of home, seesawing between cheerfulness and melancholy. Forgive me for using it, but it's a letter I'm very fond of.

"I don't understand where is this Cocoa Beach where you ask me to write to you," it said. "The city Jules Verne writes about in his book *From the Earth to the Moon* is called Tampa, not Cocoa Beach. It was from Tampa, in the southwest of Florida, that Mr. Barbicane's rocket took off—constructed more or less like von Braun's rocket, to travel at the same speed as von Braun's rocket, for a journey of ninety-seven hours and twenty minutes, the time prescribed by Mr. von Braun. And to think that the book came out in 1865, exactly a hundred years ago. As you see, I haven't gone further than Jules Verne, but I know as much as you about this useless stupid adventure: imagination always carries the seed of truth and Verne had even grasped this, that the great toy should be launched from Florida. Since I like to delude myself that there's such a thing as gratitude, I suppose that the Cocoabeachians have erected a fine monument to Verne and Mr. Barbicane. And in any case I envy you: it must be a very fine place, this Cocoa Beach–Tampa. Verne described it as a fruitful land of sweet potatoes and tobacco plants, pineapples and oranges: bring me some seeds of plants that will withstand our cold winters, the avocado you got in Brazil froze to death. It must also be a good spot for hunting and fishing, this Florida: full of crocodiles, birds, rabbits and especially fish. Ah, if only fish were seeds! I'd tell you to bring me them too: you know the trout in the stream below the windmill have gone? Poisoned, I suppose. Men are really wicked. What pleasure can they find in exterminating living creatures? I ask myself. I should like to go to Florida just for the enjoyment of seeing so many animals going free and safely through the grass. There's a lot of grass there, I bet. I can imagine the green lawns. I don't want to sound like the usual discontented old grumbler, but I can't get the grass in the garden to grow. You remember the gardener from the village dug the ground to a depth of at least three feet and spread plenty of fertilizer: nothing came up. We'll try again in the spring and let's hope. Ciao, write more often. Tell us about Cape Kennedy and the astronauts. All those machines must be interesting too —but, don't forget, the greatest interest of man is always man. From what you say, they are bright fellows, I like the sound of them. I can imagine how the Americans must love them. Ciao, let's hear from you. Your Pa."

I took a sheet of paper to answer you right away and was interrupted by a knock on the door. It was Gatha Cottee, NASA's public-affairs man or rather the guardian angel NASA had set at my heels for the duration of my Florida stay. A huge friendly man, his enormous face shadowed by an exaggerated Texan hat that he removed only when he put on his helmet, he overwhelmed me with papers and information. The package in his hand was a survey headed *Courageous Women* that contained the replies of astronauts' wives to the question: "Does your husband's work fill you with fear?" He threw the envelope onto the table, sat himself down on the bed.

"Writing your daily report for Moscow?"

"No, I write that at night when no one can see me."

Gatha and I always joked about the danger of my being a Russian spy, here on the pretext of writing a book. But there were others who didn't find it such a joke. The Americans are really odd: first they tell you everything they're doing and then they get scared you may be a spy.

"I'm just writing to my father, whose name is Ivan and who lives in Kiev. Say, Gatha, is there by any chance a monument to Verne in this part of the world?"

"Verne? Who's Verne?" asked Gatha.

"Come on, Gatha! The writer! The Frenchman!"

"Uhm. I think I've heard of him. He wrote a book that was made into a movie. I saw the movie. *Eighty Thousand Leagues Under the Sea* or something like that."

"*Twenty Thousand.* He also wrote a book called *From the Earth to the Moon.*"

"Bah!" Gatha said. "There've been plenty of books called *From the Earth to the Moon* or suchlike. My friend Caidin has written forty and he dedicated one of them to me."

"Yes, but Verne wrote his a hundred years ago."

"Oh?" said Gatha, showing a little more interest.

"And in his book the rocket is made more or less like the Saturn. There's even a kind of Apollo capsule, and it's launched from Florida."

"Ah?" said Gatha.

"It's launched from a city called Tampa."

"Tampa's only two hundred miles from here," said Gatha. "If it weren't a big city now, with lots of houses and so on, it would have been a suitable spot because it's on the coast, in the middle of an archipelago. No mountains and right on the sea."

"You know, Gatha, I think you really should have a monument to Jules Verne."

"If we had to erect monuments to everybody who wrote a book, we'd be in a spot," Gatha snorted. "But whoever put such an idea into your head?"

"My father," I said.

"He must be very odd, your father," said Gatha. And he went off announcing that we would meet at noon in the snack bar to eat, and in the afternoon he'd take me to Merritt Island, the spaceport for rockets going direct to the Moon. I went on writing to you. Forgive me for making use of this letter too.

"No, Pa, there are no monuments to Jules Verne here, far less to Mr. Barbicane. I asked an expert and he told me they haven't even any intention of making any: what I am afraid of is that they are totally unaware of the name of Verne. I have to disillusion you about a number of things, Father, especially about the grass. Here there isn't any grass at all. Or rather, there is, but it's like in Los Angeles, made of synthetic fibers. You can buy it in the supermarket at so much a yard, like buying material. There aren't even many plants, Father: the cork trees, the palms, the lilacs, the 328 kinds of trees that used to oxygenate the air are almost extinct, a few citrus trees are left. But these are getting sick. It appears to be because of the explosions that poison the air. The climate is excellent, Florida is kissed by perpetual sunshine: but the air seems poisoned. There aren't many living creatures either, Father, apart from the snakes so one of them will tempt us to eat the apple when the human race starts on its journey again. The sharks survive too: employed by NASA, I suspect, to devour the curious who want to bathe in the sea instead of in the swimming pools. In fact nobody here bathes in the sea, every hotel has its swimming pool, luxury hotels like the ones at Miami have two or three, one with cold water, one with warm water, one with salt water: and another thing that's catching on is the fashion for sunbathing in artificial sunshine instead of real sunshine;

the artificial sunshine is in the covered swimming pools and appears to be healthier than real sunshine because you don't get sunburned. As for birds, what they call birds here aren't birds at all but rockets, missiles, so if you go out with a gun and say 'I got a bird' you go straight to prison for state sabotage. Truly, here there are none of the things you imagine, Father. I've been here for two days. I've been all over the place with a character who keeps an eye on me, and wherever I go I see nothing but a shroud of sand, asphalt, salt from the sea: your Cocoa Beach–Tampa is so ugly that if you saw it you'd agree to go to the Moon, which might not be better but certainly couldn't be worse. In 1950 there were 23,000 people living in the whole zone, today there are 200,000 in Cocoa Beach alone: a Luna Park of restaurants, banks, gas stations, motels, bars, night clubs; all the rich come here, and also all those who hope to become rich. The gold rush of the last century. Not that this happens only in Florida, it happens throughout the South: throughout New Mexico, Texas, Alabama, Louisiana, Mississippi. The gold rush of the space age has landed in the very states that are the most sleepy and backward, which is to say where there was most land available: doesn't it always happen this way? But Florida is a special case, somewhat like Texas. Or more? Here the restaurants and motels have names like Satellite, Vanguard, Ranger, Polaris. The night clubs have names like Space Girls. And imagine, even the children's toys are what the cosmopioneers' children will use in the lunar settlements destined to be raised in the Valley of Eternal Light—you know, the one where Mother sees the eyes of the Moon. There are little spacesuits, tiny oxygen cylinders, perspex helmets, suncharged-battery flying spacecars; yesterday the sky clouded over suddenly and a spacecar landed on my head, I still have the bump. What else? Picture postcards for you to send your friends aren't photographs of flowers, views, girls in bikinis, but rockets, fuel depots, astronauts lying in spacecraft like Egyptian mummies. The Earth you love has been forgotten here for some time, from the desolate plain there rise only the launch towers: the cathedrals of an age that—you were right—has substituted technology for liturgy. They are tall and slender, solemn in their way, and in their way they are disturbing because they remind you that from each of them a man has been sent up. The furthest, almost by the edge of the sea, is Shepard's tower. Then come the towers of Grissom, Glenn, Carpenter, Schirra, Cooper: they're no longer of any use, but they're kept there as souvenirs. Don't you find that touching? You ask me about the astronauts. I'm also here to keep on trying to understand them. If I can't understand them, then I can't understand the world that's waiting for us, the world that surrounds them. I haven't met the young ones, that is to say those of the second and third wave, destined quite certainly to go to the Moon: they tell me they are different. I can tell you, though, that the first Seven are not always loved, as you think, in America. Naturally the government does what it can to make them loved and admired. Highly skillful government officers wear out their voices telling everyone what perfect, loyal Boy Scouts they are, devoted to family and country, and curtains of silence carefully conceal their faults. Nobody has ever heard officially of an astronaut being unfaithful to his wife. But danger waits for them at every corner, a day never passes without their being tempted by film producers, toothpaste manu- facturers, women ready to sacrifice their virtue, actresses in search of publicity: the more I hear about it, believe me, the less I envy them."

I wasn't joking in the least. Moreover, nothing that I wrote to you during my travels was intended as a paradox or a joke. It was Gatha Cottee who told me about the motel, a tale that in itself is enough to show that it's much easier to be a hero in heaven than on Earth. The motel called Cape Colony belonged to the first Seven, who had bought it with the money received from the contract with *Life*. Well, America yelled its indignation the day the Cape Colony was opened. Senators remarked that it was a scandal, religious bodies thundered that the Seven should be punished and the *Life* contract revoked. And if it weren't for Glenn, who during a weekend on the lake persuaded Kennedy to intervene, the contract really would have been revoked, certainly not renewed, and nobody would have got the thousand dollars per head that in fact they got. Nevertheless when the Houston Construction Association offered them seven little houses, the astronauts had to say no thank you, and nobody commented on the fact that Gagarin was allowed to accept the gift of a luxury apartment in the center of Moscow. Acclaimed, carried in triumph along Broadway, exalted to the level of gods before whom the gods of the movies or sport paled, the astronauts pay for it every moment. And they live in dread of making mistakes, being stoned, finishing like the fictional colleague named Jack Smurch in Thurber's story. After his epic flight, pilot Jack Smurch had become a hero, but when they realized he was only a conceited fool they gave him a shove in the back and made him fall from a hotel window to be smashed on the asphalt.

"Gatha, what if this should happen to them?"

Gatha Cottee shot me a crushing look.

"None of them is a conceited fool."

"Gatha, what if one of them were to become like that?"

"None of them will become like that."

"Goodness knows how you must keep watch on them, of course you must!"

"On the contrary. They can do whatever they want: get as much indigestion as they want, drink as much as they want, drive their cars as fast as they want. They work better if they aren't too closely watched, they produce more. And then they have hard days ahead of them: so why should we make them live like the condemned in a padded cell?"

"I'm not referring to how much they drink or eat or how fast they drive, Gatha. I'm referring to their moral behavior, their habits, their tastes."

"Well, naturally they can't lend themselves to speculations, advertising. The rules forbid it. Can you imagine a billboard in Times Square with a photograph of Cooper smoking a certain brand of cigarette? *The cigarette of space! Up in space Gordon Cooper smokes only* . . . Inconceivable! None of them . . ."

None of them disobeyed. None of them said to hell with regulations. None of them, Father. What a lesson for us who are used to telling even the angels to go to hell and who have such a fondness for that noble holy word disobey. Disobey, by God, disobey! Because what is a man, by God, if he doesn't disobey? A man or a machine? A machine . . . Cape Colony is only a stone's throw from the sea, Father, you only have to cross the road and you're on the beach. An endless interminable beach, a desert of damp and undisturbed sand that makes you exclaim my God, the sea's drying up! So you walk along it, fascinated, afraid, nobody is walking on it except you, there's nobody ahead of you or behind you, hundreds and thousands of oddly shaped shells of wonderful colors are scattered everywhere just for you, pink and blue medusas lie sighing, caressed by the waves that try to take them away again so that they may live; that sea is the sea of the world's beginning, and the silence is the silence of the world's beginning, you were wrong to write what you did to your father, and these tracks on the sand, what are they? Strange, they look like the tracks made by car wheels. And what's that sound? Strange, you'd think it was the sound of a car. But no, you're joking of course. And suddenly you jump: the car's nearly on top of you. The beach is a beach you can drive on as if it were an asphalt road, providing you don't go too fast. Poor heroes. They can't even look at the shells, the medusas, the waves without being in danger of being killed by something with an engine. Mournfully I sealed my letter, started reading Gatha Cottee's papers, the survey headed *Courageous Women:* "Does your husband's work fill you with fear?"

Marjorie Slayton's reply: "What fear? I've never been nervous about Deke's job. The Hollywood version of the pilot's wife who cries while she washes the dishes in the kitchen has always irritated me. When Deke was a test pilot I was surrounded by widows. Most of them spent their time comforting whoever was comforting them. Maybe we're too close to it all: the tragic aspect of the thing escapes us." Louise Shepard's reply: "Fear?! Why? I suppose I have the same faith in technology as other Americans: the certainty that the wheels will go on turning when the car comes to the green lights and the brakes will brake when the car comes to the red lights. If the wheels don't go on turning or the brakes don't brake, something else will work." Betty Grissom's reply: "Gus thinks that flying in a spacecraft is less dangerous than driving a car, and I agree with him. He's only had one accident in the air, the one with Gordon Cooper when they were flying the T33 jets. The plane caught fire and crashed. They both got away without a scratch. When I heard about it I was surprised but not frightened. These things happen." Trudy Cooper's reply: "I no more worry about the chances of Gordon dying in a spacecraft than I do about the chances of the ceiling falling on my head. I'm a pilot myself and fairly expert at it; before I met Gordon I was a flying instructor in Hawaii. When our first baby was born Gordon and I used to take her for rides in a Piper . . ."

Courageous women, Father, courageous women. Meeting them later, I was to be convinced of it, I was also to realize that they are good women, women able to suffer and endure: and yet there's something wrong about so much courage. Something about it I can't take. Because—pardon me, Father—what does it mean, courage? Mother also had courage when you used to risk your life for the great illusion you call freedom: but as well as courage she knew fear. Every time you left the house could have been the last time you'd leave the house and when she said so long she was very courageous and very frightened. One morning they took you. You were going to the weapons cache, they stuck their revolvers in your back and took you. Father, even you don't know how courageous Mother was. You'd left at nine, at noon you hadn't returned. Mother was making the soup and she was crying and saying: something has held him up. Evening came and you hadn't returned. Mother was weeping as she turned down the beds, weeping and saying: he'll be back tomorrow. You didn't return that tomorrow or the next day; on the next day the newspaper said: *Terrorist Leader Arrested*. Mother read it, stopped weeping, and her lovely face was like marble: the marble of despair, the marble of fear. And with that fear Mother put on her best dress, got out her bicycle and went to Villa Triste, where they tortured the men they arrested. Screams could be heard from the cellars. Mother was shaking with fear. She was shaking while she spoke to that assassin, looking him straight in the eye, telling him: my husband is innocent. The assassin had a ridiculous name for an assassin: he was called Charity. He laughed in her face and told her: you can go into mourning, Signora. So then Mother went out, climbed onto her bicycle again, began riding all over the city, looking for false witnesses who would say that her husband hadn't been looking for weapons that day but had been looking for medicine for me. Mother went around with her bicycle and with her fear for days and days, and she didn't find any witnesses, but she found something more valuable, she found that one of the torturers had once torn up a photograph of Mussolini. So Mother put on her best dress once more and went back to Villa Triste and sought out that torturer and told him: "If you don't do something to help my husband, I'll tell them that you tore up the photograph of Mussolini." I have never understood where Mother found such courage, because Villa Triste was hotter than a spacecraft breaking into the atmosphere: maybe she found it in her fear. And the assassin removed you from the Villa Triste, Father, he sent you to a prison where you remained a long long time, with the rats. Mother was expecting a baby. When she heard that you were in prison, with the rats, she was so happy that she lost the baby. Mother was courageous, but she was afraid as well as courageous. She began to suffer heart trouble during those months and since then her heart has never been the same. As her heart is no longer the same we try to prevent her from watching the television when the astronauts are going up to the top of the rocket at Cape Kennedy: and if she insists on seeing them we stay close to her with the pills. Because my mother doesn't believe in technology as the astronauts' wives do, she doesn't have their blind faith that the wheels will turn when they have to turn and the brakes will brake when they have to brake. On the other hand she has much lovingkindness and while they are staring dry-eyed at the screen, then making themselves up for the press conference that will follow, my mother weeps and sighs: "Poor boy, poor thing, look where they're putting him, look what they're doing to him."

Courageous women, Father, courageous women. But I looked at those papers that were fluttering on the floor, blown about by the wind of the air-conditioning, and I wondered what do we mean by this word courage? You had courage too while Charity went on beating you and beating you and as he continued beating he kept shouting who are the others who are they, where are you hiding the guns the newspapers the bombs, traitor you're a traitor, I'll shoot you I will I'll shoot you. Your wrists bound, your face covered in blood, the teeth knocked out of your mouth, you laughed. They told me. But as well as being courageous you were very much afraid. You were a white blur when I came to see you in prison and you were sitting on that bench, I was sitting on another bench facing you, between us there was a table, a wide table so we couldn't even touch fingers: and your whiteness was of fear, your eyes of fear, your voice of fear when you said don't cry, real girls don't cry, maybe they won't shoot me you know, maybe they'll just send me to Germany and I'll come back you'll see I'll come back, but in the meantime you must swear you'll never give away the addresses, you'll never give up fighting them, not for any reason, understand, little one. And you were afraid of me, I know. You were afraid of every tomorrow, I know, of the darkness that is every tomorrow: how can one not be afraid? Of all emotions the most human is fear. Courage itself is born of fear, hope itself, the very desire to live, to survive: so then, Christ, why weren't these people afraid? Christ, is it possible that these people can always be courageous, only courageous? But what kind of blood did they have, what kind of skin did they have, what kind of nerves did they have? And I thought then it's not true that the human race is immutable, a new race is being born in the world, a race in the face of which ours, mine, is doomed to die out, to be forgotten: like the dinosaurs, the mammoths. And it felt very cold to me at Cape Kennedy where there is never any winter and the world's rich wear swimsuits at Christmas. A biting wicked cold, and I was shivering as I left my room and went to look for Gatha in the snack bar. A thousand glistening beads of sweat covered Gatha's brow.

"Hot, eh?"

"Yes, Gatha, very hot."

"Have you read those papers yet?"

"Yes, Gatha, I've read them."

"Did you like them?"

"Yes, Gatha, I liked them."

"More than that Verne—whatever-his-name-is?"

"Jules, Gatha. His name's Jules," someone said as he passed.

I was struck first by the voice: rich, husky, the voice of a man who smokes a great deal, drinks a great deal, loves a great deal, thinks a great deal, and believes in the things he believes in. Then by the man himself: about forty years of age, rather tall and strongly built, with the heavy features of a mountaineer. His cheeks were heavy, and the lines that furrowed his cheeks in a lot of wrinkles fanned out toward his ears. His hair was heavy: thick, long and golden brown. His teeth were heavy: solid, strong, you know the kind of teeth people have who crack nuts with their teeth as if they were strawberries. Lastly, the color of his skin was heavy: something between terra cotta and rust color.

But, far from being distasteful, far from verging on the vulgar, this heavy quality became in him a strange kind of grace, a very elegant kind of strength: and indeed the man was strong, with strong shoulders and a strong neck, strong arms and strong hips, you know the powerful strength of those big horses when they approach you calm and upright, plodding on without apparent effort.

"My God, Gatha. Who's he?"

Without another word the man had gone to sit at a table, where he had set down his beer and was looking at us with eyes as sharp as needles, eyes golden brown also, and a wide grin full of kindness, amusement, indulgence, curiosity, that redoubled his wrinkles. Then, brusquely, as if we had no more to say to him and he found us boring, he stopped looking and devoted his attention to his beer. He drank with concentration, quite content to be alone, and his solitude was an island that no one would have dared approach, not even to pay him homage or ask his help. He had no need of homage, no help to give, for, whoever he was, whatever he did, he couldn't be distracted from who he was and what he was doing. His interest in others was a momentary distraction, a lamp that goes out as soon as it's lighted.

"My God, Gatha. Who's he?"

"Wally Schirra. One of the Seven."

"Ah, him."

I'd heard a lot about him. Conflicting versions, contradictory opinions. "Of Sicilian stock, I'd say. Schirra is a Sicilian name, isn't it?" "Far from it, he's of Swiss stock. There are a lot of Schirras in Switzerland." "That's right. In the French cantons." "No, the

German cantons." "Friendly, you know, open, nice with everybody. He likes people, he likes listening to them and having them listen to him. Of the Seven he's the one who's most understanding." "Introvert, you know, mathematical, cold. Remember what he called his Mercury capsule? Sigma. Sigma 7. The others had called theirs Faith, Freedom, Friendship. He, Sigma. Sigma 7." "And his sense of humor? You ought to see the crazy notes he leaves for the gloomiest people at the tensest moments. He has the knack of seeing the light side of life, the kind that never takes himself seriously and never takes anyone seriously who takes himself seriously." "Doesn't that tell you what kind of an individual he is, the way he chose a geometric symbol as a name for a spacecraft? Moreover his flight was so perfect that it hardly aroused comment in the press. He never makes a mistake. And his patriotism . . ." "Actually he detests solemn ceremonies, parades, brass bands. Pin a medal on his breast and you make him miserable, he steals away like a cat. As far as that goes . . ." "His patriotism is right out of a textbook. He'd die for the flag and yet . . ." "As far as that goes, he's cautious, prudent, always on the lookout not to be taken in: you know, like a wolf raising his hackles, pricking up his ears, stiffening as he sniffs out scents, sounds, danger . . ." "And yet, as I was saying, he's a fatalist. A rebel in his way. He judges without mercy, he'd send you to hell even if you owned the world . . ."

My curiosity aroused by such controversial opinions, I had read his biography, but I found nothing in it to prove anybody more right than anyone else. He was born in 1923 in Hackensack, New Jersey, a state that for some reason reminds me of Switzerland: so neuter, neutral. His childhood had been serene, vitaminized by love for his parents; particularly notable was his boundless admiration for his father, an air ace in the First World War and subsequently a stunt flier; for years Walter Schirra, Senior, had made his living doing aerial acrobatics, and his wife with him. While she was expecting Wally, Mrs. Schirra was unscrewing bolts, pouring out gas, leaping in and out of the cockpit: you could hardly say that flying wasn't in his blood. What else? He studied at the Newark College of Engineering, then at the Naval Academy. Captain in the Navy. He had met his wife in Washington. Beautiful woman, rigid like a statue, never a hair out of place, never a tear in her stocking, and daughter of an admiral too: Holloway. In their twenty years of marriage they had had two children, a boy and a girl. He had fought in the war in Korea and fought well: shooting down I don't know how many Migs, covering himself with crosses of merit, honors, medals. He had always been a test pilot: with illustrious results, obviously. Furthermore he was cultured and athletic. He liked skiing and he spoke French. What else? Nothing else. Isn't it enough? In order to make something out of all this I had also asked for an interview, but I hadn't managed it. I hadn't even managed to see him, not even from a distance, for a minute. And now here he was. By accident? I don't believe that things happen by accident, Father. If the Suns and the planets rotated by accident, every hour, every minute would be the end of a world.

"Do you want to talk to him?" Gatha whispered.

The man was not only drinking with concentration, he was savoring every sip, every drop as if it were the last. Yes, that was it, it was concentration more than solitude: you know, the concentration of chess players in international tournaments when it's quite useless to go up to them, to talk to them, you say listen war has broken out, listen your wife's had a baby, listen you're going to die in a minute—they don't see you, they don't hear you, and they don't care about you. And this intimidated me, Father, it held me back. "The cork trees, the palms, the lilacs are extinct . . . The birds, the crocodiles, the rabbits are extinct . . ." Father, suppose such a man could defend all this, suppose such a man could convince me that fear is not the most active and human of the emotions. Suppose that his overflowing irritating strength was nourished by the things that we love too, by the sweet green of a tree, the ecstasy of a dream: what would we be doing here, Father? What would be left to us?

"Do you want to talk to him?" Gatha repeated.

"I don't know, Gatha."

"You don't know?"

"Well . . . I . . . I wouldn't like to trouble him."

Having exhausted his concentration on the important operation of drinking his beer, the man had decided to eat something. And so he had stood up, gone over to the snack counter, picked up a tray, a fork, a knife, then a thick sandwich, and was carrying them back to his table, approaching us calm and upright, plodding on without apparent effort.

"Wally!" Gatha called.

The man stopped, with that smile that redoubled his wrinkles. The way he held the tray was interesting. As if he weren't holding it at all.

"Somebody would like to meet you, Wally," said Gatha. And he introduced me.

The man gave a slight bow: a movement between his neck and his hair. He put his tray on our table, sat down between Gatha and me. In silence. As if he wanted to concentrate on my face now, to make out who I was, what I wanted. An autograph? An affair?

"I write," I explained.

"Oh!" he remarked politely. But the information appeared to impress him very little.

"About the journey to the Moon."

"Oh!" he repeated. This appeared to impress him even less.

"So I tried to see you in Houston. But I didn't manage it."

He laughed his rich husky laugh, plunged his teeth into the sandwich, savored it well as if it were the last sandwich in the world. This was his only comment on the fact that I hadn't been able to get hold of him in Houston.

"Italian, eh?"

"Yes."

"I know Italy. Fine country. Full of trees and water. A country's always beautiful when it has these two things: trees, water. I know another country full of trees and water: Japan. And they've got the most beautiful city in the world there: Kyoto. Those winding brooks, that rustling green, that lost charm. Do you know Kyoto?"

"Yes."

"Sometimes I'd stand for hours looking at a tree, at flowing water —it was worth all the theaters in the world. I don't understand people who'll pay five dollars and fifty cents to sit in the front row, in darkness, to watch an imitation of life or somebody else's idea of life, when life's only two steps away, in the sunshine. Sometimes I'd take photographs of them."

"Of what?"

"The trees."

"Americans are always taking photographs, they photograph everything."

"So what? Is there anything wrong, anything silly about that?" He wore the wounded expression of a wounded child. It often happens with these men. Sometimes, for a moment, they seem like children.

"Yes."

"No! Not if photographs capture something, retain the joy of a single minute. Something beautiful that would be lost, something you won't see again for a long time or never see again, a person, a flower, a house. A person grows old, dies. And so does a flower, a house. There are flowers in the desert that last only for a single night: they bloom after sunset and by dawn they're gone. But if you photograph them before the dawn, you can see them again the next day or a year later or a hundred years later. We can't do without art. At least I can't. Nor could my mother, who is a good painter, nor could my grandfather, who was a well-known musician, also an art collector . . ."

He seemed to regret parting with such private information, plunging his teeth into the sandwich again, piercing my eyes with the needles of his. Once more inaccessible, adult. Instinctively I compared him with Slayton. A Slayton made of flesh, though. Shamelessly full of desires, of quite unrepressed passions, of doubts too, perhaps. And if they take away our doubts, our passions, our desires, Father, what would we be doing here, what would be left to us? Only our dreams? This handful of earth?

"We need art as we need dreams," he concluded.

"Dreams? Did you say dreams?"

"Without our dreams we wouldn't be where we are: dreaming of going to other planets, to other solar systems, and finding other Earths, our Earth, among billions of stars."

"Our Earth? Did you say our Earth?"

"Certainly. Because it's our Earth, it'll always be our Earth that we're looking for, it'll always be our Earth that we discover. I don't dream about the Moon. I know enough about the Moon to know how unpleasant and inhospitable it is. There's not one little bit of Moon that's worth the Earth or that we could bring back to Earth as a trace of civilization. I don't dream about Mars. I know enough about Mars to know that you can't live there, you can't settle it. Mars and the Moon are two ugly islands. So then, you say, what's the point of going to them? The point is to be able to say I've been there, I've set foot on them and I can go further, to look for beautiful islands. How many times, when we've been on a pink beach bordered with green, have we seen a black bare rock in the sea and wanted to fling ourselves into the water to reach it? And we've flung ourselves into the water and we've reached it, only to come back again, disappointed but satisfied because we made it. We discovered America and the whole world by going on from rock to rock: in the same way we'll discover other Earths. By God! There are more stars in the sky than grains of sand on the Earth, all the sand on Earth doesn't amount to the number of stars in the sky, and every star may have a planet, two planets, five planets: and among those billions of planets there must surely be millions of Earths. Those are what we're looking for, those are what we'll discover."

"But we've been born too soon for that."

"Too soon? Why?"

"Because we won't see those Earths. We'll have been dead for centuries by the time others get there."

"We've been born at the right time, the time for dreaming. After us everything will go so quickly, too quickly: there'll be no more time for dreaming, for appreciating. Thousands and thousands of people are flying every minute in airplanes, airplanes didn't exist a few years ago, yet the thousands and thousands of people don't appreciate the gift, don't even look through the window when the plane is taking off. They don't want the seat by the window, they want the one by the gangway so they can get to the toilet quickly. If they happen to be sitting by the window, they lower the blind and drink cocktails or watch films or TV. Ungrateful idiots. Morons. A heap of people have cried, have given their lives to rise above the streets, to fly, Icarus melted his wings by flying up toward the Sun, we've waited centuries, centuries, for Icarus to rise again: and they don't even look through the window. Ungrateful idiots. Morons. It'll be the same with space flights. There are people who cry, people who'll give their lives to go to the Moon, to Mars, to other planets: and when the others get there they won't even look through the porthole, they'll pick the gangway seat so they can get to the toilet quickly. Yes, we've been born at the right time, the time for dreaming."

Quite a while back he had pushed away his tray, having had enough of food and hungering for something different, and his voice was bubbling with passion barely held in by the dam of his rational mind. Gatha was staring at him in surprise, I was increasingly intimidated, fascinated and irritated. He was taking everything from us, Father. He was even taking our dreams, and this handful of earth, and poetry, and everything we love, because everything we love he loved too. So not even for dreams, for this handful of earth, for poetry, for the things we love, was there any need of us. Truly, Father, this meeting hadn't happened by accident. If the Suns and the planets rotated by accident, every hour, every minute would be the end of a world.

"Cheer up, what's the matter?" he said kindly. And this often happens with his type too. Sometimes, for a second, they are even capable of generosity. Or something like it.

"Nothing. I was thinking."

"What about?"

"About the new race."

"What new race?"

"Yours. Yours that is winning."

"Nonsense. We're not new at all. We're the same as we've always been, no different from those who centuries ago left Europe, the main street of the world, to come here. My grandfather was born in Switzerland, in the canton of Schwyz. He felt cramped in Switzerland, in the canton of Schwyz: so he came to America, settled in Pennsylvania. I was born near there, in New Jersey. I felt cramped there, in New Jersey, so I wanted to get away, to look for new islands. It's the history of the world, a history that repeats itself and doesn't change with generations, with races. The Phoenicians and the Etruscans and the Vikings and Columbus and Vespucci did the same thing . . . If I'd lived in those days, when everyone said the Earth was flat, I'd have been the first or one of the first to set sail to prove that it isn't flat but round. The new race doesn't have anything to do with it."

"Yes, it does. Yes, it does."

"But how, why?"

"The strength in all of you. The blind faith in all of you. Your total lack of fear . . ."

He shook his head. Then he looked at his watch and stood up.

"I have to leave for Houston, I don't have much time. But let's take a short walk anyway and talk some more."

Gatha went off grumbling that he'd see me later.

Outdoors he was much less intimidating, he seemed younger— perhaps because the wind ruffled his hair and a lock fell over his nose, covering the lines on his forehead. Outdoors his walk was oddly light, springing; following him, you forgot how big he was, and so much energy gave you both comfort and confidence. You know, those big men who entered our city on the 11th of August with their tanks. They advanced healthy and glorious, as if nothing could touch them, neither gunfire nor lightning nor divine wrath, and as we trotted along beside them we felt more ugly, ill-nourished, awkward: but we didn't feel humiliated. My foot was still broken, remember? I hopped along as little birds do and I lived in dread of not being able to run if the need to run should arise. Along that street, for example, to bring munitions to the river where our comrades were firing at the Germans. The snipers were in that street, remember? A woman had already been killed. One sharp shot, remember, and she was down, her face on the pavement. I was hopping along as little birds do and living in dread of not being able to run if the need to run should arise. But with those healthy glorious big men among us it was as if nothing could kill me. It was as if they could catch the bullets in mid-air, like that, with one hand, hold them in their fist laughing and then throw them away as if they were flies, like that. And I would walk tranquilly along that street with my munitions without the dread of not being able to run if the need to run should arise, without looking at the woman when I reached the spot where the woman lay dead: the big men gave me comfort, confidence, they were among us to defend us and they spoke our language although theirs was a different tongue. Like this man, now, here. Do you understand, Father? I mean that I felt a bond between him and us two. With his love of the Earth, of fantasy, of beauty, he was a bridge flung from his shore to ours: maybe an outstretched hand, a possible solution.

He suddenly broke the silence, stopping and sitting on a low wall.

"Let's talk about fear. Have you ever seen a bullfight?"

"Yes, of course."

"I remember very clearly the first one I saw, in Mexico City. One sunny Sunday, at four in the afternoon. The bullfighter was a boy of about twenty, with a fragile body, a nice face. The first bull entered and it was frightening. It was black and huge, with long sharp horns. The boy stood still in the middle of the ring, his feet together, firmly planted on the ground, and shouted: 'Toro!' The bull ran at him immediately, with its lowered head, its sharp horns. It brushed past the boy, who held out his cape and passed it over the bull's horns, then the bull turned back and again brushed past the boy, who held out his cape and passed it over the bull's horns, then the bull turned back again: and the boy standing still, his feet together, firmly planted on the ground, calm, fearless—while I was wondering how he managed not to be afraid, not to obey his instinct to run away. The second bull was a bad bull. The boy kept provoking it without rousing it, but eventually he managed to rouse it and then waited for it on his knees. I'll never forget that boy on his knees and that bull charging him. I'll never forget what I felt at that moment: I wanted to run away for him. But he didn't run. Calm, fearless, he waited for his bull and when the horns were on top of him he quickly raised his cape, swirled it over his head, turned the bull aside with a sweep of pink and yellow . . . with such dignity. It's very difficult to retain your dignity in the face of a bad bull. And a bad spacecraft. To do it, you must have no fear. Why wasn't that boy afraid?"

"He was."

"He wasn't. Because he knew what he was doing. He knew his bull as I know my spacecraft. He could read his bull as I read my computer. By this I don't mean to draw an analogy between a space flight and a bullfight: that would be grotesque. A bull is an animal and a spacecraft is a machine. A bullfight is a battle that has to end in tragedy and a space flight is a race that has to end without tragedy. In the bull ring you use your instinct, in space you use your brain. I only want to say that fear is lack of knowledge, fear is born of not knowing things. Fear is a dark room that might conceal a trap. But if the room is lighted, you know whether the trap exists or not: and fear vanishes."

"But a machine can also conceal a trap, a spacecraft can also kill like a bull."

"No. Because a bull isn't tested and a machine is. I've tried it out and tested it for weeks, months, years, and I know how it will respond. The chances that it won't function are infinitesimal."

"But they exist, they do exist!"

"You mustn't think of that. You'll think about it at the right moment, if that moment comes. To think about it beforehand would be a distraction and I can't allow myself the luxury of distraction. During my flight I get mad when Control Center says things that have nothing to do with the flight. "You're passing over Japan and the Emperor sends many greetings . . . You're passing over Algeria and the President sends his congratulations." Hell! Leave me in peace, later on I'll talk with the Emperor of Japan and the President of Algeria if they want to do me the honor. People say: Don't you let yourself think about other things when you're up there? No. We don't let ourselves, at least I don't let myself: I even forget my dreams when I'm up there. If I dream, if I get lost in wonder at the sight of a sunset, a color, I waste the flight and maybe my life. I love life. I don't understand anyone who throws life away for the love of danger."

"And if that moment comes, Mr. Schirra, that improbable yet possible moment, the moment when the machine doesn't function, the unforeseeable moment that bullfighters call the Moment of Truth . . . "

"I've got to face up to it without hesitation, without panic, coolly, using my brain. Like that parachutist who saved himself by using his brain. His parachute wasn't opening, the cords were all tangled.

Instead of letting himself be overcome by fear, he thought that the cords needed untangling and he began to untangle them. He went on falling and continuing to untangle the cords. Falling and untangling the cords. When he had untangled the very last one, his parachute opened. It's never the machine that kills: it's fear. I don't deny fear. I deny the luxury of accepting it."

We would never reach an understanding about this, Father. The fear I was talking about was another kind of fear, a kind of fear that he didn't know. He had been in the war, he had risked his life more times than we had, he did a job that could cause him to die sooner than we: and he didn't know that kind of fear. I envied him for this, I envied him madly, I was grateful to him for this. And I thought that's enough of our memories, our obsessions, Father. Enough. It's difficult to do without them, but enough. Our race is sick because of them, dying out because of them, so we must forget them, Father, we must stub them out as you stub out a cigarette when they tell you smoking is harmful, we must change, we must accept the bridge that is flung across from his shore to ours, his outstretched hand, his possible solution. Otherwise it is right that we should die and he and those like him should be the ones to continue life. Not I. Not you. Not people like me and you, Father.

"So then, Mr. Schirra, what is courage? What do we mean by this word courage?"

"In my case, courage is the thing that makes you refuse to go up if the machine isn't working perfectly. There you stand, ready to go, and the whole world is watching you. But there's a fault in your machine, a little fault that means your machine isn't working perfectly. Courage means stopping there, taking no notice of the whole world, and saying: 'I'm not going. I refuse to go until this machine is working the way it ought to work.' Get it?"

"Maybe."

"What do you mean, maybe?"

"Maybe. Because we'll never understand each other over this. But it doesn't matter."

"It doesn't matter?!"

"No, it doesn't matter."

"It seems to me that no one should ever give up trying to understand. And I think that sooner or later you will understand."

In the distance I could see Gatha making signs of disapproval, as if to say come on, are you still pestering him, come on, what a bore this kind of talk is.

"I must be going," I said.

He laughed his rich, husky laughter.

"Without understanding?"

"I'd have to go up there to understand."

"Up there?"

"Yes. How does it feel to be up there? How does it feel to be floating weightlessly up there?"

He shook his head slowly.

"I've been asked that so many times and I've never known how to answer. Someday I'd like to try to write about it. Like Saint-Exupéry when he wrote about the nobility of flight, the dignity there is in altitude: 'Affranchis desormais des servitudes bien-aimées, délivrés du besoin des fontaines, nous mettons le cap sur nos buts lointaines et alors seulement, du haut de nos trajectories rectilignes . . . Now freed from well-loved servitudes, liberated from the need of fountains, we set course for our distant goals and only then, from the height of our rectilinear trajectories . . .' Feeling weightless . . . I don't know, it's so many things together. A feeling of pride, of healthy solitude, of dignified freedom from everything that's dirty, sticky. You feel exquisitely comfortable, that's the word for it, exquisitely . . . You feel comfortable and you feel you have so much energy, such an urge to do things, such ability to do things. And you work well, yes, you think well, you move well, without sweat, without difficulty, as if the biblical curse *In the sweat of thy face and in sorrow* no longer exists. As if you've been born again."

Gatha was coming toward us, still making signs, laughing but: Heck, what are you still talking about?—unaware, innocent, irritating, and I'd have liked to push him away, you understand, shout at him: Not now, Gatha, go away, Gatha, be quiet, Gatha, for goodness' sake!

"Heck, what are you still talking about?"

"And when you come back to Earth, Mr. Schirra?"

"Heck, that's enough!" Gatha yelled.

"To Earth?"

"Yes, how does it feel, Wally, to come back to Earth? What's it like?"

"For me it's a great feeling of regret, a great sorrow. It starts when the retro rockets are about to fire and the time indicator shows how much time you still have left, and you're no longer weightless, and the dropping needle takes away your joy and restores your weight, your biblical curse . . . Zero, zero; three zero minutes and zero zero seconds . . . Zero zero; one zero minute and zero zero seconds . . . It's robbing you of them, implacably, robbing you of one after the other, one after another, together with your exquisite lightness, your pride, and you can't do anything about it, and while you're still thinking you can't do anything about it, there it's nearly at an end, there it's ending, there it's ended. While you're thinking that, you're here on the Earth. No, returning isn't a sigh of relief. You can love the Earth with all the love in the world: returning is regret, is sorrow."

"That's enough! Have you finished pestering him, yes or no?"

Rich husky laughter: his. Regret, sorrow: mine.

"Then so long," I said. "Thank you."

"Thank you," he said.

And he disappeared swiftly. Calm, erect, a victorious bullfighter leaving the ring, with the bull's ears, the bull's tail, and it's a sunny Sunday, the people are throwing their hats into the ruedo, the tinkling horses are dragging out the bull that is dead, in a long gush of blood.

"You look as if they'd cut off your ears," Gatha guffawed.

"My ears and my tail, Gatha. Come on, let's go."

Waiting in the car was a young and gentle man with unclouded happy eyes.

"Let me introduce Bill Douglas, the astronauts' physician. He's coming with us to the spaceport."

Dr. Douglas smiled. "Gatha insists you wanted to meet me."

"Yes. Isn't it you who awakens them the night they have to get ready to go?"

"That's me."

"I liked an expression of yours: 'They wake up as if instead of maybe going to their death they were going out to hunt geese.' "

"Is that why you wanted to see me?"

"Partly why. It's so rare to come across poets in the space age. It's as if nobody . . . well, hardly anyone can find anything beautiful to say about this business."

"We're still a bit stunned, unprepared. It all happened so quickly," said Dr. Douglas. "But it'll come, it'll come. And maybe it's already come."

"Shall we get moving?" Gatha interrupted. "It takes nearly an hour to get to Merritt Island."

15.

We were on our way. Gatha drove along a road on either side of which was nothing but a desert of sand. I was sitting between him and Dr. Douglas and my head was afire with Schirra's words, his husky voice. No, there was no escape, Father: the new race existed, he was proof of it, and we had to become like him, like them. We'd have to adapt, Father. After all, what else have we been doing for millions and millions of years but adapting? We're born naked, not clothed. Our vocal cords weren't made for speech: they served to regulate the passage of air to the lungs. It was only later that we found they could emit sound, and so we invented words. Our hands weren't made for writing, playing the piano, making jewelry. They served along with our feet to support us on the ground, it was only later that we found they could hold things, and so we began using them for writing, playing the piano, holding jewels.

"Dr. Douglas," I exclaimed, "just before we met in the bar I was wondering whether a new race of men wasn't being born, a race before which ours, mine, is destined to disappear."

"No, no," murmured Dr. Douglas. "It's still the same old race, just changing a little by adapting itself, but it's far from easy." He was silent for a moment. "In 1915 in the hills of California a man came out of a cave. He was an Indian and the last of his tribe. He looked about thirty, forty years old. The Department of Anthropology of the University of California captured him and shut him up inside the University, like you shut up a bird caught in a net, or a horse caught in a noose. Poor Indian, he only lived for two years. He had been strong and healthy until then; he was killed by comfort, hygiene, melancholy."

"That was an imposed, brutal change. Like putting me in a spacecraft and shooting me up to Mars without my being prepared for it. The change I mean is different, slower, caused by things as well as by people—"

"Are you talking about the body or the mind?" broke in Dr. Douglas.

"About both. Aren't they one and the same thing?"

"No, I'm not at all sure they're the same thing," murmured Dr. Douglas.

Gatha snorted.

"Ugh. You're boring me. Can't you talk about these things later, in the office?"

Dr. Douglas threw back his head in laughter and for a short while we were silent. The road sped smoothly by and there was still nothing on either side, not a leaf, not a flower, nothing. Only white sand and little white pebbles, shells.

"Then we'll talk about the body," I went on. "Let's start with that. With the possibility that the body itself can adapt spontaneously to what's happening. For example, that it can learn to breathe out of the air as fish learn to breathe out of water."

"Impossible, absurd. Life as we understand it depends on oxygen. Darwin's fish drew its oxygen from the water before drawing it from the air. Man will never be able to do without oxygen: when he can do without oxygen he won't be a man any longer, he'll be something else and the human race will be finished. He can adapt to weightlessness—although none of us know for how long he can adapt to it. A month, who knows? We are far from convinced that weightlessness is harmless, without long-range effects. He can adapt to great acceleration, to immobility: not to a lack of oxygen. Man will never evolve in space. He would more easily evolve underwater. For some time now scientists have been putting animals in containers of water and then increasing the pressure on the water to very high levels: seven atmospheres and more. Well, they found that these animals started breathing the water and their lungs were able to extract oxygen from it under ordinary circumstances."

"And did they die?"

"No, they didn't die."

Gatha Cottee, this time, seemed interested. "And of what use is it, Bill?"

"It's of use for going underwater and into space. When it's necessary to go up with very much more violent accelerations than at present, we can be enclosed in a container of water under high pressure and we won't break. Look, I'll give you an example. If you throw an egg on the floor, the egg breaks. But if you put the egg in a container of water and throw the container on the floor, the egg doesn't break. Put a man in place of the egg and it'll all be clear to you."

"Say!" said Gatha. "So we'd have to make spacecraft full of water."

"Exactly. Spacecraft full of water."

"Say!" said Gatha. And he stuck a piece of chewing gum in his mouth, all excited, pressed his foot down on the accelerator. Without thinking I imagined Gatha transformed into an egg that went up in a container of water and came down on Mars. In the impact everything broke except Gatha transformed into an egg. The egg rolled gently over Mars and trickled into a hole, like a golf ball. From the hole came a voice, the voice of Gatha: "Help! Sons of bitches! Bastards!" I told him, he took it badly.

"There's another system, though, Dr. Douglas," I insisted. "Cyborgs. Cybernetic organs. That is, going into space with artificial organs instead of our own: artificial lungs, artificial heart, artificial liver . . . In some ways the same as the Japanese Kamikaze system of cutting the legs off at the knee so they can straddle the torpedoes properly and steer them to the target by hand."

"Oh, no!" Dr. Douglas exclaimed. "It's possible to replace our organs with artificial organs, I know. Some of my colleagues maintain that an artificial organ is much better, that man is a faulty piece of construction, that there are no limits to the changes we can make in man: but cyborgs aren't human, they're monsters. And we want to send men into space, not monsters."

"Man is mortal, cyborgs aren't."

"I'd rather be Bill Douglas, mortal, than an immortal monster. I hope that such turpitude will never come about, and if it does, I hope I'll be dead by that day."

"Do you really believe it won't come about, Dr. Douglas?"

"No," he said glumly. "It'll come. It'll come, worse luck. It's only a matter of time."

"Ugh. This time you're really getting me down," Gatha Cottee said. "First you want to turn me into an egg, shoot me up to Mars and make me roll into a hole. Now you're scaring me with these damn cyborgs, with this talk about it being only a matter of time. The hell with you!" And he turned on the radio. "Music. I want music. Here we are. Ah!"

A woman's voice was singing an old song.

It was an old song, a song from the last war. Soldiers on their way to the front were whistling it in London from 1940 to 1945 and Vera Lynn sang it at the end of the movie *Dr. Strangelove* when the bomb had already gone off, and the sound of her voice was the only commentary on the great mushroom that opened into another mushroom and then into another so that everything would die—trees, animals, men and things. It was an old song and people thought of it primarily as a love song, but it meant so many other things besides love —it meant everything.

> We'll meet again
> don't know where, don't know when
> but I know we'll meet again
> some sunny day.
> Keep smiling through
> Just like you always do
> Till the blue skies drive the darkness far away.

> So will you please say hello
> To the folks that I know
> Tell them I won't be long,
> They'll be happy to know
> That when you saw me go
> I was singing this song

> We'll meet again
> Don't know where, don't know when
> But I know we'll meet again
> Some sunny day.

Brusquely I turned it off.
"Stop it, Gatha."
Dr. Douglas smiled strangely. "She sings well."
"Almost too well, Doctor."
"And it's a very fine song."
"A beautiful song."
"It means so many things, doesn't it? It means everything."
"Everything, Doctor."
Everything. Ourselves turned into cyborgs: artificial lungs, artificial heart, artificial liver. Turned into eggs full of water under seven atmospheres. Ourselves turned into monsters, immortal monsters, farewell man. Soon all you'll have left of man is his brain, his precious intelligent brain. But the brain itself will realize when it's turning into the brain of a monster, an immortal monster, so that alone, desperately greedy for love, for taste, for smell, it will restore man to what he was,

limited and mortal. Therefore not farewell: so long. We'll meet again, don't know where, don't know when, but I know we'll meet again some sunny day: we men, we little people, we who believe in love more than in intelligence, in smell, in taste, in ourselves made as we are, with two lungs a liver a heart and a limited brain, mortal.

"Let's talk about the brain, Dr. Douglas. It's the only organ we can't replace with an artificial organ. How will our brain, and thus our nervous system, react to the sight of other planets?"

"Ugh," said Gatha.

"How do you suppose it'll react? As it's always reacted. As it reacted the first time we went down under the ocean and saw plants that looked like fish, fish that looked like plants, colors that were other colors, unimaginable abysses. The marine landscape arouses no less terror than that of the Moon. The human brain has always had to adapt to new landscapes and the nervous system will suffer no more than it suffered in the past. The human brain is a miracle that surprises me more each day. We can foresee everything that has to do with man's survival as an animal and we can't foresee much that has to do with man's survival as an intelligent animal. It is true, yet I'm certain that the brain will make it."

"Even shut up inside that coffin called a spacecraft? At San Antonio they told me that many men lost their minds in the simulators."

"Ugh," said Gatha Cottee.

"They were weak. Our astronauts have spent days inside their spacecraft during their flights, and there are people who've spent years shut up inside a prison cell without going mad. Indeed, some have written very fine books. Superior people, of course. But the astronauts *are* superior men. Haven't you noticed?"

"No, I haven't noticed."

"What do you mean, you haven't noticed?" yelled Gatha, mortally offended. "She hasn't noticed!"

"That's because you met them in an office, across a table. Because you haven't seen them as we've seen them, the day before a launching, for example, when they'd go to bed and sleep, and I'd say: it isn't possible they can sleep, I don't believe it. I'd go in and look at them and they'd be sleeping, a healthy deep sleep. Then at one or two in the morning I'd wake them up. They'd all wake sleepily and say: let's go. At first I couldn't understand why. Then I understood."

"Why?"

"Have you ever been caught in a bombing raid?" Dr. Douglas asked.

"Yes."

"Have you ever gone to bed thinking there'd be another raid during the night?"

"Yes."

"And what did you do?"

"Let me think . . . I used to sleep."

"It's the same with them. They know the raid will come—so they might just as well sleep."

"There's nothing superior about that."

"Yes, there is. Because when they wake again to the realization that the raid is coming, they're happy. And they don't consider the fact that they might be going to their death; I don't believe they even concern themselves with this. They're so confident of their own ability, of their own invulnerability, that there is no reason for them to have insomnia and spoil their happiness. To die . . . who's ready to die? They have a desperate wish to live, and so they awake eager to live, and they're happy. An inexplicable happiness. When they come back down instead . . . you may have heard it."

"Yes, I have."

"They're glad to be back, obviously. And eager to talk about it. But . . . you would think they were looking for something they'd forgotten."

"Yes, I know. Schirra told me . . ."

That husky voice: "As if the biblical curse *In the sweat of thy face and in sorrow* no longer existed . . . " The biblical curse, Schirra, or the peace? Don't you forget the peace when you are back on the Earth? I wonder, Schirra, if you ever read that science-fiction story, the one about the astronaut they send somewhere or other, doubled up in his capsule like a foetus in the maternal womb. Like a maternal umbilical cord, a tube takes care of keeping him alive, nourishing him. He has nothing to do except remove this tube when he leaves the capsule. The journey takes nine months: the length of a pregnancy. And it seems to be a journey he took once before, a comfortable sweet peaceful journey, but he cannot remember making it. When the nine months have passed and he arrives at his destination, he remembers that other journey—in fear: it is the journey he made to be born . . . After the baby has spent his appointed 266-or-so days in the tranquillity of his mother's womb, he is abruptly shoved out by a 100-pound propulsive force into the hostile world, full of startlingly unfamiliar conditions. The first shock is the drop in temperature from the mother's cozy 98°F. to a room temperature some 20° lower. His eyes which have seen nothing but darkness are suddenly assailed by light. He moves from a wet world to a dry one . . . But he doesn't want to be born again, to be born, he's all right inside. If he's born again, if he's born, the first thing will be a long wail: and after that wail will come the effort of eating, drinking, sleeping, the effort of living in a hostile world full of startling nastiness, and grief, and disgust. No, he doesn't want to cut the cord again, he doesn't want to go out into the light, he doesn't want to live, he doesn't want to die. And he stays inside. Hello, hello, hello, they call from Earth, hello, hello, are you reading us? Hello, hello, hello, remove the tube, remove it! But he doesn't remove it and he stays there inside, forever.

"And I'd give a lot to know what they see up there," I said to Dr. Douglas. "In spite of everything, my strongest feeling toward them is envy. Jealousy and envy. If only I could go up . . ."

"Who told you you couldn't go up?"

"A centrifuge." I told him how I'd lost face in San Antonio. Dr. Douglas' shoulders shook with laughter.

"That doesn't mean a thing. It's an old story, the flight from the centrifuge when you're seeing it for the first time. I could get you to go in it and in less than a week I'd get you up to seven, eight G."

"But I saw a man pass out in it!"

I told him about Sergeant Jackson.

"Because they took him up to fourteen G. The astronauts go up to eighteen, twenty, twenty-one: but it's not that indispensable. They might have to withstand eighteen G during the re-entry, but usually the highest acceleration they have to withstand when a rocket lifts off is six G. Anybody can withstand six G for three minutes. What nonsense, that's not what's needed to make an astronaut. Physical superiority counts for nothing: the main thing is that they shouldn't have any serious condition. Some slight condition doesn't make any difference. Everybody knows Gordon Cooper had gallstones and had his gall-bladder removed some years ago, but Gordo is a perfect astronaut. And as for Slayton's heart defect, I might be wrong but I'd be ready to go up with him tomorrow."

"Then what is needed, Doctor?"

"First, a great curiosity, an unbounded total curiosity. Then, a great deal of intelligence. And lastly, courage. I don't know how one can pick out courage, but I know that's what's needed."

"And what do you mean by courage?"

"Courage . . . Look, courage is the quality that makes you wake up in the morning as if you were going out hunting instead of maybe going to your death."

"Only . . . ?"

"Amen!" shouted Gatha.

It seemed impossible, but here there were huge trees full of health and oxygen, and broad downy leaves that lovingly swathed their branches. Strong green beautiful trees that for centuries had withstood lightning, fire, insects, savage rain, drought and the gusts of fuel that poison the air. They flourished there like a mirage. I clutched Gatha's arm.

"The trees! The trees!"

"So what?" said Gatha, surprised.

"She's noticed that there are trees here," Dr. Douglas explained.

"Yes," said Gatha. "We still haven't cut them down. We haven't had time yet."

Dr. Douglas looked at me in silence. Then he offered me a cigarette.

The trees rose solid as a rampart, the last boundary of the Earth, and beyond stretched the spaceport for the space flight to the Moon: a silence of sand and water, a handful of islands thrown down by God on the seventh day when He couldn't think what else to do with them. Before NASA arrived, the landscape must have made one think of Genesis. Now it made you think only of what it was: an archipelago of 87,000 acres destined to be transformed into a city, the most hallucinating city that human imagination has ever conjured up. Before it such adjectives as enormous, gigantic, cyclopic become meaningless; the skyscrapers of New York, children's toys. The tallest and biggest building seemed to touch the clouds.

"Gatha, what's that?"

"It's the Vertical Assembly Building, the biggest building in the world."

"And what's it for, Gatha?"

"It's to house the rockets that will go to the Moon—already assembled, of course. But naturally this isn't all there'll be. There'll be heliports, railroads, banks, hospitals, post offices, houses, shops, police stations and the NASA headquarters. Cape Kennedy will be abandoned, like a little old station for steam engines."

"And what's that platform on the little island down there?"

"That's the launch pad for the Saturn. It's mobile and can be taken to pieces. It stands on the furthest island so as to avoid disasters at the moment of the Great Explosion. The island is called Complex 39 and it's joined to the island of the Vertical Assembly Building by an isthmus that is becoming a very long crawlerway: about three and a half miles. The launch tower slides from here to the launch pad along the crawlerway. Of course it holds the rocket with the astronauts already inside."

"Extraordinary."

"Complex 39 alone cost a billion dollars," he added proudly. "Not bad, eh? Now, this will be the Operations Building, where the astronauts will live for weeks before the space flight."

"A kind of spiritual retreat. Like nuns before they take their vows." Dr. Douglas smiled.

"What?" said Gatha. And he blinked his blue eyes: he couldn't even conceive that anyone could talk ironically about it. He pointed out those steel nightmares as if they were the Sistine Chapel, Giotto's Tower, the Acropolis, to his proud eyes they really were works of art to which he had made his little contribution. The evening before, finding him tired and depressed, I had asked him a question I would have liked to ask Dee O'Hara days before in Houston. "Why, Dee?" "Why, Gatha? Who makes you do it? Why?" And he had said: "So that I can say I was there." They all said it. Journalists who could have credits in *The New York Times,* publicity agents who would have triumphed in Hollywood, secretaries that any firm would have been happy to employ, all working like Dee and Gatha Cottee at Cape Kennedy, in Houston, in San Diego, in St. Louis, Huntsville, El Paso, Washington, Boston, New Orleans, exploited, badly paid, pushed around, and if you ask them why, they answer you obstinately: "So that I can say I was there." Their faith knows no doubts, their enthusiasm is free from uncertainties. Like Christians, Buddhists, Communists and Moslems, spacemen constitute a religious sect: ready to sacrifice and deaf to irony.

"Well? Aren't you going to say something?" Gatha stammered in disappointment.

What could I say to him, Father? I couldn't think of anything that would make him happy. Those towers that were too tall, those buildings that were too big, they were only the history of man, a history that was going on as it was destined to go on. Thousands of years earlier I would have seen a similar sight in Egypt when those huge blocks of stone were raised by the strength of men's arms to build pyramids and temples, and you would say "What's the use?" And the climate, the sand, the urge to amaze themselves and everyone else with those pyramids and temples was the same. And the motive that drove them was the same: not only a thirst for power, not only a competitive spirit. Unwittingly, childlike, these men were looking for God.

"Aren't you going to say anything at all?" Gatha repeated, disappointed.

"I don't know, Gatha. It reminds me of the Pyramids."

"The Pyramids were much lower and they used them to put the dead in," said Gatha, vexed now.

"Nevertheless . . ."

"Nevertheless?" asked Dr. Douglas.

"Yes, nevertheless: something has just crossed my mind . . . Dr. Douglas, if an astronaut dies during a journey, what do his companions do with him? Do they leave him on the Moon, do they bring him back, or do they abandon him in space like sailors burying their dead at sea?"

Gatha moved away as if he'd been stung. Dr. Douglas became very grave.

"It's a problem to be faced. We've thought about it, but we haven't come to any conclusion. My view is that we should ask each man before he goes whether he would rather be buried on another planet, or be abandoned in space, or be brought back home? If a man dies on Mars, or near Mars, it's clearly advisable for him to be buried on Mars. But . . . I don't know. Certainly his companions would want to bring him back home, we always try to take a dead man back home. But a spacecraft isn't a submarine, with refrigeration and all the rest. A spacecraft, the Apollo in particular, has very limited room and . . . you see . . . it's not only that the body would decompose because there's air in the spacecraft and air in the pressurized spacesuit. It's that traveling with a dead man close to you, so close to you, would be dangerous psychologically. I think that to abandon him in space would be the best solution."

"And what would become of him in space, Doctor?"

"Are you sure you want to know?"

"Yes . . . that is, no . . . but I have to know."

"Well, then. Without his pressurized suit—because with the pressurized suit he'd decompose—he'd become more or less like what you see in the hall of mummies in the Cairo Museum. He'd become like the kings buried in the Pyramids."

"And then?"

"And then he would continue to circle the Earth or circle another planet at the same speed the spacecraft was moving at when he left it."

"Forever?"

"Providing he was sufficiently far from Earth or from the Moon or from another planet—sufficiently far, that is, not to re-enter their gravitational orbit—he could keep on going around for centuries, for millions of years. Until the moment . . . until the moment when he would fall into the Sun."

Gatha had been listening angrily with his back turned to us. He swung around abruptly and said: "But, Bill, would we see him?"

"Yes, I think we'd see him," answered Dr. Douglas.

"And what would we see, Bill?"

Dr. Douglas smiled gently.

"We'd see a star."

———

So, on our return, we were all a little tense, as if we were sorry certain things had been said, and nothing could relieve our embarrassment. We were all silent. We looked for topics of conversation and found none, we tried making remarks and they fell flat. Sitting there between these two men who were so different and yet shared such a bond, I felt like an intruder and a fool: after all, I had been the one to drag in the accursed Pyramids, to start that talk about the dead. And so I was pierced by a strange indefinable anguish, almost a foreboding, but of what I didn't know, Father. It had nothing to do with the Moon certainly, already visible in spite of the blueness, a pale white reflection. It was more to do with myself, with the journey whose end I couldn't see. When I'd left Mother had shaken her head saying: but what a notion, my daughter, she's mad, now she wants to go to the Moon, yes to give me something else to worry about, it isn't enough that I never know where she is, what she's doing, a letter as big as a bedspread and then nothing for months nothing; and myself saying: what nonsense, Mother, the Moon, America isn't the Moon. Talk, just talk, for me America is the Moon, it's an excuse for going to the Moon, I know you'll get there in the end, and what for, I don't know, don't you know the Moon is only cheese? Cheese, Mother? Cheese, Gruyère cheese. And why Gruyère of all cheeses, Mother? Can't you see it's full of holes? Mother had added a postscript to your letter: "Take care of yourself and bring me a bit of cheese with holes in it." I looked at that pale white reflection.

"The cheese is out already."

"The cheese?" Gatha shook himself. "What cheese?"

"If you weren't so ignorant, you'd know what she's talking about," Dr. Douglas remarked with a short laugh of relief.

"I am not ignorant," grumbled Gatha, hurt.

"Yes, you are, because you don't know what the Moon's made of."

"The Moon is made of rocks, lava and dust."

"No," I said. "It's made of cheese."

"Who says so?" Gatha laughed.

"My mother says so. The Moon is made of cheese with holes in it."

"That strikes me as a very sensible hypothesis," said Dr. Douglas, "and it poses an economic problem."

"Meaning?" asked Gatha.

"That up there there's a fountain of infinite riches. An immense storehouse of cheese with holes in it."

"Say!" said Gatha excitedly. "We'll have to go and get it. The problem is how to do it."

"We'll steal the Saturn and the Apollo spacecraft," I said.

But I wasn't amused. They were, though, greatly.

"That, never," said Gatha, proclaiming all his devotion to NASA.

"Would you rather have the storehouse fall into the hands of the Russians?" exclaimed Dr. Douglas.

"Oh, no! Not that." Gatha thought for a moment. "But if we steal it, everybody'll notice."

"Obviously we'd have to act with cunning," said Dr. Douglas.

"I have a plan," I announced. "We must attack the Moon when it's on the wane, when it's at the three-quarters. That is, attack it on the dark quarter. It's a bit awkward, but robbers always work at night. And of course we'll have flashlights."

But I wasn't amused. I wasn't really paying attention.

"Blue flashlights," said Dr. Douglas. "I'll hold the flashlight, Gatha, and you can do the digging."

"Of course it would be my job to do the digging, as usual," Gatha complained. "And what'll the girl do?"

"I do nothing," I went on. "I direct and supervise. When we've emptied the first quarter, we'll load the cheese into the LEM and bring it back to Earth. In the meantime the second quarter will also become dark, so we'll leave again to empty the second quarter. Repeat procedure, repeat trip to attack the third quarter. The last quarter will be the hardest because we'll be working in the light and people down here on Earth will begin to suspect that there's something amiss."

Now I was quite amused. And they were also, vastly.

"We'll start a rumor of a lunar eclipse," said Dr. Douglas. "I have a friend who's an astronomer and he'd do it for us."

"We'd have to give him something."

"We'll give him some cheese."

"That eclipse is a great idea."

"People will believe it's an eclipse and they'll never suspect that we're stealing the cheese."

"Everyone'll be in the streets to watch the eclipse."

"Without realizing we're stealing the cheese."

"Then they'll expect to see the Moon again and the Moon won't rise."

"It won't rise because we've stolen it."

"All of it."

"But what'll we do with it when we've stolen it?"

"We'll make cheese sandwiches, cheeseburgers, we'll grate it on our soup, and we'll sell the rest."

"At top prices!"

"No, at lowest prices. That way we'll ruin Switzerland."

It ended the embarrassment, the silence. Even my anguish had passed. We spent the last twenty minutes of the drive working out the basic terms of a long contract, considering whom we could accept as shareholders, such as the astronauts, who are good fellows and deserve it anyway—after all, we were stealing the objective for which they'd been preparing themselves so hard, we had to make good their losses for them. Oh, how Mother would have laughed if she'd heard us! What a daughter, she'd have said, what a crazy girl, she's even managed to corrupt the physician who looks after those poor boys, and then that Gatha, who must be a really fine man, you see it's not for nothing I worry when she's traveling around, now she's going to ruin Switzerland that I like so much because it never has any wars. She would have laughed as she can laugh, the full-throated laughter that comes only to those who have wept a lot.

Still guffawing, I picked up the telegram the porter was holding out to me: some interview postponed, damn it. Still guffawing, I opened it. It was your telegram, Father, and it said: "Return immediately, Mother is seriously ill."

Part Two

16.

Mother lay in bed and her eyes stared at me like the eyes of one who has beheld the great darkness but managed to flee in time: frightened, stunned. Her jet-black hair had suddenly turned a dull gray, her hands that were never still dropped pale, exhausted, boneless, her lips tried to form a smile.

"Have you brought me the cheese with the holes?"

I looked at those hands, I felt her pulse to assure myself she was alive, alive, and my heart kept time with hers, that heart which was so tired. What did I care about the Moon now? The Moon had never existed. Cape Kennedy, Houston, San Antonio, Los Angeles had never existed, and all the future was in that pulse. All that remained to me of my broken journey was a dull anger, a feeling of rancor.

"No, Mother, I haven't brought you the cheese with the holes. No. Mother, Mother."

Spacecraft, pressurized spacesuits, centrifuges: but why didn't they invent something to prevent heart attacks? Cyborgs, urine that changes into pure water, weightlessness: why didn't they study instead how to heal a heart that's breaking? They were going to throw their fistfuls of algae on Venus, they were going to give life to another planet, and with every broken vein the life of my mother was in danger of the great darkness. They were packing their suitcases for the Moon and for Mars, those knowledgeable children, and they still didn't know how to cure the Earth's illnesses. But what does the space age mean if in the space age the heart of your mother is breaking?

"You'll have to go back, then, to get me the cheese with the holes."

Their pretentious talk. Their infantile lies. "In five hundred years man will have learned how to defeat death . . ." "We shall be able to eliminate every cause of death or at least be able to treat them: death from old age, death from illness, death from accidents . . ." "The resurrection of the body is a possibility: we have already resuscitated chicken spermatozoa and dried-out seeds, it's all just a problem of biochemical technology or surgical technology . . ." "The body doesn't die as soon as the heart stops beating, and the heart can be replaced: very soon we'll be able to do it . . ." Soon? How soon? Soon today, soon tomorrow, soon in fifty or a hundred years? Soon for me means immediately, now, this minute, while I feel her pulse, while I look at her lifeless hands, her dulled hair, her frightened eyes. Are you really able to perform all those miracles? Then do it soon, by God, drive away that darkness now, assure her now of that immortality. If you don't, you're just liars and charlatans.

"No, Mother. I don't want to go back and get it for you, the cheese with the holes."

The smile broadened.

"I know what you're thinking."

"What, Mother?"

"You're thinking about the men who can go to the Sun and can't cure my heart."

"Not to the Sun, Mother. It would burn them."

"Well, anyway, up there."

"Yes, Mother."

She was silent for a moment, searching for the right words. Then she found them.

"One afternoon I was in the garden. I was reading and a pigeon fell at my feet. Just like a stone. I bent down to pick him up and he was gasping for breath, he was dying. I felt bad for him and I wished I could cure him. But I didn't know how. None of us would have known how."

"No, Mother."

"Then I thought about you when you used to study medicine. Pity you gave it up. Perhaps you would have known how to cure him."

It was her way of saying that I didn't have the right to think certain things, to curse. Because I did nothing myself to make life immortal. The others were at least trying: I was only criticizing them, nothing else. A cicada in a world of bees. I'd given up being one of the bees many years ago when I sat at a typewriter for the first time and fell in love with the words that emerged like drops, one by one, and remained on the white sheet of paper, one by one, and every drop became something that if spoken would have flown away, but on the sheet as words became solidified: whether they were good or bad. It was like falling in love with a man when you already love another man, losing your head over him and leaving the other: even though you know the other is better, more reliable, a man with whom your life would have been well spent. A betrayal, in short. And when you betray one man for another who's maybe worth less, the least you can do is not to insult the man you betrayed, to accord him your respect. That was what Mother wanted to say. And she was right. But the fact remained that the man you'd betrayed wasn't really worth much. The fact remained that he was a good deal less reliable than he seemed, the whole of science was a good deal less reliable than it seemed. And I hadn't given up much when I gave up the microscope, the scalpel, pathology.

"No, Mother. I wouldn't have known how to cure him."

She had a flash of tender irony.

"Then when are you going back to get me the cheese?"

"I'm not going back, I told you."

"Oh, you'll go back."

But I didn't go back for four months. And it's curious how I remember those months: tedious and lethargic, like a long long sleep, Father. I went around Europe and I was bored. I wrote about people who were considered interesting and I mixed with the same people as before and I was bored. I only livened up when I started talking about my broken journey, and I only talked about it to Mother and to you. Mother had regained her strength little by little: at least she was very much better. She spent much of her time in the country with you. I would come every now and then to see you and tell you about the things I'd seen, the people I'd met. I enjoyed myself. I also enjoyed the way you reacted: arguing with each other over every trifle. Mother, for example, supported Slayton, she liked him because he had heart trouble too, and she defended him furiously against your indifference.

"Poor boy, to think that they should treat him so badly, poor blessed creature."

"Blessed creature, my foot! He even bombed us, that blessed creature."

"What a way to talk! They made him do it, didn't they?"

"He volunteered, what are you talking about?"

"Whether he volunteered or not, they've no right to treat him so badly."

"If you ask me, the nicest one is that one with the horses and the cows. That Shepard. All he cares about is horses and cows."

"Rubbish! Didn't he try to make a profit during his interview by selling them? He could have given them to her, couldn't he? He's rich enough! What would he lose?"

"He raises them to sell them, not to give them away to the first girl he sees."

"That one with the sick heart, he'd have given them to her, he's kinder."

"Don't kid yourself. Couldn't your daughter have bought them from him?"

"But, Pa, where would I have put them, the horse and the cow? In my suitcase?"

"You could have sent them, couldn't you?"

"I'd have taken the horse," said Mother.

"The horse, nonsense! What would you do with a horse? I'd have taken the cow."

"The horse."

"The cow."

Mother liked Glenn too because he went to church and said those beautiful things about God. But you liked Dr. Douglas, "the only one who's quick on the uptake, I'd say," and the doctor who killed the mouse. I began to suspect that your mouse hunts were not due to hygienic reasons but to the personal hatred that had matured in prison: "He had nobody to bite when he was swelling up in there, your mouse." Then you turned your back in irritation. You turned your back at other times too: when I was describing the marvels of the Apollo capsule, for example. "I'm not convinced. I'm not interested." But you stole the space food I'd brought from Downey, California, didn't you?

They were four little bags and they contained dehydrated lobster, dehydrated toast, dehydrated dessert and powdered coffee-with-milk. They were the only tangible proof that my journey had really happened, that I hadn't been dreaming. Ignoring your protests—"Putting this rubbish where everyone can see it!"—I gave them a prominent position in the book room, as if they were pieces of Chinese porcelain.

The first to vanish was the little bag of toast. One day when I arrived it had gone.

"Who's taken it, dammit?"

Mother threw me a glance of supplication.

"Don't get angry, I'll tell you."

"Who took it, Mother?"

"You know, the fish . . ."

"Don't try to tell me that the fish came out of their bowl to take the astronauts' toast."

"No, not the fish. Your father."

"Father?"

"Keep calm and I'll tell you. Your father was looking for some dry bread to crumble for the fish. And there wasn't any. So he went over there and took your toast. He even needed a hammer to break it up: it was so hard, nothing would break it. I kept telling him you'd be cross. But he went on hammering at it, you'd have thought he was hammering at the Moon."

The second one to vanish was the little bag of dehydrated lobster. Another day when I arrived it was gone.

"Who took it this time?" I asked with resignation.

"Who do you expect took it? I took it," you said without batting an eyelid.

"You promised me you wouldn't take any more."

"I promised you nothing of the kind and you know I can't stand having rubbish like that among the books."

"What did you do with it, Pa?"

"I put it in the pig food."

Mother groaned.

"Such a fine souvenir in the pig food. I didn't want him to, you know. I didn't want him to do it."

"But why, Father? Why?"

"Why, why, why! The farmhands don't give the pigs anything but apples and bran. They'll grow up stupid. Even pigs need phosphorus. It says so in that book *The Country Gentleman*. Lobster contains phosphorus, doesn't it?" You looked at me uncertainly. "It *was* lobster, wasn't it?"

"Yes. It was lobster."

"Uhm. Seeing it like that, it looked like anything but lobster. Just a lot of red pebbles. But in the pig food they swelled up like bread rising."

Now all that was left was the dessert and the powdered coffee-with-milk. Determined to save them, I entrusted them to Mother.

"Here, Mother. I make you a present of them."

"Really?"

"Really."

"Can I do what I like with them?"

"You can do what you like with them."

Mother would treat them with respect. She keeps everything, Mother: empty perfume bottles, odd little stones, creased bunches of ribbon, novelty Easter eggs, anything. She put the two little plastic bags in the glass case where she keeps the little things I bring back for her from every trip: next to the stone from the Parthenon, the Kyoto doll, the bit of rubber I gathered in Malaysia, the topaz I bought in Brazil, the ring from Calcutta. Then she locked the glass case so that you wouldn't get any ideas. But you got them all the same. And you contrived something I believed impossible: you managed to corrupt Mother. You corrupted her slowly, silently, without asking her for anything, without making a false move. The tale of what happened was told to me by Mother. Do you mind if I quote this too?

"For days he'd kept on saying: but I wonder what they taste like, I must admit it was stupid of me to give the toast to the fish and the lobster to the pigs, I'd be interested to try the stuff myself, after all we ought to know what they get to eat those astronauts, sometimes we talk and we don't know what we're talking about. You see, maybe it isn't bad stuff, it might even be a good invention, I'm not at all prejudiced. He kept standing in front of the glass case, looking at them, and in the end I just left the key in the keyhole. You know him, if I'd said to him: go on, take them, he'd never have taken them, he's so proud, but given the freedom not to take them he'd end up taking them, and when you gave them to me you said I could do what I liked with them, did you or didn't you? I left the key in the keyhole before I went to bed, he was getting up at seven the next morning to go shooting. I didn't hear a sound when he turned the key and took the little bags. He came back from his shooting about noon and he was very pleased with himself: he made no excuses, nothing. He just said: but you know what, it was good, that dessert! I added some water like your daughter said, I waited a little, and it was really very good: you know what those little seeds were? They were raisins. And the coffee-with-milk was excellent too, sugared and everything: a little water in it and in five minutes breakfast was ready. They're not so stupid after all, those Americans, you know, we must tell your daughter to bring us some more of these little bags when she goes back to America: they're fine when you're up in the hut waiting for the birds." And I wrote to Downey for some more. They sent me a parcel of them, there must have been forty: dehydrated peaches, dehydrated roast chicken, dehydrated onion soup, and they all finished inside your stomach while you aimed your gun at the thrushes and the chaffinches. I wonder what the American Senate would say if they knew that forty-four little bags of precious space food, prepared with great effort and at great expense by the scientists at Downey, had finished in the stomach of the fiercest enemy of the Moon while he was in a shooting hut in a thicket at Greve in Chianti. My God, the least they'd do would be to cancel my visa.

During those months I also saw Stig and Bjorn again. The paper sent me to Scandinavia to do a feature on the monarchies and so I saw them again, making up for my broken promise to meet them in New York. They had both written to me after searching vainly for me in New York. I'd written back explaining my unexpected departure and so a correspondence had started that strengthened our swift friendship. Bjorn, who always addressed his letters "To the Girl of the Moon," was the most assiduous and also the one I got along with best: his sentences oozed regret for the world that back there he had scorned. I found him at the Stockholm airport, still gay and attractive, his camera slung around his neck. He bounded up to me, crushing my bones, and announced that we were going to have dinner with Stig that very evening, Stig would show his color slides. Stig was spending some vacation time up in the hills, there was still snow on the hills so he came on his skis to show us the fork in the road that led to his house: he was looking more like James Stewart than ever. His house was warm, his wife was very sweet and I liked his daughters: in their quaint English they asked me to tell them about the Moon, which Stig would never talk about at all. "It's not worth it," he would say. Happily I obliged them. It was like old soldiers meeting to talk about what they did together in the war. It gave one the urge to get back to the trenches. After dinner we looked at the color slides: San Antonio, Houston, the astronauts, the Apollo spacecraft, and while Stig's daughters shouted with excitement and it seemed that Stig was sleeping, I caught the expression in Bjorn's eyes. An expression, I'd have said, that contained a thought like my own: "We were wrong. Stig is still wrong. It *is* worth it." When the slides were finished, he spoke aloud the words I'd been repeating silently to myself for some time:

"I'm going back. I want to go back."

Another factor contributed to my making this admission: that feature I was doing on the monarchies. The deeper I plunged into the out-of-date putrefied world of kings and queens, their idiotic dynastic problems, their grotesque privileges, the more I understood the people of Houston, Cape Kennedy, Downey: I needed them as a comfort, a salvation. Agreed, old Europe was still preoccupied with certain idiocies, with ill-bred princesses who marry friends of Generalissimo Franco, with heirs to the throne whom they won't allow to marry the shoemaker's daughter, the queen who has miscarried again, poor dear, and so they haven't got an heir: but young nations are thinking about flying to Mars. And my fingers were burning with the need to write about something truer, more serious, closer to what is waiting for us: the anger that tore me when I saw my mother lying ill belonged to a distant past, my rancor toward the knowledgeable children who don't know how to heal a broken heart was now finished. Like perjurers who when they're in danger commend themselves to God and promise to be good, to make sacrifices, to light candles if they come out of it safely, and then, when they're safely out of it, go on exactly as they did before and even forget to light a candle, so did I deny those cries, that moment of lucidity and common sense, and I revived the fable of my spark of light. When I returned to Milan I stuck up in my study a huge map of the Moon that had been sent to me by the advertising office of Nestle's Powdered Milk. On the Mare Copernicum was printed: *Feed Your Babies on Nestle's Powdered Milk,* but it looked beautiful to me. At night, with the field glasses I use for watching the races, I looked at the Moon. I couldn't see much more than you can with the naked eye: but she looked stupendous. And one night when there was a full Moon (how consuming it was, that whiteness, Father, how consuming) I wrote to NASA at Houston to tell them I was coming back. Among the things I asked to see was a rocket launching: I had never watched a rocket launching except on TV. Among the people I asked to see were the new astronauts of the second and third groups: in short, the twenty-three to whom it would doubtless fall to land on the Moon. A reply came from Paul Haney, the director of the public-relations office, the man who had interrogated me so astutely on my arrival: there would be two or three launchings during the month of May, he would do his best about the astronauts. "The astronauts heard about you and Gatha Cottee and Bill Douglas wanting to steal the Moon to dig the cheese out of it, so you enjoy a certain popularity. Some of them are anxious to know if they can participate in the affair. They say that with Bill and Gatha you'll never make it, you need an astronaut, and they offer themselves as pilots for the most fantastic theft in the history of the cosmos. You'll be welcome." And at this point something happened that I feel I may be allowed to relate, Father, because it demonstrates pretty well the muddle I was getting into again, the cracks in a world I was missing in such a tormenting way. The protagonist in my story is a gentleman I've never seen, but I know he lives in Washington and he's called Paul Smith. Let us proceed in order.

The Americans, as everybody knows, are generous: without a doubt the most generous nation on Earth. And also the nation that holds money in the highest respect. With the combination of these two virtues, and bearing in mind that I was a good girl after all, the Foreign Correspondents' Center of New York informed me that it would be very happy to get me a study grant for the second trip, to lighten the indisputably violent expense. The study grant was to be provided by a para-governmental body called the Governmental Affairs Institute, one of whose sources of money is the Ford Foundation. It consisted of twenty dollars a day, plane tickets for traveling from one state to another, and was for a period of forty-five days: not one more, not one less. The Governmental Affairs Institute was, in fact, very keen on encouraging cultural exchanges between the various countries, it had encouraged four thousand exchanges to date, among its beneficiaries they mentioned the Polish vice prime minister Piotr Jaroszewicz as well as the prime minister of Tanganyika Julius Nyerere. This news put me up in the clouds. More than anything else I found it comforting that in Washington they had finally become aware of me and my overwhelming and inimitable authority on European culture and the journey to other planets. Then I thought it very right and proper that the Ford family, with all their billions, should pay for my plane trips, my motels, my cigarettes. After all, wasn't I setting my story in America, ignoring alternatives and possible rivals who—to be fair—cut quite a good figure in space affairs? Between myself and the Ford family there would be only an exchange of courtesies; in Naples they have a saying: "I give this to you, you give that to me." I replied: very honored, thank you, accept without hesitation. And at this point Mr. Paul Smith came onto the scene. Or should I say Smithovic? The more I think about Mr. Smith, the more I am convinced that the whole world is developing the same faults, Father. As far as I'm concerned, Mr. Paul Smith could quite well be called Paulov Smithovic and live in Moscow.

Mr. Smith's letter was polite. He said how happy he was that I accepted the study grant from which the Polish vice prime minister Piotr Jaroszewicz had benefited as well as the prime minister of Tanganyika Julius Nyerere, and enclosed a questionnaire for me to fill in. The

questionnaire was long and anybody with any sense would have realized
as soon as he read it that the wisest course would be not to fill it in at
all. Some of the questions ran like this: "Do you believe in God? Which
church do you attend? Are you on a diet? Which illnesses have you had?
Do you have any contagious disease?" Let's be clear, asking a guest
whether he has contagious diseases strikes me as not particularly
charming but wise: you invite someone to dinner, maybe, and he gives
you a cold or tuberculosis or leprosy. Asking him if he's on a diet is
downright sensible: maybe you'll cook him stuffed pheasant and he can
only eat boiled rice. And it goes without saying that Mr. Paul Smith
didn't have to bring me anything to eat, he only had to provide me with
the dollars to buy a couple of sticks of chewing gum and a sandwich
every now and then. But asking a guest whether he believes in God
strikes me as being tactless at the least. You might ask him in the
course of conversation, I don't know, in an interview: I do so myself.
But to ask it in a questionnaire, I may be wrong: it strikes me as
tactless. At all events, being a person with no sense at all, I filled in the
questionnaire: I had no contagious diseases but as a child I had had
measles, mumps, scarlet fever, and since I'd grown up I had broken an
arm, a foot, a leg, in addition to which I had been operated on for
mastoids. Churches I didn't attend: not even on Sunday. The matter
of believing or not believing in God was my own affair: such deep
questions are not in the same province as diets. Mr. Smith replied with
a cold letter that ordered me to list all the people I intended to see, the
cities, the counties, the towns I intended to visit, the unforeseen
eventualities I thought I'd be able to face.

I was a bit irritated, nevertheless I made out a list. I intended to
stop at New York; at Houston, Texas; at Huntsville, Alabama; at Cape
Kennedy, Florida; at Los Angeles, California. I intended to meet the
new astronauts, Wernher von Braun, Ernst Stuhlinger—the man who is
building the spacecraft for Mars—and I intended to watch the launching
of a rocket. I was unable to list unforeseen eventualities; my life was
one long unforeseen eventuality. Mr. Smith answered with a still
colder letter in which he acknowledged receipt of the above and
announced that I would be provided with an interpreter throughout the
entire journey. In order to inform the interpreter, he would like to be
informed of the exact day and hour I would be leaving Cape Kennedy
for, I don't know, New Orleans, then the exact day and hour I would be
leaving New Orleans for, I don't know, Kansas City. And then I lost

my temper. I wrote to Mr. Smith as follows. Unfortunately I don't have a copy, but my letter went more or less like this:

"Dear Mr. Smith: Your intention of giving me an interpreter is truly delightful but I don't want an interpreter because I speak English quite well and understand it still better; if necessary, as you see, I can write it. Besides which I don't want an interpreter because I like to be by myself: I hate feeling watched, followed, spied on. If such a thing happens, I escape by very skillful stratagems. For the same reason I cannot provide you with a precise schedule of my movements: besides I never know myself when I am coming and when I am going. It may happen, for example, that I'm in St. Louis and suddenly get the idea of going straight to Mexico City to buy a sombrero. So I go to the airport and five hours later I'm in Mexico City. You may find this odd, my father says it's crazy: but people who write are always a bit crazy. However, the FBI, which is an excellent organization, will be able to keep you scrupulously informed of my movements. And it goes without saying that I should prefer to do without them: this is the very reason why I have never insisted on going to Russia to collect the material I need for my book. Indeed, I am certain that in Russia I should finish up being shot in front of the Kremlin for Great Indiscretion and Gross Lack of Discipline. It is thus unpleasant to think that such a ceremony could take place before the Lincoln Monument. Sincerely yours, etc., etc."

A deathly hush ensued. As if Mr. Smith-Smithovic had melted away into nothingness. Worse: as if he had never existed. Letters reached me from all over America, even from Washington, but never from Mr. Smith-Smithovic. And, I admit it, I was unhappy. Not on account of the suspicion, which grew daily, that I had lost the Ford family dollars, but because I'd got fond of Mr. Smith-Smithovic by now, by God: not hearing from him any more made me feel like a foundling. Could he be ill? Dying? Dead? In mid-April I asked for news of him at the Foreign Correspondents' Center. The Foreign Correspondents' Center answered that Mr. Smith was very well, that the Governmental Affairs Institute was again very happy to welcome me as it had welcomed the Polish vice prime minister Piotr Jaroszewicz and the prime minister of Tangyanika Julius Nyerere, that I could get ready to leave. So, full of faith, full of love for Mr. Smith-Smithovic, who evidently didn't want to bother me with unpleasant arguments, I spread the news that I was going. I was going with a study grant given by the

Ford family: and the announcement was not once greeted with mere indifference. There were those who impulsively congratulated me, those who jealously envied me, those who treated me with great respect, those who told me to drop dead. Those were the days when I learned to distinguish friends from enemies, the sincere from the false: and this too was attributable to Mr. Smith-Smithovic. One friend who one day confessed to my vast embarrassment "I love you" would no longer say hello to me, he was so angry. Another whom I had considered very hostile, on the other hand, hugged me with tears in his eyes. As for Stig and Bjorn, they answered humbly that I was truly important, by God, if I was being treated like the Polish vice prime minister Piotr Jaroszewicz and the prime minister of Tangyanika Julius Nyerere. And in this atmosphere I sent my telegram to the U.S.A.: "Coming, coming, coming." Then I packed my bags and Mother shook her head indulgently: "I told you so, I did, I told you so." You growled your usual disapproval, Father, but at the bottom of your heart you were proud that the Ford family was standing the expenses of your daughter.

The telephone call from the American Embassy, via USIS, reached me twelve hours before my plane was due to leave. They said, laconically, that my study grant had been canceled.

"Impossible!"

"It appears not."

"But I'm leaving in twelve hours."

"We're sorry, it is very embarrassing."

"Couldn't they have told me sooner?"

"That's what we said ourselves."

"Was this Paul Smith's decision?"

"Dammit, yes."

"And does he send me no other message?"

"Well . . . actually . . ."

"Come on, out with it. What does he say?"

"He says that if you're going to America to see the cherry blossoms, you're late: spring is over. If you're going to America to see the launchings, you're early: no launchings are scheduled till next year."

Nice adorable Mr. Smith-Smithovic. Just as well the banks open early in the morning in Italy. You won't believe it, Father, but I wasn't at all angry. Indeed, I was happy. One feels taller, more beautiful, younger, when one buys all those dollars and reflects that one is saving the Ford family the expense. One feels more of a Ford than the Fords:

one's chest swells, one steps out freely and the mob opens before one like the Red Sea before Moses. Nice adorable Mr. Smith-Smithovic. I owed this experience to him too. When I reached New York I telephoned a firm in Tokyo whose slogan is *Say It with Flowers* and sent to Washington a great bunch of Japanese branches covered with cherry blossoms.

17.

The man was flying in the New York sky as in those dreams when you're sleeping happily and think you're a butterfly, a bird, you only have to lift a finger in order to leave the ground, light as a feather, and go floating upward, higher and higher—you know those dreams, Father? Sometimes it's like swimming in the air with the air stroking your face, whispering, and your arms are wings that touch the rooftops, the spires, the trees; sometimes it's floating like a feather, a silent drifting with the wind, without even moving, and you wish it would never end. But it ends. You open your eyes, plummet down, stuck to the ground, and you're no longer a feather, a butterfly, a bird: you're just a lump saying "Tonight I dreamed I was flying" and then you look jealously at the feathers, the butterflies, the birds.

The man looked more like a hornet: but white. He had white overalls, a white helmet, a white handlebar, the harness that bound his midriff was white, the cylinders strapped to his shoulders were white, the exhaust tubes were white, thin, curving downward like a hornet's antennae. From the tubes came a continuous high buzzing: the buzzing of a hornet. Like a hornet, he was flying alone and determined, as if looking for something to eat or to sting: you instinctively feared he was looking for you and you ducked your head in fear, thinking fearfully: here he comes, he'll sting me, he'll eat me. More like an insect than a man, it took you some time to realize that it wasn't a hornet but indeed a man: a man exactly like you flying about as in those dreams we dream when we are happy. Not swimming through the air, though. No drifting on the wind either. Standing upright, head up, shoulders back, legs held stiffly together as if he were standing at attention. His arms were bent at right angles. His hands gripped two handles on the handlebar. His feet were dangling a little because he had nothing to rest them on. He was wearing brown boots that were the only dark spot in all that whiteness.

The man had flown off a roof and now he was going around the globe at the New York World's Fair. A great steel globe with steel meridians and parallels, steel continents, nothing for the seas, and hollow inside. Through the grille that was made by the junction of the meridians with the parallels you could see him, even when he was flying lower down on the other side of the world. He flew up and down, suddenly stopping still and considering us, then abruptly flying on again as if he didn't like the look of us, then suddenly changing his mind again and coming back to bestow a smile on us. He flew around like this, with alternating smiles and hesitations, for three minutes: finally he came down. Not dropping like a stone, though, nor with the rather sad somersaulting of someone descending by parachute in a clumsy intricacy of strings: gently, gracefully. He landed light as light on the asphalt, turned off the motor, held out his hand to me and said: "I'm Robert Courter." If he'd said to me: "I'm a butterfly, I'm a bird, I'm an angel," I wouldn't have batted an eye, I'd only have thought that Mother was right, angels do exist. Besides, what else could he be if not an angel? He was an angel named Robert Courter.

"I saw you from up there," said the angel.

"Oh!" I stammered.

"And I came down a little early," said the angel.

"Oh!" I stammered.

"Did you like my flying?"

"Oh, yes!" I exclaimed.

"Do you want anything before we start talking?"

"Oh, yes!" I exclaimed.

"What?"

"I'd like to go up!"

"No, can't be done."

"Why? Is it dangerous?"

"No, it's not dangerous."

"Is it difficult?"

"No, it's not difficult."

"Then what's the reason?"

"It's because this damn contraption costs a hell of a lot of bucks and if you broke it it'd be yours truly who'd have to cough up the dough out of his own pocket, get me?"

He suddenly stopped being an angel and became Mr. So-and-So, American citizen, thirty-eight years of age, married, with children, by profession rocket man. Before becoming a rocket man he had been a pilot and had fought in the Second World War and in Korea. He was here because the Bell Aerosystems Company was exhibiting these damn contraptions to the damn people who bought their damn tickets for the damn Wonderworld at the damn New York World's Fair. As for the Bell Aerosystems Company, it was the damn company that made the things: yes, in Buffalo, near Niagara Falls, they're also making the Atlas engine, that is the rocket for the Gemini capsule, but a lot he cared about that, all he cared about was being stuck here at this damn Fair, just as well he had two damn colleagues who took turns with him: there are three rocket men in America, which in other words means there are three in the whole world, Russia isn't using rocket men at present. Who were the other two? They were the two damn characters who were taking off his rocket belt: what, couldn't I see them? Say hello, boys!

"Hi," they mumbled as they removed his cylinders and harness.

They were very much alike, especially their faces. The kind of face, Father, that you forget the moment you've seen it and if you want to remember it you have to look at it again or find a photograph. All I can recall is that they were very much alike and very suntanned. Or perhaps not, perhaps they weren't, but pilots do nearly all have suntanned faces.

"I'd have liked to try it to see what it feels like," I insisted to the rocket man.

"What do you suppose it feels like?" he answered. "It feels like being someone up there. Period."

"I was wondering if you felt light. Or rather, in what way you felt light," I continued.

"Well, as for feeling light, you feel light. Damn light. How do you suppose you feel?"

"I don't know, I can't imagine. Except when I'm dreaming."

"When you're what?" exclaimed the rocket man.

"When I'm dreaming. About flying, for example. Don't you ever dream?"

"I sleep sound, damn sound. I don't dream about stuff like that. I fly when I'm awake."

"I see."

"Well, do you want to know how this damn contraption works or not?"

"Of course, sir. Thank you."

The damn contraption worked like a perfectly ordinary rocket. It was ignited by turning the handles of the handlebar, like the handles of a motorcycle. By means of these the rocket man could also control his ascent, descent, every maneuver he made. He could go forward, backward, down, up, around and around, or stand still. The fuel, hydrogen peroxide, was in two tanks strapped onto his shoulders: as big as the oxygen cylinders for underwater fishing. The exhaust tubes that I had compared with a hornet's antennae were some distance from the body so as not to cause any injury. The rocket belt was that harness that reminded one a little of the plaster cast they put around your chest when you break your ribs. It was fastened to the body with two straps and was also attached to the legs at the groin. It was made of Fiberglas. The duration of flying time was three minutes, but in future it would be for very much longer: as much as several hours. So said Dr. Wendell Moore, the rocket engineer who had invented the machine. Naturally I realized the infinite uses to which the rocket belt could be put. To mention only one, there was the military use. With the rocket belt, men could get over rivers, minefields, obstacles of any kind, and during landings they could fly from the ships to the shore without getting wet. It wasn't for nothing that the Army had bought it. NASA had also bought it, for use on the Moon. It would be very useful on the Moon for getting over rocks, craters, slippery lava, plains of dust where a man could easily sink down. And then in space it would be irreplaceable: there was no other way of leaving one spacecraft and steering toward another. Once he's out of his spacecraft, an astronaut can only float: he's stuck there like a damn pear on a damn plate. But with the rocket belt he can move about, go wherever he wants. The rocket man had flown with the damn contraption for Dr. von Braun, who had been ecstatic about it. The other feller had been ecstatic too, whatever his name was, the one that works on the damn craft for Mars, yes, Dr. Stuhlinger.

"And what are its uses here on Earth, sir?"

"Well, here on Earth it could be used a lot of ways, couldn't it? You could use it instead of the automobile, the helicopter, the bicycle, the bus. But it's better than any of them because it can land anywhere: on a damn rooftop or on a damn pavement, on a damn balcony or on a damn windowsill."

It seemed that I could hear your voice, Father: now we won't even be able to sleep with the windows open at night in the summer; even if you live on the eightieth floor, you'll sleep with the nightmare of seeing people land on your balcony. Robbers, rejected lovers, sex maniacs, who knows what? Especially a woman: do you think it's wise? You could be snoozing peacefully at the top of your skyscraper and pouf! There you are, strangled, or cleaned out, or involved in painful arguments. You're right, Father. And those interpreters of Mr. Smith-Smithovic, who's been humiliated by my cherry blossoms? I looked at the rocket man in great anxiety.

"Do you know Mr. Smith, by any chance?"

His mouth gaped open in genuine surprise.

"Mr. Smith! Which Smith? America's full of damn Smiths."

"Mr. Paul Smith of Washington."

"Never set eyes on any damn Paul Smith of Washington."

I lit up like a Christmas tree, Father.

"So even if a very important man said he needed one for cultural exchange or something, you wouldn't give him one, would you?"

"Cultural . . . what?"

"Cultural exchange."

"Never heard of it."

"Which means they couldn't be used for that, then."

"It can't be used for anything, not a damn thing that I don't know already. Period."

"Thank goodness for that, angel."

"What did you say?"

"Nothing, sir."

"Well, anything else you want to know?"

"No, thank you, sir."

"Can I go up?"

"Of course."

"Have some damn papers."

He gave me an envelope full of information and photographs, put on the belt of dreams again, made ready to go up for the damn people who'd bought a damn ticket for the damn Wonderworld at the damn New York World's Fair. The crowd was yelling with excitement. Spitting out curses on them, the rocket man turned the handles. One heard a little explosion, like the sound of a revolver with a silencer, and then a high buzzing sound. And the rocket man lifted off toward the sky. He flew around the great globe, smiled, went forward, came back, smiled, went forward, came back, smiled again, climbed higher and higher and became once more a white hornet, a butterfly, a bird, and then at last he was an angel.

I had come back into the future, Father. And I was beginning to regret it again.

18.

Manhattan was an embroidery of old skyscrapers, reminder of a past civilization. On a forty-third floor on Fifth Avenue, shut inside my office, I was waiting for Dr. Willy Ley, scientific author and friend of Wernher von Braun. As I waited I stood with my face pressed to the window: on the terrace of the skyscraper opposite, a man was watering the plants in his hanging garden, geraniums, rhododendrons, azaleas. Every day at the same time, at five in the afternoon, he would water the plants in his hanging garden: and always in the same solicitous sorrowful way. Once I had met him in the subway and I'd said to him: "You are the gentleman I see every day at five watering the plants in your hanging garden in a solicitous sorrowful way." And he had answered: "Yes, I love plants so much."

So what? What's so extraordinary? you'll say. Oh, nothing, nothing really. It rains so seldom in New York, plants have to be watered. Especially when they're geraniums, rhododendrons, azaleas. But, Father, his plants didn't need any water: they were plants that had never been born and would never die either. Plants without thirst, without life. Plastic plants: like the grass in Los Angeles, remember? What? The gentleman must be mad? Oh, no! He wasn't in the least mad. In a city like New York it's impossible to grow plants that are authentic plants, and he, who loved geraniums, azaleas, rhododendrons, had plastic ones. But so as not to go mad, you see, so as not to go mad, every day at five o'clock he would water them.

It was for a not so very different reason that I was waiting to meet Willy Ley, a man about whom everyone in America speaks with admiration and respect, and whom everyone always advises you to meet. Having fled from Germany at the age of twenty-eight because he wasn't a Nazi, in 1935 Willy Ley took refuge in New York and here he lives with his six thousand books and his lucid statements about the future. Indeed, they call him a prophet of the future, and the reason I was meeting him was to ask for his help: to rid me of all my doubts before I went on with my journey. I had told him this on the telephone. And he had answered me kindly: "All right. I'll come around to your place. Tomorrow at five." He arrived on the dot of five o'clock, a heavily, massively built old man, with asthma that made his large stomach heave, and the most disturbing eyes I had ever seen. Beneath his very white eyebrows, the eyes were almost blind. They stuck out as if they might fall out altogether at any minute. And yet they saw. Nor did it take you long to realize that they saw very far: beyond the blue sky and beyond any words. He even saw the question I was silently turning over in my mind: "But was I right to come back, Mr. Ley? Is it truly interesting, the future that lies ahead of us?" He lowered his great body onto a chair which creaked, fixed me with those blind eyes and said: "You did right to come back. You are right to go on with your journey because ahead of us lies a future that is very interesting. Very, very interesting."

I opened my arms wide.

"I'm not sure, Mr. Ley. At times I am fascinated by it and at times it revolts me. At times I feel full of courage and at times full of fear. At times it makes me burst out laughing and at times it makes me weep."

"But over this I cannot help you: nor should you ask me to help you. You must find the answer to your doubts within yourself, in what you see and understand, and it will take time."

"Have you found the answer, Mr. Ley?"

"Yes. I have found it, together with the truth. And truth is to be found at neither one extreme nor the other. Nor is it to be found halfway between the two, as has been said for centuries. It stands rather to one side: the side of the future. I believe in the future, I've been believing in it for thirty years, with optimism, with faith. I believe in it because I know what it will bring us."

"Yes, yes. But those rocket belts, those automobiles, those submarines instead of ships . . ."

He nodded his head in agreement, lighted his cigar, smiled at my astonishment.

"Of course submarines will replace ships."

"But—"

"Didn't steamships replace sailing ships?"

"Yes, but—"

"Didn't automobiles replace horses?"

"Right, but—"

"The other fundamental change to take place will be in air travel. It's obvious that rockets will be used instead of airplanes. For the reason that supersonic planes vibrate too much, make too much noise and don't go fast enough. The fastest jet can take two hours and fifty minutes to go from Rome to New York. A rocket takes only forty, forty-five minutes, because it flies through the stratosphere. Six years ago von Braun and I planned a rocket-line project, and we both agree that in 1990 there will be more rocket lines than airlines. No, rocket passengers won't need to be strong like the astronauts. At present the acceleration to which you're subjected at lift-off is six or seven G and lasts for three and a half minutes, but with the system von Braun has in mind, acceleration will be barely three G and will last only one minute. Anybody will be able to bear it without wearing pressurized suits and playing at being space pilots. Landing will be no problem either. Today a capsule landing is full of drama—but rockets are still primitive today. The ones von Braun has in mind for the rocket lines will have wings like an ordinary jet and so they'll be able to land on a runway like ordinary jets. In other words, they'll lift off on the rocket principle and land on the airplane principle."

On the terrace of the skyscraper opposite, the man was still watering his plastic plants so as not to go mad.

"Agreed, Mr. Ley. But what price will we pay for all this?"

"Ahead of us, inevitably, is a technological society: ours is an age of technology. In the nineteenth century the most advanced science was astronomy, then it was the turn of chemistry, then biology, then technology—and no science has ever developed as rapidly as technology. This is only the beginning, though, and once technology has invaded every other scientific field—"

I broke in, exasperated.

"Nobody will say *I* any more, everybody will say *we*. Nobody will consider the individual any more, everybody will consider the group. It will be total collectivism, Mr. Ley, and we shall have lost the freedom to be alone. Does that seem proper to you, Mr. Ley?"

"It seems logical to me rather than proper," he said. "We won't be able, we are not able to allow ourselves to be alone. In a technological society, which is to say a society based on technology, work must be done by many people together, and consequently every individual is destined to be part of a group, to say *we* instead of *I*. Beethoven was able to write his symphonies by himself, von Braun cannot build his rockets by himself. He cannot because the Saturn is too big to be built by one man alone. Not even von Braun knows Saturn from the first bolt to the last: he knows one part of it. And his assistant X knows another part, his assistant Y knows yet another part, and von Braun cannot say: '*I* built the Saturn,' he has to say: '*We* built the Saturn.' To start with, von Braun used to talk like you: he always used to say *I*. Then he began to say *I and my assistants*. Now he says *we*. He has understood that today not even a genius can say *I;* today even a genius must talk in collective terms. Because without collectivity he can't be a genius, he can only be a would-be-genius."

"And should that make us happy, Mr. Ley? Should we light candles to the good Lord for sending us von Braun instead of another Beethoven?"

"Yes, because He's already sent us Beethoven and today we don't need Beethovens any more, we need von Brauns."

"What for, Mr. Ley?"

"First, for building a base on the Moon. It isn't enough just to land on the Moon, we must build a base there with telescopes, laboratories. And Beethoven couldn't build a base on the Moon, but von Brauns can build it. And then we need von Brauns in order to go to Venus, to Mars, to investigate asteroids: we have a great deal to do in the next thirty years. Lastly, we need von Brauns in order to go to Alpha Centauri. Beethoven can't get us to Alpha Centauri. I love Beethoven. I love him much more than von Braun. But I want to go to Alpha Centauri. And not with my eyes shut, listening to a symphony: with my eyes wide open. Like this."

On the terrace of the skyscraper opposite, the little man was still watering his plastic plants so as not to go mad.

"Von Braun can't get us to Alpha Centauri either, Mr. Ley. It would take four light-years to reach Alpha Centauri and we'll never be able to travel at the speed of light."

"Nonsense. Of course we shall. Not on our first journeys, obviously. The first journeys to Alpha Centauri will take not less than ten years and . . ." He relighted his cigar, which had gone out. He began puffing at it thoughtfully. "Ten years to go, ten years to come back. A twenty-year journey. It's a long time. No ship here on Earth has ever journeyed for as long as twenty years. What a problem, what a problem. Not from the technological point of view, obviously, but from the psychological point of view. What will those men do shut up inside their spacecraft for ten years and then for another ten years? They'll sleep, von Braun answers. They'll sleep an artificial sleep: six or seven years on the outward trip, six or seven years on the return. I don't agree. You can't ask a man to sleep uninterruptedly for twelve years of his life. I maintain and always will maintain that they must stay awake and lead a normal life. We should have both men and women in these spacecraft and let them procreate during the journey so they don't get bored."

"Procreate during the journey, Mr. Ley? Bring children into the world in a spacecraft? Raise children in a spacecraft?"

"Yes, certainly. Children who'll return as fifteen-year-olds, eighteen-year-olds, twenty-year-olds, and thus more inured to interplanetary travel than their parents. Perfect astronauts."

"Creatures who've never seen trees, the sea, fishes, birds, grass, houses, blue sky, Mr. Ley! But can't you imagine what it would mean to be born and grow up in a spacecraft, in perpetual darkness, in perpetual space? What would happen to their poor eyes, what would happen to their poor minds the day they returned to the Earth they'd never known!"

"Not what would happen, what *will* happen. I'm not romancing, my dear. What will happen is this: they will discover a paradise that we start seeing when we're kids so we don't appreciate it. They'll discover it and they'll be happy and they'll say: 'Look, it's like being born twice.' "

On the terrace of the skyscraper opposite, the little man was still watering his plastic plants so as not to go mad.

"Listen, Mr. Ley: if our planet is so beautiful, why go to Alpha Centauri?"

"Because this planet will die, will grow cold just as it grew warm, and we must make ready to leave before the new ice age comes upon us. Our solar system is five billion years old. It will go on for at least another five billion years. But before the end the Sun will have begun to lose light—to die, in other words—we must have learned how to reach other solar systems. Not other planets like Venus and Mars, bound by the same fate as ourselves: other solar systems."

"Earths like this, you mean. So many people have already told me the same thing. And what if it's only fantasy, only hope, nothing more?"

"Fantasy, hope, nonsense! It is mathematically certain that our galaxy includes other Earths, and mathematically certain that our galaxy is inhabited by other intelligent creatures like ourselves. Perhaps not made like us, but doubtless with a brain or something like a brain, situated in the head or something like a head. We shall soon know."

"Soon, Mr. Ley?"

"I believe I shall still be alive when we'll know: by communicating with each other, obviously. For some time we've been trying to communicate with the radio messages of Project Ozma. The trouble is that our instruments are disturbed by continual interferences and they are not sufficiently sensitive. However, once we have the base on the Moon, such obstacles will no longer exist. And the day we meet them and tell them—"

"But how will we tell them, Mr. Ley? How?"

"By mathematics. Mathematics doesn't vary because of biological variation: two plus two make four anywhere in the cosmos. By chemistry. Chemistry doesn't vary with variations of temperature and so on: only the reactions vary. By . . ."

He got up to leave and gave me a tremendous smile. A smile that filled me with terror because a suspicion had crossed my mind, Father, an absurd irrational suspicion. So I hoped madly, desperately, that he would leave quickly, quickly, quickly! He knew too much, that man, he was too sure of what he said. His eyes were too different from our eyes. They weren't Earth eyes. My God! Where did he come from, that man? Where? And what was he about to say to me? What? This.

He raised his finger.

He pointed it at the sky.

He looked right into my mind.

He said silently: Don't be afraid.

" . . . by pointing a finger at the sky. As if to say: Brother, I come from up there. That's how we'll tell them."

———

When the elevator took him away with a rush of icy wind, I seemed to be paralyzed, even incapable of grasping that now it was growing dark and that the last part of our conversation had taken place almost in darkness. The secretaries had left the office at five, just before he had arrived. There was nobody left on the forty-third floor but myself. And yet, Father, yet my terror seemed to have vanished as in a bewildering dream. I sat down. I looked at the telephone, which was ringing. I didn't answer. I didn't want to speak to anybody and I didn't want to see anybody. I didn't want to go to the hotel and I didn't want to eat. I didn't want anything at all except to stay there by myself and think. Or not think. Who knows? New York was aglow with lighted windows: thousands and thousands of stars framed in the blackness of the cosmos. Mother, yourself, the people I loved were all thousands of miles away, Father. And all my yesterdays were thousands of miles away. And this office was a spacecraft already started on a very long journey: to some remote planet up there. "I maintain and always will maintain that you must stay awake and lead a normal life: procreate during the journey so you don't get bored." "Yes, Mr. Ley." My companions were in some cell close by, sleeping. But soon one of them would awaken, any one of them, and on that plastic couch we would conceive, without love, according to the commands of Mr. Ley, a son to bring back with us in twenty years: my son. Day by day, month by month, year by year, my son would grow up inside this spacecraft: without ever seeing the blue sky or anything resembling blue sky, without ever seeing the sea or anything resembling the sea, without ever seeing trees, houses, animals or anything resembling trees, houses, animals, without ever seeing the Earth or anything resembling the Earth. Day by day, month by month, year by year, I would try to tell him about the Earth and this would be his bedtime fairy tale while he was small, a story to use in teaching him when he was older. While he was small he would believe it all, he would smile at my tales of fairies that look like fishes and flies, but when he was older he would laugh and say: I'm too old for fairy tales now. Then I would make him read books, I would show him pictures and films, I would say to him no, my son, I'm not telling lies, down there they really do exist, animals, houses, trees, the sea, the blue sky, the light: until he would be convinced and would look at me with hatred, with a rancor that precludes forgiveness, and he would reply then why did you make me be born here in the darkness? And he would grow wicked. He would know nothing of goodness, sacrifice, love: this son conceived without love on the plastic couch in a spacecraft according to the commands of Mr. Ley. Neither I nor his father would be able to explain to him what is good and what is evil because all goodness and all evil would be shrunk like a dry prune into what was happening among ourselves and in the sterile language of books. Neither I nor his father would be able to explain to him what is beautiful and what is ugly, because all beauty and all ugliness would be diluted to the point of rarefaction in all that space and in what he could see of that space through the porthole. Neither I nor his father would be able to teach him anything about anything except numbers and that which derives from numbers, and so he would know everything about mathematics, certainly, everything about chemistry, certainly, he would discover God knows what equations, God knows what chemical reactions: but this would be all he would have to build his life on until the

age of twenty. Then, after twenty years, we would bring him back to
Earth, this creature of the Earth that did not know the Earth, and we
would fling at his eyes the fairy tale we used to tell him when he was
small: the animals, the houses, the trees, the sea, the blue sky. We
would explode in his ears the whistling of the wind, the splashing of the
waves, the rustling of the leaves. We would fill his nose with the
perfume of flowers, his belly with the warmth of an embrace in bed, so
that like a storm, like a terrifying catastrophe, the truth would explode
over him, the truth that everyone, even the poor, possesses: and that he
had never possessed. And, shattered, unprepared, terrified, he would
ask only to leave again, to go back into the darkness, the silence, the
nothingness. And so he would go, leaving us on the Earth, too old now
to go away again, and to start with he would have a feeling of relief, but
little by little a feeling of regret for what he had seen, heard, smelled,
understood would make him unhappy: and day by day, month by
month, year by year he would learn to be sorry that he had not stayed,
he would suffer over it, he would weep with anger, and everything would
start all over again. On a plastic couch he in his turn would conceive a
son to bring back to Earth when he was twenty years old, with books
and photographs he would tell him the fairy tale of the blue and the
green, but he wouldn't believe it either, he would grow up without
believing in the blue and the green, in goodness, in sacrifice, in love:
until one day, suddenly, like a storm, a terrifying catastrophe, the truth
would explode over him too, and he would shout his curses on us. He
would curse himself, life, the Earth, the Sun that was dying, his accursed
fate of going to look for other Suns, God no! No! No! No! Like a
falling man clutching for a hold, I switched on the light, called the
elevator and escaped down into the street: the black nightmare was
over. Fantasies flourish when you're alone and the light is out. But
were they just fantasies? Are they really, Father?

Hallucinating reality denies it and shows that there was nothing
impossible or absurd in my nightmare. Nothing, Father. Not even my
suspicion (ridiculous when you look back on it) that Mr. Ley came
from very far away. Journeys that take ten years there and ten years
back will come: and longer ones will come too. That teams of men and
women should procreate in spacecraft is an idea put forward by many—
Mr. Ley wasn't raving mad. Nor was he raving mad when he spoke of
other Earths inhabited by creatures with a brain or something like a
brain situated in the head or something like a head. More honest men,
better men find a problem in this new knowledge and, mindful of what

we did to the American Indians, ask: Will we do the same to them too? Will we also steal their hills and their valleys, their springs and their forests? Will we exterminate them too with our bullets and our whiskey? Will we reduce them too to reservations and slavery? They used to be a happy people. Then we landed, so sure that we were more beautiful and good, more intelligent and more cultured, and we judged them as savages, inferior, desperate. We found their terra-cotta faces ugly, their language ridiculous, their brains like something that's something like a brain situated in something that's like a head. So, utterly without compassion, deaf to right or wrong, we took their green and their blue, we hunted them like rabbits or buffalo, we poisoned them like cockroaches or mosquitoes, and out of our assassination we built the most heroic era: the glorious tale of the pioneers who went to find new Suns. We wept for our scalped heads, justly, blessedly scalped, over our graves we raised stones and crosses: but we used the terra-cotta bodies as manure for the fields of corn. And we told our children that all this was our sacrosanct right because we had been more beautiful and good, more cultured, more intelligent, we had invented chewing gum, the jukebox, Coca-Cola, Pepsi-Cola and Seven-Up, plastic flowers, plastic hearts: because we had a real brain situated in a real head.

No, there was nothing impossible or absurd in what I had learned that afternoon, and Mr. Ley might quite well have been born in a land much further away than Germany. The hallucinating reality went beyond General Motors and radio-controlled cars, rocket lines and my son born in a spacecraft: there were, for example, people in New York who demanded interstellar laws. Already. Lucid cool people with their heads well screwed onto their shoulders, magistrates, lawyers, not dreamers, poets. There was lawyer Andrew Haley, general adviser to the American Rocket Society, seventy years old, office on Park Avenue, who was studying a code of interstellar law. Already. Interstellar law, he would say, is a subject to be dealt with with all urgency: do there exist meta-laws to regulate the relations between the inhabitants of the various planets, an Intersidereal Tribunal to adjudicate future relations between the various galaxies? Not in the least. There exists only a ruling drawn up in 1919 at the Paris Convention and according to which "every power has sovereign rights over the space above his territory." But in 1919 nobody was thinking of going to Venus and Mars, Alpha Centauri, so their concept of distances was therefore different. How far does space extend? As far as the limits of the atmosphere? Beyond the stratosphere? As far as infinity? A space station rotating and floating between Venus and the Earth occupies whose sky? The sky of Venus, the sky of the Earth, sky jointly owned by the Earth and Venus? The right to settle those planets, the Moon, whose is it? The first who plants the flag there, or he who subsequently occupies its surface? Columbus was an Italian in the service of a Spanish queen when he discovered America, but this doesn't make America belong to Italy or Spain. Amerigo Vespucci was another Italian, Giovanni da Verrazano was another Italian, but this doesn't make them speak Italian in America.

In 1956, at the first International Astronautics Conference, held in Paris, some wise ones made long speeches on the lack of laws to govern space travel and the ownership of the planets. If a nation owns the stretch of sky between the Earth and the limits of the atmosphere, he pointed out, then the stratosphere becomes no man's land, the Moon becomes no man's Moon, and anybody can claim possession; first, therefore, it is necessary that space, the Moon, the uninhabited planets should be considered independent territories under the control of the U.N., which should also govern trade, settlement and the naming of these regions. But in recent publications others have gone further, tackling the problem of the Indians of the sky. We must have legal rulings for eventual meetings with any eventual inhabitants of other planets, it was written, whether they be less or more intelligent than ourselves, more or less ethical-minded than ourselves. Our only means of assessing intelligence is our own intelligence. Our only means of judging what is right is our own justice. These are both the fruits of a certain evolution, our own evolution. So we must be ready to meet an intelligence and a justice that are the fruits of different evolutions. For example, we must forget our principle of "Don't treat others as you wouldn't like to be treated yourself" or "Treat others as you would like to be treated" and establish instead a principle that says "Treat them as they would like to be treated." The first thing they want, seeing that they're alive, is to live; so we mustn't kill them, we mustn't land on their territory in such a way as to damage it, we mustn't go there at all if we aren't invited. Agreed: but at this point there arises the problem of communicating with them, of knowing whether they want us or not, you'll say. Exactly, Father. But NASA have thought of that too. How? Like this.

First, the dolphins. The first step was taken in the aquarium where the neurophysiologist John C. Lilly, under contract to NASA since 1962, directed Project Dolphin. Excluding man, said Dr. Lilly, dolphins are the most intelligent animals of our planet. If they had legs and arms, or at least hands with thumbs, they would be something to be reckoned with. They understand everything, they can learn anything— or if not, anything that can be done without legs or arms, without hands that have thumbs. And they have a complete vocal language: they talk, they sing, they laugh, they cry, although at a speed three times greater than ours. By recording their talk on tape and then playing it back at a third of the speed, you can hear conversations or quarrels of which the only mystery consists in the fact that they are spoken in a language unknown to us. If we can succeed in deciphering their language, then by the same device we can decipher the language of creatures that live on other planets. And it goes without saying that Dr. Lilly is optimistic. His system, in my opinion, is as inadequate for communication with the Martians as the capsules of Glenn and Cooper were inadequate for reaching Mars. Let us suppose, for example, that an astronaut who has qualified in the aquarium lands on Mars, meets a Martian and talks to him with the device that he used for talking to the dolphins. At the very least the Martian will hook him, flour him and fry him. The astronaut and the dolphins have in fact something in common: a language that, like our senses of touch, smell, hearing and sight, derives from terrestrial evolution. If the Martians, products of a totally different evolution, have senses of touch, smell, hearing, sight and consequently also a language without anything in common with our own, what's the use of talking to them with the device you use for talking to dolphins? You might just as well talk to them in English or Russian or Ethiopian.

In such a case the Project Ozma that other people talk about is very much better. Initiated by NASA in 1960, Project Ozma consists in launching intersidereal messages by the radiotelescope at Greek Bank Observatory in Virginia, but it has one serious defect: it is very slow. On the day when Dr. Frank D. Drake sent out the first message, a journalist asked him when he thought he might get a reply and Dr. Drake exclaimed: "Not for at least fifty years, obviously. I sent it to Andromeda." Nor are certain astronomers listened to when they say: "I am far from convinced that it is a good idea to request messages or reply to them. We are the youngest planet in our galaxy and we have been civilized for only a brief moment in our history. Let us keep quiet, for heaven's sake. If we discover civilizations that are more advanced than ours, we'll be the ones who'll wind up on fenced-in reservations because nobody can alter my suspicion that we are the ones who are the Indians of the sky." However, nobody listens to this kind of advice,

Father. We can't allow ourselves such a luxury. To slow down the space race would be like stopping a ship full of passengers and goods in mid-ocean: it would spell economic disaster for any country. And the psychosis of going is by now in everyone. In the space age can't we even generate life without that act which mammals call the act of love? Can't we freeze death, resuscitate the body? The test-tube gestation that Aldous Huxley prophesied in *Brave New World* is considered with growing favor: the day when we shall be born in bottles, pre-selected, trained, organized, is not far off. Nor is the day when we shall be able to resuscitate, become physically immortal. NASA research workers realized it while they were trying to find a way of sending astronauts to solar systems hundreds of years distant. What happens if they're dead when they get there? They resuscitate themselves, of course. It's enough to drive one mad, Mr. Ley. These things don't affect you, I know. You come from a long way off, Mr. Ley, but we are only at the beginning, and so some of us are filled with fear: the same fear that overcame me when I realized that your almost blind eyes could see me even in the dark. And so there are some of us who are afraid we'll go mad: afraid as I was the evening after our meeting in New York.

———

This man was called Constantine Generales and he had known von Braun in 1935 in Zurich, where one was studying medicine and the other engineering. They lived in the same hotel and their favorite pastime was studying the effects of acceleration on the human body. They used to tie a mouse to a bicycle wheel, the rascals, and spin the wheel round at 21 G: a kind of centrifuge, in short. The mouse would burst like a grenade, covering the walls of their room with blood. This pastime continued until the day when the landlady, particularly touchy about her wallpaper, threw them out, shouting: "Get out of here." As a result of this, space medicine was temporarily brought to a halt, but the two remained friends, such close friends that von Braun's youngest son is called Constantine, books written by Generales are dedicated to von Braun and books written by von Braun are dedicated to Generales. They see each other very frequently even though one lives in Huntsville, Alabama, and the other in New York. His office is on Central Park West and it was here that I saw him: a gaunt man of fifty with a long nose and a little voice, two hands that were leafing through some certificates or other to show me that his intelligence quotient was 183, which is to say something comparable with the intelligence of Leonardo da Vinci and Einstein put together.

"How long can a spacecraft last?" Dr. Generales attacked, once he felt he had convinced me sufficiently of his intelligence.

"I don't know, Doctor."

"What, you don't know?"

"No, Doctor."

"And you're going to see my friend von Braun without knowing how long a spacecraft can last?"

"Yes, Doctor."

"Then I'll tell you: it can last for a century, even two. And how long can the human body last?"

"Eighty, ninety years."

"Call it seventy: allowing for the fact that at fifty an astronaut isn't worth a fig."

"Yes, Doctor."

"Now take an astronaut when he's thirty and send him to Alpha Centauri. But not at the speed of light: at thirty or forty thousand miles an hour, let's say. What happens?"

"The spacecraft gets there and he doesn't."

"Very good. He gets there, but he's a corpse, at best a centenarian. For him to get there as an adult or with his faculties intact we'd have to send him when he's a child. Agreed? But then what does he know, what can he do?"

"Nothing, Doctor."

"Nothing. Very good. But if we take the astronaut when he's thirty, put him in the refrigerator at the temperature of liquid helium, freeze him in apparent death for the length of the entire journey, then defreeze him and bring him back to life in the neighborhood of Alpha Centauri, he will land at the same age he was when he left. Clear?"

"Clear, Doctor."

"Then why not use the same system here on Earth? What we call death is not complete death, it's only the heart that stops, we all know that. The cells, although they deteriorate, go on living for a good while. So if we refrigerate a dead body before the cells deteriorate, that body is conserved indefinitely and death becomes something temporary: a waiting for resuscitation. Resuscitation is very easy when the cells remain intact, we are constantly bringing hibernated microorganisms back to life, the only obstacle at present is the brain. The brain deteriorates very quickly: a few minutes after clinical death. But my colleague James Connell at St. Vincent's Hospital here in New York is quite certain he'll solve the problem in a few years. If he doesn't solve it, there's only one solution."

"Which, Doctor?"

"It's very simple: to die with a refrigeration expert at your bedside. In short, to die and be promptly plunged into liquid helium, which is like saying in the refrigerator."

"I understand, Doctor."

"After all, a refrigerator is more attractive than a coffin."

"Certainly, Doctor."

"In my opinion, everybody should have themselves put in the refrigerator instead of being buried. There should be hibernation banks instead of cemeteries. But, you'll see, in fifty years there will be. Every hospital, every police station will be furnished with a hibernation bank where we can stay free of charge until the day we know how to cure the illness that was killing us. But even if it were expensive—one thousand dollars, maybe, two thousand, I don't know—we could buy our space in the hibernation bank on the installment plan. Don't we buy TV sets, cars, vacations in the Bahamas on installments? So we could certainly buy immortality on the installment plan."

"Certainly, Doctor."

"There's also another way this method can be applied. We can have ourselves put in the refrigerator before we die and decide how long we want to stay in it—twenty years, fifty, a century or two—then have ourselves defrozen. That way we can rid ourselves of our curiosity as to how the world will be in fifty, a hundred, two hundred years, and in the meantime we can have a nice nap."

"And if they forget to defreeze us, Doctor? Then what have we gained?"

"That's part of the unpredictable. There's always an unpredictable element. The only fact about which there's nothing unpredictable is that resuscitation is possible and that in the future death will be a meaningless word."

"Then life too, Doctor, will be a meaningless word."

"What nonsense! We'll be producing so much life, even if it's artificial, that we won't know where to put it. At a certain stage we'll have to sterilize people to stop them producing more life. On the other hand, it's better not to be born than to die, isn't it?"

"I don't know, Doctor."

I don't know, Father. My knees were giving way as I left his office on Central Park West. I kept on walking and instead of the walls of the houses I was seeing blocks of ice, one after another, each one identical to the next, and inside each block a yellow corpse waiting with closed eyes for the Resurrection of the Body. The blocks were on end, so the corpses were standing upright, young, old, children, and at the feet of each one dangled a card with its Christian name, surname, age, date of death, 1965, 1978, 1993, 2000, but at precise intervals a block would go crack, shatter into little cubes of ice, a corpse would open his eyes and go away unnoticed, weeping. It was the year 2000 and New York was already the city they are prophesying: the sky was buzzing with rocket men and rocket women, the air was poisoned with fuel fumes and I was moving along a mobile pavement because I was very very old and so very tired. My son who had been born in a spacecraft had left again with his fairy tale of green and blue, his bewilderment and his despair; soon he would return, old himself now, and I didn't want to see him, I didn't want to see the reproof in his eyes, and so I was letting myself be taken along by the mobile pavement and asking only one thing: to die. The thought of dying gave me a sense of peace, a happiness I had never known, gave me a sense of rest I had been thirsting for, but the sight of those blocks of ice was enough for me to be overcome with tiredness again because I knew that they wouldn't let me die, that they would condemn me to live. Wherever I might go to hide my body, they would find it, and immediately too, in time to put it in a block of ice at the hospital or the police station. And there I would remain, like a perpetual curse, waiting to be resuscitated, to open my eyes on my son and my son's son—my enemies. That evening, Father, I nearly did go mad. You know what saved me? A very simple precious thing: a sense of humor. And do you know where I found it? In the remarks of somebody called Frederik Pohl, who writes science fiction. Do you want to hear it, Father? Imagine, says Frederik Pohl, poisoning your uncle, the rich one, in order to grab your inheritance, then living in luxury for a hundred years and having yourself frozen for another hundred years to see what the world will be like then. All right. But if some imbecile freezes your poisoned uncle, or if freezing of the dead is obligatory by law, then—how shall we put it? How will you feel on the day you're resuscitated and there before you stands the old bastard, resuscitated too, waiting for you to open your eyes so he can take you to prison? Bad, I tell you. Very bad. You would curse the idiots who played this practical joke on you until you were blue in the face.

After all, there were some people of wit in New York. I packed my bags to go to Huntsville.

19.

It was a green little city such as you can still find in Alabama and in other Southern states. Deer, foxes, squirrels filled its woods; cows, bulls, calves grew fat on its pastures, and its fields all grew cotton. In May, when the cotton bolls burst in white puffs, those fields look like clouds come down to earth, a soft quilt into which the pickers sank and then surfaced again. The pickers were Negroes. Immersed up to their knees in all that whiteness, they stood out dark like treetrunks and their arms were like branches that with swift fingers tore off the cotton puffs and put them in sacks. As they worked they sang melancholy spirituals that kept their movements simultaneous and alike: "Jesus—Jesus, Halle-lujah! Jesus—Jesus, Halle-lujah!" And at every hallelujah the clouds would part a little, the soft quilt would diminish, the whiteness would become painted with earth again. In September, when all the cotton would be gathered and they would sow cress, the cattle-raising contest would begin to choose the candidate to go to St. Louis, Missouri, where each year they elect the champion milk-producing cow of America. Sometimes this would trigger off brawls, enmities that lasted for whole seasons. You'd have liked Huntsville at that time, Father.

The longest street was called Milk Street, another street was called Cotton Street, and here stood the wooden houses with sugarloaf roofs, organdy curtains at the windows, rocking chairs on the porch. On the porches, in the evening, old men would sit smoking their pipes or women doing their knitting. The wooden houses belonged to those who were neither rich nor poor. The houses of the rich, on the other hand, stood on a hill called Snob Hill and were built in neo-classical style with columns along the façade, high green hedges around the lawn. The houses of the poor—that is, the houses of the Negroes—stood on the edges of the fields and were huts made of corrugated iron or stones. Every now and then it happened that a Negro grew tired of living in a hut made of corrugated iron or stones, and he would start drinking to forget it, and so he would annoy a rich man from Snob Hill, or else a rich man from Snob Hill would grow tired of being annoyed by a Negro and would have him beaten: but it didn't make the town unhappy. Whites and Negroes knew that such things happen in any part of the world, sometimes worse things, and we can't expect an earthly paradise. There were no real barriers of race and color in Huntsville: whites and Negroes, rich and poor, good and bad, they were all alike and on Sundays they would mingle their sins at Mass. After Mass they would walk around the square together. In the square there was the Town Hall: of stone and brick, with oblong yellow-and-blue windows, and a great flight of steps to give it an air of importance. There were always pigeons cooing on the steps and people would sit there in winter to bask in the sunshine, in summer to keep cool. In front of the Town Hall there was the statue of a frowning man with a mustache and a gun— John Hunt, veteran of the War of Independence, who had founded the town in 1805. The statue, raised on a tall pedestal, was barely three feet high, the least pompous statue you could raise, but it was enough for them and anyway it was after John Hunt that the town was named Huntsville.

John Hunt had taken thirty years to build Huntsville. After another thirty years the Civil War had broken out and Federal troops had destroyed everything. But the citizens of Huntsville had built it up again as it was, with its wooden houses, its neo-classical villas, its huts of corrugated iron, and everything had returned to what it was: a small green quiet place, without ambition and without curiosity. The only ambition of the women was to find a husband, the only curiosity of the men was to know which cow would go to St. Louis. For them all the world ended down there beyond the woods full of deer, foxes, squirrels: the Moon was a lighted torch to illuminate the streets, the stars were spangles sewn into the sky to make the nights precious. They hadn't the remotest suspicion that the stars might be planets like the Earth, the remotest notion that the Moon might be a place where one could land: nor did they have the remotest idea that the bombs would serve for flying in space. A war had broken out in 1940 much more catastrophic than the Civil War. But it had broken out far away, in Europe, in the Pacific, and they had hardly been aware of it. Besides the absence of some boys who would never return, it had left no mark. It was as if they had emigrated to New York or Canada. Nobody had actually seen them die, actually seen them put in their coffins. A German had come to America: a German who had brought a lot of other Germans with him and who was living at Fort Bliss, Texas, where, they said, he was launching diabolical rockets. His name was von Braun. But nobody had seen this German, nobody had seen those rockets, so that basically it was as if he were still living in Germany and the rockets didn't exist. And in such a state of indolence or ignorance or happiness (isn't that happiness?) dawned that day in 1950.

Father, shall we construct such a day? Let's see: I like to think that that day Huntsville was on holiday by reason of the most extraordinary thing that could happen on the terrestrial globe: the cow Lily Flagg had won for the third time the title of Champion Milk Producer of America. For the third time: she had already won it in 1948 and 1949. The best cows from all the states took part, dozens of cows, hundreds of cows, fat cows, strong cows, cows with udders like blown-up balloons, hard as salami: but Lily Flagg had beaten them all, just like that. Could you imagine anything that would distract Huntsville from such a triumph? And for this reason it was a great day, a holiday. Let us watch together, Father, the scene that fills the square. In the middle, garlanded with roses and ribbons, washed and groomed better than a racehorse, stands Lily Flagg, all white and patient. Behind her, not far from the little statue of John Hunt, stands Lily Flagg's portrait, and covering the portrait a banner inscribed:

TO LILY FLAGG
CHAMPION OF AMERICA
THE PEOPLE AND THE MUNICIPALITY
OFFER
PROUD AND HEARTFELT THANKS

Around the banner is the town band playing the Huntsville song: "Huntsville, city of heroes, Huntsville, city of the brave . . ." On the left the people are holding up placards: *Lily, we love you,* and making ready for the picnic. On the right there is a platform with flags and officials, in the front row the mayor, who is making a speech. "There are those who celebrate victory over another nation or a battle won," says the mayor, "we are celebrating victory in milk production and the success of a cow. There are those who send beautiful girls to beauty contests or strong young men to the Olympics," says the mayor, "we send Lily Flagg to beauty contests and Lily Flagg to the Olympics. We've had enough of bombing and worldly vanities," says the mayor, "we prefer to bombard each other with milk and show off our butter." "Long live Lily Flagg, our heroine!" reply the citizens of Huntsville as they raise their placards. And in the fields the bolls of cotton burst in white puffs, the clouds seem to have come down to Earth, a soft quilt into which the pickers sink and then surface again. With placid docile eyes Lily Flagg looks at the crowd, beneath her is a great white lake that smells of cream. The picnic begins. A splendid picnic: the fanfares are joyously sounding, the doughnuts are frying, the firecrackers are exploding. But suddenly a bigger explosion is heard, then a roar, then a whistling, and as everyone flees, knocking over doughnuts, placards, flags, as Lily Flagg lies fainting among the roses and the ribbons, the holiday is over. Von Braun has launched his first Redstone missile.

Since then (how many decades, how many centuries ago?) Huntsville is no longer Huntsville: it is Rocket City. Gloomy stone missiles, statues to the Atlas and the Redstones, are everywhere and they look like steles in a space cemetery: the sight of the pigeons covering them with their droppings is the sole comfort to anyone who loved Huntsville. The pigeons—who knows why?—are the only creatures that have survived the massacre: when the woods were shaved like some uncouth beard, stags, foxes and squirrels became rare. Cattle-raising is finished: like Lily Flagg, certainly dead of fright without ever giving a drop of milk again, they all found themselves with dry udders. Now, Father, the Moon is no longer a lamp lighted to illuminate the streets, the stars are no longer spangles sewn into the sky to make the nights precious: the Moon is a state to be settled, the stars are worlds to be conquered. Now experts on astronomy and ballistic science, the citizens of Huntsville put on a grave air when they talk of them; the boys at Butler High School, as they wait for the sound of the bell that marks the end of class, measure the time in terms of countdown: four . . . three . . . two . . . one . . . ding-a-ling! Go! And these same boys are learning to keep cotton in their ears so as not to be deafened when a missile is fired. Missiles are being fired all the time, day and night, the air is continually rent by explosions, by reddish blasts. In Huntsville, or rather Rocket City, you live in a perpetual bombardment, a nightmare of noise and shouting.

The most terrible noise comes from that Saturn that is going to the Moon and is one and a half times taller than the Statue of Liberty, eighty times bigger than the capsule that carried John Glenn. The voice of a giant that rumbles and roars like Niagara Falls in autumn. When it whispers, the earth trembles up hill and down dale, walls quiver, windows shatter, your eardrums hurt beyond endurance. There are more deaf people in Huntsville than anywhere else in the world, and nobody is sorry for them. Whose fault is it, they say, if they didn't put cotton in their ears? NASA had told them: Put cotton in your ears.

They disobeyed and now they're condemned to perpetual silence. Poor things? And why? They can always emigrate with state compensation. You can recognize them in the airport waiting room because they are wearing those very complicated spectacles for the deaf and in spite of their spectacles don't understand a thing: when their flight is called on the loudspeaker, they go on sitting there looking at the ceiling. So then somebody calls them, signs to them to go out onto the runway, and they reply thank you, I don't want to sit in the sun, I'd rather wait here. And so they miss their plane. Those who remain, out of resignation or laziness, so loathe the Moon that they never raise their eyes to look at it, and if they see it accidentally, this is what happens.

I had never seen a man spitting at the Moon, Father. But I even saw this that evening when I reached Huntsville. I was walking round my motel, I remember, and the Moon was clear. In the middle of the parking lot stood a man with his hands in his pockets. Quite still, his hands in his pockets, he was staring at the Moon. Suddenly he flung back his head and spat. Spat hard and straight: his spit like a little rocket. Like a rocket indeed his spit went upward and, as far as I could tell, never came down again. So then I approached him, fascinated, and tried to open a conversation. The man listened to me without hearing and then began talking to himself. "I spit on it," he was saying. "I spit on it, I spit on it! That whore of a Moon." A pause. "And that pimp of a rocket Saturn!" Another pause. "And those . . ."

Saturn's father is called Wernher von Braun. Saturn's uncle is called Ernst Stuhlinger. Its relations are all Germans although since 1955 they have possessed American citizenship. A hundred and twenty Germans with curt gestures and whiplash voices who only soften when they speak of Saturn—spoken with infinite gentleness: our baby. Or else: our biggest baby. During the Second World War, when they lived at Peenemünde in Germany, they had given birth to smaller babies, called with equal gentleness the V2. Read V for vengeance. The V2's, we know, bombed London. In seven months 3,000 dead, 6,800 wounded. It was no accident that Hitler considered von Braun the most valuable scientist of the century. The paradoxical chapter in the story of the journey to the Moon begins here and with this man whom the Americans haven't yet decided whether to love or hate.

A great many of them, it's perfectly true, love him: such as young people born since the war; such as lovers of Germany, who are very numerous in the United States. They love him and look on him as a Christopher Columbus of space, a hero of science fiction, and attribute to him all the virtues in the world: passion, organizational ability, optimism, imagination, the very merit of having redeemed America for her loss of face over the first Sputnik. A great many others hate him, those for instance who accuse him of learning Chinese now, just in case, and sure, they say with anger, he's a good engineer, an expert mechanic, but he's also a tremendous opportunist. When he found he had to choose between the Americans and the Russians who were advancing toward Peenemünde from opposite directions, he chose the Americans. But only because they seemed the stronger. No, they say, you can't really like the idea of this von Braun practically controlling the space venture, you can't really like the idea of his being greeted like a hero and, at times, carried in triumph. He and his 120 confederates who live in Huntsville, all entrenched in the same district as if in a fortress. Many writers, and journalists too, boast of having written volumes about the journey to the Moon without ever mentioning von Braun, Stuhlinger and their friends.

Honestly, Father, I find this ridiculous. And although I am one who doesn't forget, who never loses a chance of refreshing the memory of the forgetful, this you know, I find it dishonest and unfair to deny von Braun what is von Braun's, to leave him out of a tale of this kind. You may not agree, but that's how I see it. Let's be perfectly frank about it, Father: didn't upright men like Fermi and Oppenheimer make the atom bomb that pulverized Nagasaki and Hiroshima? This was said also by Erik Berghaust, author of an excellent book on von Braun, *Reaching the Stars*. An American citizen, though a Norwegian citizen until the age of twenty-four, Erik Berghaust lost his parents in the massacres in German concentration camps, was arrested by the Gestapo, was beaten, joined the Norwegian Resistance: yet he's very fond of von Braun and von Braun is very fond of him. Friendship, like love, can sometimes blind us. I advance these arguments at the outset, Father, to show you that I am not writing this chapter to annoy you: indeed I am writing it with some reluctance. And this allows me to give him the space and consideration he deserves, to say outright that I quite like the man. That astounds you? It astounds me too. But here is what I wrote in my notebook immediately after our meeting: "Interviewed von Braun. He's very tall and big, with a wrestler's shoulders, heavy paunch, the florid complexion of a beer drinker. Handsome face, though. His hair is very fair, his eyes are very blue, his teeth are very white: typical specimen of the pure Germanic race. He talks with an undeniable Prussian accent, manages to make the softest words sound hard: such as *Moon*. As he talks he stands erect like a general addressing a stupid recruit and his smile is so cold that it seems more like a threat than a smile. Odd: by all rights he should be unlikable and yet he isn't. For half an hour I made myself dislike him. To my utter astonishment I found myself feeling just the opposite."

The point is that nobody would deny his overwhelming personality, his forceful intelligence, a demoniacal ability to influence whoever is looking at him and listening to him. He knows about everything, he has a finger in everything, he's a pilot, a writer, a parachutist, an athlete, a violinist, a swimmer, a mountaineer, a skier, a pianist, he shoots, gives lectures, he's a fisherman, underwater swimmer, tennis player, theologian and so many other things that I shouldn't be surprised if he were also an excellent cook, did delicate crochet work, sang beautifully *Figaro qua, Figaro là,* and was a lightning translator from Sanskrit. You sometimes come across types like this, it doesn't make them any better than other folk, but one thing is certain: they are different from other folk. And the man is not an ordinary man. He never has been, and, well, it's also true that life has always been kind to him: apart from giving him a strong body and mind, it gave him a father called Magnus von Braun, baron, banker, landowner, Minister of Agriculture, owner of the magnificent Wirsitz Castle in East Prussia where on March 23, 1912, Wernher was born, to the great joy of the whole family. Even if he were a second Leonardo da Vinci (for the sake of argument), Leonardo would still have been the more remarkable on account of being only the illegitimate son of an ignorant peasant woman. Wernher von Braun's mother was no ignorant peasant, she was the Baroness Emmy von Quistorp, a rich and energetic woman and a noted astronomer. The day when Wernher was baptized according to Lutheran practice, when he was about eight years old, the Baroness Emmy didn't buy him the traditional gold watch, Berghaust tells us. She gave him a telescope with which to study the stars. And he studied them. By the age of thirteen he already knew enough to set himself the problem of inventing a vehicle for getting close to the Moon: in fact, he bought Hermann Oberth's book *The Rocket for Interplanetary Space* and began to read it. But being weak at physics, very weak at mathematics, he couldn't make head or tail of it. So he went to see Oberth, told him that he couldn't make head or tail of it, and Oberth advised him to go and improve his knowledge of mathematics and physics.

Seven years later he had taken degrees in mathematics and physics at the Institute of Technology in Charlottenburg. "I was filled with the romantic desire to go freely into the sky and explore the universe. At night I would stand spellbound looking at the Moon and telling myself how near it was, how near."

The Moon that was so near incited him to a deeper study of astronomy: he went to Berlin to learn astrophysics. But here he became convinced that the problem was not how to go to the Moon but how to keep a man's mind and body alive during the journey. He left Berlin and moved to the Eidgenossische Technische Hochschule in Zurich, where he met Constantine Generales and did those experiments with the mice. Then he returned to Germany and was taken on by the army as a civilian employee to work on the construction of rockets with liquid propellant. He was twenty-one years old. By the time he was twenty-four he was in charge at Peenemünde. It was Baroness Emmy who suggested his choice of Peenemünde. Wernher was looking for an uninhabited zone with a large area of water where he could fire his rockets in peace and she said: "Why not Peenemünde? Grandfather used to go duck-shooting there to be by himself." Strange that the same thing happened to Peenemünde that was to happen to Huntsville fifteen years later; the man seems destined to ruin every quiet spot. Berghaust says that at Peenemünde he wanted to work on space travel. But in the spring of 1939, when Hitler shook him by the hand for the first time, von Braun made no mention of the Moon. Explaining to Hitler the features of the A5, a forerunner of the V2, he said that it was a formidable weapon, a weapon that would pulverize the enemy. Pretty absurd, isn't it, Father, that the spacecraft for going to the Moon should be basically the same as what Hitler used for killing people? Von Braun told him that aerial bombardments were nothing by comparison, and it was an odd meeting, this meeting between the Nazi dictator and the Christopher Columbus of space. Hitler ordered that von Braun be helped, financed, he followed him in his endeavors to turn the A5 into V2, which is to say a rocket capable of flying at supersonic speed and reaching the hated England in the twinkling of an eye, he suggested that thirty thousand V2's be built immediately with which to annihilate London, and then another thirty thousand with which to annihilate Moscow, and then another thirty thousand with which to annihilate New York. And Dr. von Braun began constructing V2's with which to annihilate London, Moscow, New York, the whole world apart from great Germany, and so that day came, that very sad September 6,

1944, when the first V2 fell on Chiswick by the Thames. After
Chiswick another 1,115 were to fall on England, 518 in the center of
London. The last one fell on March 27, 1945, one month before the
death of Hitler. "If the Germans had launched the V2's six months
sooner," Eisenhower was to say, "we'd have found the invasion of
Europe very difficult, maybe downright impossible." This was the story
we would have to tell the Martians and the Venusians when, filled with
admiration, they watched us coming down in our spacecraft and asked
us: "But how did you do it? How did it happen?"

Well, it happened like this, dear Martians, dear Venusians, it simply happened that in January 1945 Germany was on the brink of defeat. The Russians were advancing from the east, the Americans from
the west, and the artillery was thundering ever closer to Peenemünde,
where both were anxious to arrive on account of the V2's: both knew
that Baron von Braun's favorite duck-shooting village contained a treasure. Barricades of reinforced concrete had been erected around Peenemünde, the documents had been locked in metal boxes full of acid
that would destroy them immediately when the lid was raised, a thousand V2's had been evacuated to safe caves. Von Braun called together
the men he trusted most and, Erik Berghaust reminds us, made the
following speech: "Germany has lost the war. But our dream of going
to the Moon and to other planets isn't dead. The V2's aren't only war
weapons, they can be used for space travel. To one end or another, the
Russians and the Americans will want to know what we know. To
which of them will it be better to leave our inheritance and our dream?"
(Or would it be more accurate to say: "Germany has lost the war. Here
our lives aren't worth a penny. We'll either be hanged by the Americans
or shot by the Russians. With which of the two do you think we can get
out of it by offering in exchange these very efficacious rockets?") The
reply was unanimous: "The Americans!" The Americans hadn't seen
their own cities bombed, their villages burned, their children deported,
their men and womenfolk shot to death. The Americans weren't nur-
turing hatred or vengeance. The Americans were very rich. "The
Americans!" Sigismund, Wernher's elder brother, had been at the German Embassy to the Vatican when the Fifth Army had taken Rome, so
that by now he had been with the Americans for more than two years
and was doing fine, what's more. Magnus, his younger brother, always
listened to Allied radio broadcasts and said that if it was up to him the
Americans would already have taken Berlin. "The Americans!" They
absolutely ought to try to surrender to the Americans. And fortune

helped them: in February Colonel Walter Dornberger, military commandant at Peenemünde, received orders to evacuate the five thousand men of Peenemünde and the remaining missiles to Bleicherode. The evacuation took place a few days before the Russians entered Peenemünde.

At this point the most paradoxical chapter in the story of the journey to the Moon is colored by a love episode: the farewell between Wernher von Braun and his cousin Maria von Quistorp, daughter of Alexander von Quistorp, Emmy von Braun's brother. At that time Wernher was thirty-three years of age, Maria only fifteen. But Wernher had loved Maria since the day he had seen her baptized, an event that I imagine must have taken place according to Lutheran practice when Maria was at least eight years old, and no other woman counted as far as he was concerned. So he must have gone to say goodbye to her in the von Quistorp castle near the Baltic Sea, and there followed this Wagnerian farewell scene, he enormous and fair, she slender and fair, he looking at her with his blue eyes, she looking at him with her blue eyes, he saying to her: "Auf Wiedersehen, Maria," she saying to him: "Auf Wiedersehen, Wernher." Behind them the waves of the sea smashing against the rocks, in the distance the thunder of gunfire. Those who have described the scene before me have made beautiful pages of it, really touching. I can't. This is the third time I've tried and each time I put less feeling into it: let those who have more than I do add their own, Father. You know that it's not that I don't respect the feelings of others. It's that I can't work up any sentiment over Wernher von Braun and his love scene in the castle. I'm being uncivil, I quite understand this, but as fast as I tell myself you're being uncivil I think of other farewells that were taking place while the guns thundered. Such as the farewell between an Italian girl and an Englishman who has fallen down from the sky, who is leaving to try and reach the lines. The girl is fair, about fourteen years old, the Englishman is the first man who has ever stroked her cheek. The Englishman is fair, about twenty years old, the girl is the first woman who has ever wept for him. They had met by chance in the ruins of a house and she had given him her bed, gone into the kitchen to sleep, for fifteen days. Nothing has happened, yet everything has happened, in those fifteen days. And so he has said to her: "I must go," and she has accompanied him past the German roadblocks to where a gun is thundering. "Ciao, then," says the girl. "Ciao," says the Englishman. "Let's hope it doesn't rain," says the girl. "Let's hope it doesn't rain," says the Englishman. And his eyes are very bright, so bright that they seem to be underwater. The girl looks at him and sees that a drop of water is running down his nose, down his lips, down his chin, she has never seen such a long tear as the tear of this Englishman, and the tear is finally lost in his neck: remember, Father? You were there too, Father. When the tear reached his neck, he turned and went away. I watched him going, fair, thin, defenseless, a boy almost as young as myself, and suddenly my childhood was finished, my fourteen years were finished, and my capacity for forgiveness: nor would it be brought back by laughing playing weeping for men who were not this one. I had become an adult in one moment and in one moment I became old: two months later when they told me he was dead, they'd found him in the woods with two bullet holes in his throat, the Germans had stopped him, he'd tried to get away and the Germans had shot him in the throat. Just there where his tear had disappeared. In short, I think of other farewells when I try to write about the Wagnerian farewell of Wernher and Maria, and I couldn't care less about their sadness beside the Baltic Sea. They saw each other again, they did, now they are married and doing very well in the little house in Huntsville. If von Braun has the force of intelligence I credit him with, and if one day, by chance, he happens to see this book, he will understand: I hope he will. End of romantic interlude. Let's get back to Peenemünde, Father. Or, better, dear Martians and dear Venusians.

"We absolutely must place the baby in the right hands." It is April 30, 1945, the radio announces that "Hitler died a hero's death in the battle of Berlin" and almost all Europe is now freed from the nightmare. Like angels in uniform, the Allies cut the barbed wire of the concentration camps, liberate the ghosts of starved humiliated creatures, horrifying to behold, and the vise tightens, tightens, tightens. They are coming from everywhere, these liberators or avengers as the case may be, they come from the north, from the south, from the west, Americans, Russians, French, English, and in the middle are the Germans, like mice caught in a trap clutching a useless piece of cheese. Donnervetter! If we can get out by throwing them the cheese! Von Braun sends Magnus to discuss the terms of surrender with the Americans. Magnus is the one who speaks English best. He goes off on his bicycle and after a few hours comes back: "It's done. Here are the passes for six automobiles. The escort jeep will be here soon." "Did it go well?" "Very well. They all seemed to be expecting us, anyway they seemed happy to see me." Then the escort jeep arrives and von Braun finds himself in General Patton's barracks before two officers who interrogate him very, very kindly. One of them is Dr. Richard W. Porter, who, like a Hollywood talent scout, is looking for "desirable elements" to take back to America. The other is General Roger Toftoy, coordinator of the Technical Intelligence Service in Europe and charged with requisitioning what remains of the enemy equipment. He has already gleaned a lot of Tiger tanks and now he wants the babes, the V2's. Von Braun tells him where they are: part in the secret caves in the Harz Mountains and part in a factory at Nordhausen. The General gives a start: Nordhausen is about to be handed over to the Russians. He quickly interrupts the conversation and grabs the telephone: the Russians will have Nordhausen but not the contents of the factory. Within twenty-four hours both cave and factory were emptied, the babes sent on their way to New Orleans. It was to take sixteen Liberty ships to load that kindergarten, and when the kindergarten was finally unloaded at New Orleans, and from there transferred to New Mexico, Toftoy was to be made chief of the Rocket Department.

As chief of the Rocket Department it was his job to select a hundred of the technicians and scientists to send to America with von Braun. So he went to question them in the ex-school at Witzenhausen where they were spending their time mending bicycles and radios. Toftoy was such a good and naïve man. He wondered, I read, whether he would find the hundred who would go to America, among the five hundred from Peenemünde, and in order not to run the risk of any failures I hear him asking them: "Do you prefer to work with Russians or with Americans?" Without fail each man replied: "The Americans! The Americans!" They all wanted to go to this America that they had expected to annihilate with their V2's, they seemed like Jews being offered a crossing to the Promised Land. Flattered, distressed, surprised, Toftoy turns to von Braun, who suggests a group of a hundred and twenty-eight. Agreement is reached over a hundred and twenty-seven: the one left out is Dornberger, military head of Peenemünde. The English view him as a war criminal, want him as a sacrificial goat to expiate the 1116 V2's launched against Great Britain. Toftoy hands him over to the English and it really looks as if the commandant of Peenemünde will finish at Nuremberg with a noose around his neck. Instead he finished by picking up the ruins of London for two years. What saved him was the fact that he drained the acid from the metal boxes containing the documents, the effort he had made to hand over

the babes to Toftoy, the testimony of von Braun. Ten years later he too
was to have an American passport, and you know what he does today,
Father? He manufactures rocket belts at the Bell Aerosystems in Buffalo. Yes, yes: the rocket belts of the angel who was flying at the Fair.
This is something else we shall have to tell the Martians and the
Venusians when, paling at the tale we relate, they exclaim: "But what
strange types you are down there on Earth, you really do act like people
from another world. And then?"

And then the first group of twenty Germans left for America, led
by von Braun. It was September 1945. The second came in January
1946: straight to El Paso. The third and last group arrived in April
1947, with their families. They were obviously in military custody
but they couldn't have cared less. All they cared about was getting U.S.
citizenship and in this hope they accepted everything, imitated customs,
habits, bad habits. In America people always chew gum? They chewed
gum. In America people drink whiskey? They drank whiskey. In
America people listen to jazz? They listened to jazz. America is an
octopus that swallows up anyone who lives there longer than a month.
There's no country, there's no religion that absorbs and transforms like
America, you know that? After a month in America you think you're
still European or African or Asian, you think you've resisted, that you
haven't let yourself be swallowed up, absorbed, transformed: but one
morning you wake up and you realize you're more American than an
American born in Chicago. It's happened to Italians, to Chinese, to
Russians. But even so, no group of Europeans has ever insinuated itself
into American society with the ease and speed with which the hundred
and twenty-seven of Peenemünde and their families insinuated themselves. Congress made them wait ten years for their U.S. citizenship, it
could have given it to them after six months. You met a German who
spoke English like a German and you asked him, just for fun: "Pardon
me, where are you from?" He would reply: "I'm a Texan." It was no
accident that during the six years the Germans spent in Fort Bliss there
were no incidents, no unpleasant quarrels. The worst that might happen
was that a child who had been called "Nazi!" by another child might
run home to his mother crying: "Mutter, was ist ein Nazi?" And his
mother would say: "Nothing, it's an old-fashioned word." And the
child would stop crying. "I thought it was a rude word, Mutter."
"Rude word? Why?" However, the rude word was never spoken to the
daughter of Wernher von Braun: by now father and husband. In 1947
von Braun had written to ask Maria to marry him. Maria had replied

yes certainly, von Braun had gone to Germany to marry her, and the new family in Fort Bliss included a little girl named Iris, born one year after the marriage. It included also Magnus and Emmy von Braun.

The Baron and the Baroness had followed their son to Texas after his marriage to his cousin Maria. Following the Yalta agreement, their castle and lands in Silesia had passed to Poland, and moving to Fort Bliss seemed an acceptable though difficult solution. Lovers of Bach and Brahms, they must have grown pale with horror whenever they heard jazz, and the motto "Do It Yourself" must have made them shudder in a wish for servants. In vain their son tried to convert them to the space age, to the customs of the great country that welcomes anyone: they stared at him with moist blue eyes, politely, and repeated that they wanted to go back home. They did go back in 1953. Von Braun didn't have much luck in America with the older generation. At a certain point he wanted Oberth there, the professor who had pushed him into studying mathematics, the great Oberth who ranks with the American Goddard and the Russian Tsiolkowsky as one of the three fathers of missile science. Oberth came, was received with great honors, and after six months announced that he was going to return to Germany. With the younger ones, however, von Braun was luckier. His brothers Magnus and Sigismund followed him without hesitation and stayed. Magnus later became an engineer with Chrysler, and Sigismund settled in Washington as Ambassador from West Germany. They were very tough years, those first years at Fort Bliss. Also, because there wasn't much to do apart from firing V2's into the sky of El Paso, von Braun was bored. To overcome his boredom, he worked with Ernst Stuhlinger on the project of an expedition to Mars and wrote a book on the same subject: *Project Mars*. When he had finished it he sent it to a publisher in New York who rejected it as "impossible and unconvincing." So then he sent it to another publisher, who also rejected it as "impossible and unconvincing." Eighteen publishers rejected it as "impossible and unconvincing." Five or six years were to pass before the book was published in Germany, then translated in America. The same publishers asked Wernher von Braun for a science-fiction story and he did one for them: the story of some astronauts who land on Mars and find a great civilization of green men. The green men are dressed like ancient Romans and live in glass buildings. They immediately learn English and one of them leaves with the astronauts to settle in America. What a relief it must have been, Father, to abandon Fort Bliss for the city of Lily Flagg.

Von Braun and the hundred and twenty-seven Germans moved to Huntsville, Alabama, on the sly, after the outbreak of war in Korea. When the first Redstone climbed up into the sky and Lily fainted amid the roses and the ribbons, the citizens of Huntsville didn't really know what was happening. They only knew that there were those Germans in the town and, whatever they were up to, they weren't at all welcome. "The last time our boys saw Germans was to shoot them in Germany, therefore we're not at all eager to have them here," the mayor had declared. And the town had picked up his cry. They closed their doors in the faces of the intruders, they turned their backs on them in the street, nobody wanted to lease a house to them. Paraphrasing the posters that had already appeared in South Carolina and Georgia when whole villages had crumbled before the bulldozers to make room for the construction of atomic-energy research establishments, an old lady who had heard talk of rockets hung the following heart-breaking slogan from her window: "It's hard to understand why our peace should be destroyed in order to destroy the peace of other cities." The hundred and twenty-eight didn't bat an eye. They bought plots of land, built their own houses, waited with Teutonic patience for their U.S. citizenship. It can be granted after five years: when five years had passed they had to wait a further five years, Washington didn't feel ready to take the step. Then Washington was ready and the ceremony was like a surrender: the surrender of all who love green things and cows and birds and can say: "It's hard to understand why our peace should be destroyed in order to destroy the peace of other cities."

The surrender took place in the main hall of the high school, in the presence of twelve hundred citizens of Huntsville, and nobody screamed, nobody booed. The atmosphere was the same as on the day of that interrupted picnic for Lily Flagg. Flags, trumpets, jollity. The mayor erect on his platform. The town band playing "Ja-da" and "Tea for Two." And, instead of Lily Flagg, the New Citizens: with white carnations in their buttonholes. The mayor, no longer angered, was bursting with satisfaction. "I am happy," he said, "that you have chosen us. I can recall no other group that in choosing America gave us so much pleasure. You bring strength and vitality to our little town." Then Toftoy spoke and said that in the course of thirty years of Army life he had never known a better group than this one consisting of the hundred and twenty-seven Germans. Then von Braun rose to his feet and all the arrogance of his aristocratic family seemed to have vanished in peasant joviality. Big, suntanned, blue-eyed, you'd have said he was about to open a baseball game: the women were mesmerized by him. Up on the platform he flung wide his arms, smiled: "This is the most beautiful day of my life. You know, it's like getting married for the second time." And the next day a reporter oozed with sentiment: "We are forgetting that ten years ago we were sending mass raids against them, these poor Germans." That reporter wasn't in London during the war. Nor was he in Poland, Czechoslovakia, Denmark, Norway, France or Italy. And maybe this was why he was feeling so Christian. It's easy, isn't it Father, to say let-us-love-one-another-we-are-all-God's-children? It's easy when you have been living in Huntsville, Alabama, from 1938 to 1946. A platform, a couple of ribbons, a band playing "Ja-da" or "Tea for Two" and stop, boys, no more rancor, no more memories, let us think rather of Mars, of the Moon. Turn the other cheek, Jesus said. Anyway all's well that ends well, isn't it, Father? and here ends the most paradoxical chapter in the story to tell to the Martians and Venusians. I go into the enormous building of the Marshall Space Flight Center and introduce myself with a big smile to Joe Jones, publicity man, who takes me to Wernher von Braun.

20.

He entered without warning and the room suddenly felt as full as an eggshell full of egg even though it was a very large room, the kind with a long table used for conferences, and the walls suddenly seemed a fragile shell that he could crack if he gave a good push, and there was suddenly not enough air. He had sucked it all in with a single breath, and in its place there lingered a slight scent of lemon. I was vaguely disturbed, wondering where I had already smelled that scent of lemon, but I couldn't remember, Father. It was a fragrance of long, long ago.

He was wearing a gray belted raincoat. A lock of hair had fallen across his extremely high forehead. Perhaps it was this lock of hair that made him seem younger than his fifty-two years: he looked about forty-five, no more. He was carrying a briefcase under his arm. He put the briefcase on the table and looked at me with eyes so pale in color that you might have thought he was blind. Then he held out his huge hand, the hand of a strangler, and reached for mine. He had to stoop to reach it: I barely came up to his chest. His voice came down to me from some distant inaccessible height.

"I cannot apologize enough. I am eleven minutes late."

"It doesn't matter."

"It does matter. And I'm sorry, because I cannot spare you more than half an hour. I am never late."

"I know."

"You know?"

He smiled at the unintended irony. He took off his raincoat, flung it onto a chair, turned back to me as if he had forgotten something.

"My name is Wernher von Braun."

"I know that too."

He smiled again. He folded his arms, watching me.

"What is yours?"

I told him. He repeated it, trying it out slowly, as you taste a wine to see if it's good.

"Oriana . . . A good Proustian name. Fallaci . . . Fallasci or Fallaci?"

He wasn't joking, he wanted accuracy. I gave him accuracy.

"It's Florentine to say *sci* instead of *ci*. A Florentine mistake. I come from Florence."

"Florenz! Ah, Florenz! A Yankee, then."

"A Yankee?"

"A Yankee, a Northerner. Important point. Yankees are always proud of being Yankees, Northerners in fact. Northern Italians regard Southern Italians as Yankees regard Texans."

He wasn't joking now either. He was still looking for accuracy. I increased the accuracy.

"Florence isn't North or South. Florence is an island in the center of Italy, a kingdom apart."

"A kind of aristocracy, eh?"

"Yes, that's what we think."

"And this is why you all speak ill of everybody else?"

"Of ourselves too, though."

"Out of coquetry, not conviction."

"You know us well, Mr. von Braun."

"Of course. Germans all know Florenz. Germans are romantic. Shall we get started?"

He went to the conference table, sat in the chairman's place, which is to say his own. At that moment there entered a little man with a red obsequious face and stooping obsequious shoulders: his public-affairs officer, Bart Slattery. He was late too, and breathless. He worriedly asked our pardon, hastened to introduce us. Von Braun silenced him with a brief gesture.

"Already done, Slattery. We already introduced ourselves. The young lady is an Italian Yankee. She comes from Florenz. Already done, Slattery."

Slattery took refuge in a chair that completely engulfed him. He was all humble and obedient, his face was lifeless and anxious. He looked at von Braun as a pupil looks at his master and seemed to be asking: In what way can I serve you, my lord? There now, he could serve him by reminding me that Wernher von Braun has no time to lose, he could spare half an hour at the most. Again von Braun silenced him with a brief gesture.

"Already done, Slattery."

Slattery slumped even deeper into the engulfing chair, crushed by his restlessness, and looked at his stopwatch to indicate that the half-hour began as from that minute. Then he looked at von Braun, who this time approved with an imperceptible movement of his eyebrows. I took a deep breath and went into the attack.

"Mr. von Braun, I'll omit the preliminaries and put a question to you at once. The question is this—"

I was interrupted by a white slip of paper that came sliding across the table in front of me and stopped by my hand. It came from Slattery, who had written on it: *"Doctor* von Braun. *Not* Mr. von Braun." The word Doctor was written with angry force and in big capital letters: DOCTOR. I stared at him in stupefaction, my face flaming, and threw a quick glance at von Braun in the secret hope that he would call him a fool. But von Braun was busy examining a fingernail, for all the world like someone who has noticed nothing. Perhaps he had noticed nothing. Don't you think so, Father?

"The question is this, Mr. von Braun. Here people talk of the journey to the Moon as they do of the trip from Huntsville to New York and repeat that, for America at least, it will take place by 1970—"

Another white slip of paper came sliding in front of me, sent by Slattery. Enraged. "DOCTOR von Braun!!!" But von Braun was examining his fingernail. Goodness knows what was the matter with that fingernail of his.

"Will it really take place by 1970, *Doctor* von Braun?"

Slattery nodded happily and preened himself in his chair. Von Braun quit scrutinizing his fingernail, finally convinced that it contained nothing of interest.

"Providing the people of America are willing to pay—yes, there's no doubt of it. It's an enterprise that will cost hundreds of billions of dollars, and it can be realized only if Congress continues to finance it. This is my one big if. A financial if, not technical. From the technical point of view I do not foresee any delays. Obviously there are certain difficulties, but all perfectly surmountable. It's only a short journey: eight days there and back. Going to the Moon is a picnic."

"A picnic?"

"A picnic, a trifle, a party trick."

"For you, on paper, I don't doubt it. Perhaps not quite such a picnic for the astronauts who make the landing."

"No. I am inclined to think that landings can be made almost anywhere on the Moon without excessive difficulties. Naturally there are areas that will be inaccessible to our craft; the Moon is quite a big place and the lunar surface is not uniform. There are mountains on the Moon, and plains, and areas thickly covered with dust, and areas as slippery as frozen snow. But there are also areas where movement will be relatively easy. At least I hope so. We know almost everything about the Moon, but not quite everything."

"Yes, of course. And what about the percentage of risk, *Doctor* von Braun? What is the percentage of risk to the three astronauts?"

"Uhm . . . Fifty percent of the risk is that before they set off they'll die in a car crash here on Earth: they drive like madmen. Uhm. The other fifty percent is that they'll die going to the Moon. Uhm?"

"With the difference that you don't always die in a car crash, but an accident on the Moon and you're dead in no time. Uhm? A hole in your spacesuit and that's it. Uhm?"

Bart Slattery was fidgeting. He picked up a slip of paper, then his pencil, and seemed about to send me another message. But he didn't send it, since he saw I'd got the message anyway. You mustn't say *uhm* when Dr. von Braun says *uhm*.

"A hole in your spacesuit, you say. But a hole in a ship sailing the seas will also make it sink to the bottom. A hole in a plane will also make the plane crash. In theory a plane might crash every time it flies. I truly see no difference between planes and ancient Phoenician ships and today's spacecraft and spacesuits. Sailing across the Mediterranean in those fragile Phoenician vessels was very much more risky than sailing through space with the Saturn rocket and the Apollo capsule. If those vessels were hit by a storm or foundered on a rock, the sailors died just like astronauts who are hit by an interstellar storm or who tear their spacesuits on a rock on the Moon."

"But would you go to the Moon, Dr. von Braun?"

"Indeed I would. I'd go like a shot. I wouldn't hesitate for a moment."

Bart Slattery nodded, quite overcome. He was beginning to get on my nerves. I glowered at him and he glowered back. Von Braun sat stiff and still, arms folded and legs crossed, watching our little skirmish but taking no part in it.

"It seems odd, then, that there shouldn't be a little place for you in the Apollo capsule. A scientist would be useful, wouldn't he?"

"That's exactly what I say: the question whether to include a scientist or not has been a burning issue for years now. I, for example, am willing to argue that a good geologist will observe aspects of the lunar surface that no astronaut, however good he is, will note. The particular formation of a rock, for example. So I repeat that scientists should be included. But they answer me that the aim of the first journey is simply and solely to succeed in sending up three men and bringing them back to Earth alive and finding out from these three men the good and bad points about the spacecraft. They must be able engineers, men who are young and cool enough to cope in the event of some emergency. Test pilots. Types who wouldn't be afraid to jump out of a burning plane or leave the spacecraft to repair any damage. And I'm afraid that as a test pilot I don't really have the necessary qualifications. I . . . maybe they'll put up with me on flight number 10 like you put up with a grumbling old uncle, to make me happy."

Bart Slattery sighed to show how deeply he shared in his lord's disappointment. Von Braun didn't even deign to look at him.

"Perhaps you'll manage to go to Mars, Dr. von Braun."

"Mars is another story. The main difference between a journey to the Moon and a journey to Mars is that Mars is very much farther away and consequently entails an extremely long absence from Earth. We reckon two years there and back. No, going to Mars isn't going to be an eight-day picnic. And even if Stuhlinger is right when he claims that it will only take nine months there and nine months back, it still makes a journey of eighteen months. Plus the month to be spent on Mars. We'll want to spend at least a month there, surely, and then we'll have to send a lot of people to Mars: a regular fleet with doctors, scientists, archeologists. We'll want at least one archeologist in case we discover traces of an extinct civilization on Mars. We'll need at least one doctor with all those astronauts, even if only in case an astronaut gets toothache or stomach ache. And how can he control the spacecraft if he has toothache or stomach ache? Should he leave the controls? In short, before we can go to Mars we must reach a much higher level of technical knowledge, and I'm very much afraid that a flight of this nature won't be possible until ten or twelve years after the first journey to the Moon."

He said this in the offhand manner in which he might have said: I'm very much afraid that a flight of this nature won't be possible until two or three centuries after the first journey to the Moon. And I was on the verge of thinking he must be joking: but he wasn't joking in the least, there wasn't even the flicker of a smile on his granite face. His voice was solemn. The voice of a teacher instructing a slightly stupid child. Like a slightly stupid child, I sought confirmation of what I'd heard.

"I'm not sure that I've understood, Dr. von Braun. Do you mean that we'll be able to go to Mars by about 1985 or 1990?"

"Exactly. By about 1985 or 1990. Do you think that's too far off, uhm?"

"I think it's terrifyingly close, Dr. von Braun."

"Quite the contrary, I would say. We should be able to get there very much earlier. If only we had decided sooner to study these things . . ."

And this time he smiled, believe me, Father, with such an unshakable faith. Galileo must have spoken like that when he said: "The Earth moves: it moves, all the same." Columbus must have spoken like that when he said: "The Earth is round and we shall reach the Indies." With the speed of a light that flashes on and off at the flick of a switch, my hostility turned to respect. And for a second, please don't be disturbed, I couldn't have cared less that this was the man who gave Hitler the V2. Forgetful, fascinated, I gave reign to childish curiosity, puerile enthusiasm. Mars with its canals, its blue hills, its diamond glaciers. Mars with its mystery, its buried cities, its cities perhaps still intact. And us up there in thirty years! Providing I wasn't struck down by illness, providing I didn't accidentally shoot myself, in thirty years I'd still be alive and I'd have seen the first journey to Mars. I would die thinking: I managed to see the first journey to Mars. So what did I care about the past, about past wrongs and errors? What did I care, since the future held the promise of such an amazing dream? I attacked him with enthusiasm.

"Go on talking, Dr. von Braun. Go on talking, please. Do you also expect to find life on Mars?"

"There is no doubt that at least inferior forms of life exist on Mars. Highly reliable astronomers note beyond any shadow of doubt that vegetation on Mars blossoms or withers according to the changing seasons. There is vegetation on Mars. What kind of vegetation I do not know, we do not know: but in spring it swells and broadens, in autumn it shrivels and dries. Experiments on Earth show that certain bacteria can live and propagate themselves in a hostile atmosphere such as that of Mars. Naturally when I speak of life on Mars I allude to a form of life quite different from our own, a life that has had two hundred million years to develop or to die. It may be that in an age which to us seems extremely remote Mars once possessed other forms of civilization. It may even be that we shall find traces of it when we land there: providing that these too have not been swept away by the millions and millions of years. I am convinced that in two hundred million years—indeed, in a hundred and fifty—life on Earth will be more or less what it is on Mars today."

"You mean nothing? Nothing left at all?"

"Not quite nothing. Primitive vegetation, lower forms of animal life. The last flickers of something that is dying down."

"But nothing that resembles a human being, Dr. von Braun? I don't mean something that is anatomically, chemically, physically constructed like the human body. I mean something that moves and possesses intelligence."

He shook his head. "That's an old argument, that one about intelligent creatures on Mars, but I hold to my belief that only primitive vegetation can be found on Mars today. I don't expect to find little green men, no. And yet . . . yet . . . you see, I don't want to be definite about these matters. Nobody can be. Everything is possible, you know. We'll have to go up there to know for certain."

"And the flying saucers? Those flying saucers that were discussed for years? What if they weren't figments of the imagination? What if they were real?"

He shook his head again. "I read an official report on what you call the flying saucers and what we call UFO, Unidentified Flying Objects. The report spoke of six thousand instances. Only a percentage of two percent were inexplicable."

"Which means a hundred and twenty flying saucers that were maybe not figments of the imagination, that were maybe not optical illusions, that were maybe really objects that came from other planets?"

"Uhm!"

"Why uhm? Have you another explanation, Dr. von Braun?"

"No, but I don't feel inclined to have doubts about that two percent. A lifetime spent on experiments with rockets and telecontrolled missiles has taught me to treat visual testimonies with extreme caution. If you talk to three spectators after a rocket-launching and ask them how the rocket went up, whether it went to the left or the right or straight, no two of them will say the same thing. Our eyes deceive us, and as for these extraterrestrial objects that from time to time enter and fly in our atmosphere, I can only say that I have never seen them and I don't believe in their existence until I see them for myself."

"Let's get back to the little green men, Dr. von Braun. When you were at Fort Bliss you wrote a science-fiction book, and the story was set on a Mars inhabited by little green men."

"I did that for my own amusement. A ridiculous and idiotic book and, apart from anything else, surpassed by our actual knowledge. When I was young I used to read a lot of science fiction, but not any more today. Science fiction is now surpassed by reality, what we are doing is much more exciting and incredible than what science fiction was foretelling years ago. Reality travels faster than imagination did in 1945. When Stuhlinger and I were talking of going to Mars, everyone laughed at us behind our backs. Today we're preparing to go to Mars and the journey to the Moon is already *démodé*. We shall prepare to go to Venus—"

"To Venus!"

"Yes, we'll get there."

"And what if we find somebody when we get there? I know the supposition is absurd, but it's not so absurd if Venus really has an atmosphere and oxygen and water, if Venus is like the Earth."

"Not so absurd."

"Well, then. If we find somebody, how shall we explain who we are and where we come from and what we want?"

He fell suddenly silent, and when he spoke again he seemed to be talking to himself about a grievous problem that could never be solved. "How to talk to the Venusians, how to explain to them who we are, where we come from, what we want: my God. I could make some joke about, seeing it's so difficult for us to communicate among ourselves, it will certainly be more difficult to communicate with the Martians. But that wouldn't be answering scientifically or honestly. So . . ."

"We could take photographs with us and explain ourselves through them" was Slattery's importunate contribution. "Or we could make drawings on the ground." Poor Slattery, he'd managed to keep quiet for such a long time. So quiet I'd even forgotten about him. But here he was, emerging inexorably from the cloud of his awkwardness to spoil everything. Like a gust of wind, his voice swept away the canals and the blue hills and the diamond glaciers of Mars, the rivers of Venus and the seas and rains and the faceless creatures whom we do not know how to tell who we are and where we come from and what we want, swept away the magic and the poetry of the whole adventure: and brought us back to Earth, back to the V2's, back to that scent of lemon, to my wondering where I had smelled it before, and my deciding that I couldn't remember. In this scent of lemon von Braun incinerated poor Slattery with a look.

"Excellent idea, Slattery. Excellent idea. We'll make a note of it."

Slattery made himself as small as he could, trying to earn forgiveness by making himself useful.

"May I mention something, sir?"

"Mention it, Slattery, mention it."

"The half-hour will be up in ten minutes, sir. Or rather nine."

"All right, Slattery, all right."

That scent of lemon. Asking myself where I had smelled it before. Telling myself I couldn't remember. I could remember only that it was a fragrance of long, long ago. Long, long ago. But whose was it? I'd better forget it. I tried to forget it.

"Let's get back to the Moon, Dr. von Braun. Tell me, what are the chances that the Americans will get there before the Russians? I'm thinking of something you once said to one of my colleagues who asked you what the Americans would find on the Moon. 'The Russians,' you told him."

"It was just a joke. I don't know to what extent the Russians are giving priority to their Moon program. They have money problems too and I doubt whether they know themselves just how far Russia can stand the cost of such an undertaking. Briefly, I don't know whether they, like us, are worried about making an early landing on the Moon. Moreover, what we ourselves want is to make a successful landing, not to get there first at any cost. The Moon itself is not the sole aim of our work, it's a moment in a program, an exercise. The Moon is useful to us for learning how to get from one planet to another, how to get there and how to get back. Nothing else. Haven't you ever seen footballers training on the field during the week, doing gymnastics? Well, the Moon is our gymnastics. As Mr. Kennedy said, we must learn to navigate new oceans and each man will learn to navigate in his own way."

"Does that mean that the Russians can learn without going to the Moon? Does it mean that the Russians can skip the Moon?"

"I mean that they can choose other stages than the Moon. For example, if the Russians were to say: 'We want to build a huge inhabited space station, this is the focal point of our program, a space station interests us more than going to the Moon,' it would not be less important than going to the Moon. So, you see, it hardly matters whether one gets there first or second. All that matters is learning to navigate new oceans. The ocean called space is full of islands, and when two men build two ships to navigate an ocean separately, they aren't necessarily trying to reach the same island. It's perfectly possible that the first man wants to go to one and the second to another. In such a case, what does it matter that one arrives first and the other second? It wouldn't even matter if they were both aiming for the same island. The important thing is that they should get there, and get there safe and sound. I hope I've made myself clear."

"Perfectly clear."

God, that scent of lemon.

"But the fact remains that this is a race, Dr. von Braun, and the eyes of the world are on the race and, as in all races, the one who wins gets the applause and the laurels. I know that from the scientific standpoint this may seem absurd, but from the human and political standpoint it's no such thing."

"But this is precisely why Mr. Kennedy chose the Moon: because everybody knows what the Moon is and where it is and everybody understands what we're talking about when we say we're going there. How many people know that Mars is a planet? How many realize what a space station means? Most of the world population don't even know that beyond the atmosphere the force of gravity ceases to exist, at least by Earthly standards, and so they can't imagine a space station that will stay up in space instead of falling down to the Earth. I hope I've made myself clear."

"Perfectly clear."

God, that scent of lemon. Oh, Father, that scent of lemon.

"And what would you say is the reason why the Americans are behind the Russians in the space race?"

Von Braun breathed in and out, puffing like a bellows, as boxers sometimes do before a fight.

"The simple truth of the matter is that the Russians began their long-range and military missile program five years before the Americans, and so now they are ahead in a very important field: how to launch heavy craft. This is not a field that can be explored in a day, nor can we catch up with them in a day. It isn't easy to make up five years. Let me explain: the war was hardly over when the Russians began to concern themselves with the problem of launching heavy craft, long-range missiles, etcetera, and the United States, being still in possession of a powerful air force capable of defending the country and bombarding at long distance as well, thought there was no real need to spend time and money on the question of launching heavy craft or long-range missiles. Rightly or wrongly, I would say wrongly, they contented themselves with maintaining efficiency in their planes while Stalin was building up a missile force capable of carrying very heavy nuclear bombs over the United States. Subsequently it was therefore an easy matter for the Russians to convert these war weapons into spacecraft and put themselves ahead of us. They are not ahead in everything, though; only with regard to the tonnage of space ships and the duration of human space flights. With regard to scientific space research, for example, we are in the lead. We have launched more artificial satellites than the Russians. We've launched Tyros and Relay and Syncom and Telstar and Echo, so that we are far ahead in the system of satellite communications, meteorological satellites, in . . ."

That was when I had smelled that scent of lemon. During the war. But where? Whose was it? When exactly?

"Tell me, Dr. von Braun, do you think that conquests in space increase or decrease the danger of war? And do you think the Moon can be used for military purposes?"

"I am not in the most suitable position to comment on the military uses of the Moon: but everyone is agreed on the fact that the Moon in itself is of very little strategic interest, I would say none whatever. A man on the Moon can be of use only for the scientific exploration of the Moon: only the space immediately surrounding the Earth can be of military use. As to the increased or decreased danger of war, I don't know. This is a tremendous question that no engineer or philosopher or scientist could ever answer. My personal hope and indeed my conviction is that the navigation of space will decrease the likelihood of war, inasmuch as a space war would be collective suicide, total ruin even for the one who started it. To my mind, these rockets that can be tremendous destructive weapons are or can be also the most powerful guardians of the peace. Yes . . . it's perfectly true that the greatest technological discoveries have been prompted by war, consider nuclear physics and aviation, radar and medicine, war demands the maximum yield from scientists and industry . . ."

That was it. That day in July. Those German soldiers. In the deserted convent where we were hiding. That was when I'd smelled that scent of lemon. They all washed with a disinfectant soap that smelled like lemon and when one of them pressed close to you in the street you at once smelled that scent of lemon: a sharp pungent scent that penetrated through your nostrils right into your heart and your brain. We all loathed that scent of lemon. You can tell if somebody's a collaborator if he smells of lemon you used to say, Father. If he smells of lemon it means he's washed with German soap, and if he's washed with German soap it means he keeps company with the Germans. The boy who sat next to me at school used to smell of lemon, and you said there you are, that's why he's always wanting to know where we'd gone to avoid the bombing. That day in July was a month after school had broken up. The sun was hot and we were in the orchard which was enclosed by a wall and nobody could see us. We'd planted beans in the garden, and the wheat we'd already gathered was heaped up by the well. Soon we would thresh it and then we would give it to the baker in exchange for flour. For a sack of grain the baker had promised us half a sack of flour. I was thinking about where we would hide the newspapers when the grain became flour; beneath the wheat were my newspapers that spoke of liberty. The sun was hot that day, the cicadas were chirping and suddenly we heard the loud noise of a truck. I clambered on top of the wall and the Germans were getting out of the lorry, great birds dressed in gray-green with tommy-guns on their shoulders. "Warn the two Yugoslavians," you said and fled: into the fields. A great many days were to pass before we were to see you again and know that they hadn't taken you. The two Yugoslavians were on the first floor of the convent and it was too late for them to escape into the fields by the time I reached them and said: "The Germans." They followed me down the stairs and into the garden and lowered themselves into the well. The well was dry and they were able to get down it very easily because of the bricks that stuck out like steps. So they lowered themselves quickly down the well, and then they told me to hurry and replace the lid which was made of iron and was very heavy. It was too heavy for me so it took me some time to move it and when I'd finished the first German was already coming into the garden. Perhaps he saw me and this was the cause of their downfall. Perhaps he saw me, but he didn't say anything and just stood there, and the others came and stood there too, clutching their tommy-guns at the ready, the way you would when you surrounded a place to look for someone. The sun was hot that day, but I suddenly felt very cold as I slipped the newspapers out from under the wheat and stuffed them into the watering can, which was very big and green. Then I carried the watering can into the cell where we slept and then Mother started burning the newspapers in the stove which had been lighted to bake the bread. As she burned them she poked them with a bit of iron to make them burn more quickly. I watched them burning and it seemed like throwing away precious food when you're hungry. It had cost so much effort and been so dangerous to print them and get them here and keep them hidden. The sun was hot that day, and the burning newspapers added to the heat, and Mother was sweating with fear and heat, but I felt very cold. From the end of the corridor their tread reached us, heavy and inexorable, sounding as if there were a hundred of them. The footsteps echoed like a waterfall, like a torrent, and as she prodded the flaming newspapers she kept saying: "God they're coming, God let's hope they burn soon, God they're coming, oh they're coming." They were hammering on the doors as they came, all the cells were shut so they were hammering on the doors with their tommy-guns and raucously shouting to open up, but nobody opened because there was nobody in there apart from ourselves and the Yugoslavians, and so they broke down the doors, which went crack! Then they reached our door, and they kicked on the door with their great boots, shouting to open up, and I opened the door, and I stared at Mother to get her to keep calm. I opened and was surrounded by that stinking scent of lemon. Sharp, pungent, almost like a gas that penetrates through your nostrils right into your heart and brain . . .

". . . but it is also true that space flights provide the perfect substitute for the stimulus that generally comes from wars. In addition to which they permit collaboration: in the field of meteorological satellites there is already collaboration with the Russians. In the future we shall be able to reach agreement with the Russians concerning the development of a lunar base: you fly with your rockets and I fly with mine, when we're up there we'll build a base together. A lot of people say: but how will anyone be able to live up there on the Moon where there's no air nor water nor any of the things we need in order to live? It will be like in an airplane, I tell them, where we eat our steak, drink our champagne, are looked after by a charming hostess. When man is provided with an Earthly environment, man can live anywhere. And he will do it. We shall get used to the Moon as we have got used to planes, and the old argument that man is meant to stay upon the Earth no longer means anything. Man is meant to stay wherever he wants to stay and go anywhere he wants to go."

"Then it would be appropriate to ask oneself where all this going will take us, Dr. von Braun. Science is proceeding like a curious child, discovering things of which we know nothing, causing things to happen that we'd never imagined: but, like a heedless child, it never stops to wonder whether it's doing good or ill. Where will all this going take us?"

"Very far. Just as we've been taken far by the discovery of new seas, of new continents, by the settling of new lands. And nobody can tell in advance whether it will bring good or ill. Until now man has done nothing but bring about a heap of trouble: but it has been through these very troubles that man has advanced and new civilizations have been built to replace those which have been destroyed. So I do not think that we are doing anything ill. Men must always travel farther and farther afield, they must always widen their horizons and their interests: this is the will of God. If God didn't want it to be so, He wouldn't have given us the ability and the possibility to make progress and to change. If God didn't want it, He would stop us. Yes, of course I'm religious. Look, I've known a lot of scientists and I've never known a scientist worthy of the name who could offer an explanation of nature without some notion of God. Science tries to understand creation, but religion tries to understand the Creator and nobody can avoid trying to understand the Creator. It's a poor scientist who deludes himself that he can do without religion and God: the kind of scientist who scrapes the surface without looking beneath it. I try to look beneath the surface, and I see good there . . ."

They looked beneath the surface and saw the two Yugoslavians. They tossed aside the lid which had seemed so heavy to me, then they peered down the well and saw the two Yugoslavians in it. Mother and I could tell that they'd found them by the way they were laughing. As long as I live, Dr. von Braun, I shall never never forget the way those Germans laughed when they saw the two Yugoslavians. Laughing open-throated, tickled to death, one of them dropped his tommy-gun and clutched his stomach with laughter. The two Yugoslavians believed in God too, Dr. von Braun. The elder one had once had a great discussion with my father and had said just the same: that you can't explain nature without some notion of God, etc. And they said that God is good and is on the side of the good, that if God didn't approve He would stop us, etc. But God didn't stop those Germans who aimed their tommy-guns down the well and ordered the Yugoslavians to come out. God let them do everything, those Germans, and so the two Yugoslavians came out, climbing up the bricks that stuck out like steps, commending themselves to God that He should not let them be killed: but God didn't hear them and the Germans took them away, together with their scent of lemon.

". . . I see ethical principles there. Two factors are necessary to make man accept ethics: one is the belief in the Last Judgment, when every one of us must account to God for his use on Earth of the precious gift of life, the other is the belief in immortality, which is to say the continuation after death of our spiritual existence. Because we have a soul . . ."

As well as a soul the two Yugoslavians had a little tube of explosive which they had forgotten to leave in the well. It was a little tube not much bigger than a bit of candle and they'd stolen it from the drain where I'd hidden it. We heard that it had been found in the pocket of the elder one, and the next day they were both in a sealed truck that took them to Germany, and they never came back from Germany, did they, Father?

". . . we have a conscience and we know that nothing in nature can disappear without leaving a trace. Nature allows no extinction, it allows only transformation: if God applies His fundamental principle to the whole universe, and He does, there can be no doubt of the existence of immortality. And we work in this awareness of immortality, subject to the eternal cycle of life and death, true links between the past and the future. The future of the generations to come depends on what we discover today, with conviction that we are doing good, with the help of God. I hope I've made myself clear."

"Perfectly clear, Dr. von Braun. Perfectly clear."

"That's thirty-cight minutes, eight more than the allotted time," said Slattery.

"I have to go now," said von Braun.

"It has been interesting," said I.

"Very interesting," said Slattery.

"The future is always interesting," said von Braun.

"More than the past," said I.

"Much more than the past," said Slattery.

"Clearly," said von Braun. And he left, in a scent of lemon, leaving the room as empty as an empty shell, as an empty well. We should never remember what's past, Father: but there's always a scent of lemon to bring it back to us, together with its flotsam and jetsam, like the waves of the sea.

21.

It had been to get away from the flotsam and jetsam, that scent of lemon, that I had gone to New Orleans. When you're oppressed by a memory, the only thing to do is get a change of air and I didn't feel like staying on in Huntsville hearing other voices as abrupt as the sound of a whiplash, as curt as the sound of shots, the nightmare of so many years ago. A harsh exclamation, a stiff gait were now enough to make me jump: his tiny eyes filled with alarm, Joe Jones had looked at me without understanding, and in the meantime he had offered me coffee. Something had happened in Joe Jones' office just after the interview with von Braun. A man had come in, I had had my back to him, and Joe had said: "Yes, it's her, an Italian." Then the man had drawn a little closer, I still had had my back turned, and in a hearty fashion he had shot a: "Goot mornink, Zignorina" at the back of my neck. In a hearty way, but I had shuddered and jerked my head, my arms, the sudden shrinking movement of men when they're shot in the back and seem to get shorter, you know what I mean, and I hadn't been able to turn around, to reply at once: "Good morning." At last I had replied, but the man, maybe only surprised, maybe hurt badly, was by then going out again: a gray head above a blue suit.

"Who was that, Joe?"

"Dr. Ernst Stuhlinger, the scientist who's constructing the spacecraft for Mars. But, say, what came over you?"

"I wasn't aware, Joe. I'm sorry."

"You must tell him when you see him. You've got an appointment for tomorrow."

"Tomorrow?"

"Yes. He's a good man, you know that? He's the best of the lot. You shouldn't treat him like that."

"I'm sorry, Joe. I didn't do it on purpose."

"I don't get it. What on Earth did the Germans do to you?"

"Nothing, Joe. Nothing." And without even canceling my appointment with Stuhlinger, I had left that evening for New Orleans, determined to spend there the days that separated me from Houston and from the new astronauts.

I had liked New Orleans. It's so beautiful, Father. The most beautiful city in America. The only one where time goes by without leaving bruises. I had liked the wrought-iron balconies that trim the white houses with delicate lace, transparent mantillas, endowing them with verandas, colonnades, charm. I had liked the Spanish patios with their wells covered in green ivy and their pools full of water lilies, the coolness that invites you to be lazy. I had liked the stone-paved streets with their big lights two hundred years old and their old French names, Rue Ste. Anne, Vieux Carré, the antique shops full of exquisite little objects. I had liked the carriages drawn by horses wearing little hats, and with fringed canopies to shade you from the sun. I had liked the rich quarter with its huge houses, the houses of *Gone with the Wind,* elegant, grand, neo-classical columns on the façade and gables in the roof, gardens inhabited by ghostly silence. I had liked the poor quarter, with the Negroes piled on the doorsteps brooding in hatred and filth, clusters of hostile proud eyes. I had liked the Mississippi, that river which is now a lake, now a sea, now a river again, and flows slowly, heavy with water, the boats plowing through it, and at dusk there is still a showboat that passes gently by, a great ghost with music playing on board. I had liked the oaks planted in 1783 by Colonel Denis de la Ronde, now tall cathedrals wrapped around by parasite plants that dangle in shreds of brown veiling, in those great parks! I had liked the restaurants, the French and Spanish food, the stuffed oysters, the murderous drinks of ice and rum to sip in the sultry heat while you cool yourself with a fan and a streetcar goes ringing by and is still a streetcar named Desire: there are still eighty-five streetcars in New Orleans. And then I had liked Bourbon Street, where you can listen to the last *real* jazz on Earth, the jazz you'll never hear in theaters, on records, and it's dying out because young folk no longer want to play the trumpet, the piano, the double bass: NASA, who have brought their space industry even here, pay more than music. In the dive where I had stayed until morning the woman at the piano was seventy-one, the trumpet player was seventy-six and the man who played the double-bass was seventy. They were Negroes and they were sweating because they loved what they were doing, not for money. Anyone who wanted to listen to them could sit on broken chairs, wooden benches, and you didn't have to pay, and you'd have liked all this, Father. A notice hung on the wall.

FIVE DOLLARS FOR THOSE WHO WANT TO GO TO PARADISE
TWO DOLLARS FOR THOSE WHO ARE RICH

ONE DOLLAR FOR THOSE WHO HAVE IT
NOTHING FOR THOSE WHO HAVE NOTHING

When they were tired they would go out to get drunk on whiskey, on drugs. When they felt the devil in their blood they would come back and send us up to the stars. The old trumpet player was blind, beneath his eyelids he had two holes. He spoke only French and he liked songs that were a bit dirty. He would suddenly throw aside his trumpet, bound to his feet like a leaping monkey and yell: "Le cochon, hop! Le cochon, hop!" The old woman would cry from time to time, who knows why? Yes, I had liked New Orleans. I had even liked the cockroach I found in the bath at my very expensive hotel: black, tubby, glorious, with his dignified insolent gait, make way for me, hygienists, I'm a cockroach! I could have spent months and months in that sleepy sweating town, with the same voluptuous laziness that makes us relish the warm bedclothes on winter mornings when we don't want to get up. Nevertheless here I was in an airplane taking me back to Huntsville.

This was how it had happened. I had no sooner reached New Orleans than I was struck by the thought that I had behaved badly toward Ernst Stuhlinger, and I had telephoned him to apologize, inventing an excuse. A friend of mine who had been living in New Orleans for years was lying in a hospital, gravely ill. I had come to see her and expected to stay with her until Friday afternoon, then I'd be going on to Houston, where interviews had been arranged for me with the new astronauts. I was very sorry, etcetera. With patient courtesy Stuhlinger had asked me to give his good wishes to my friend, and had unexpectedly wound up: "I'll be at your service from Friday afternoon on. If you arrive on Friday evening, my wife and I will be happy if you'll come to dinner. Send a telegram to let us know." Farewell, Bourbon Street. Farewell, showboat plowing along the Mississippi. Farewell, oysters, glasses of rum to sip in the sultry heat. Farewell, Rue St. Antoine, Vieux Carré, wrought-iron balconies that clothe the houses in transparent mantillas. It was Friday morning and the plane was losing height over Huntsville, over its woods blackened by the rockets. Looking at those burned branches, now yellowed, I wondered what kind of man he was, this man who first frightened me with his Germanic "goot mornink" and made me run away to New Orleans, then induced me to come back like a child who's sorry; first he let himself be insulted and then he invited me to dinner. Actually, I knew nothing about the German who was constructing the spacecraft for Mars, except for two things that to me seemed very beautiful: he rode a bicycle and hadn't been a Nazi. True. And I was sorry that the plane was late: almost an hour late, my God, the Germans are so punctual, and I was going to be forced to offer painful explanations and apologies. At the bottom of the steps I looked around for a telephone and was hit by the same voice, full in the chest this time.

"Goot evenink, Zignorina. Zignorina Fallaci?"

———————

I had thought he was tall, watching him going away, perhaps because he was walking stiff and straight. But he was almost short. I had also thought he was broad-shouldered, but he was thin. Seen from behind, he had had gray hair, but front-faced he was bald, with only a few hairs at his temples.

"Yes, that's me. You must be Dr. Stuhlinger?"

A face sculpted and chopped out of wood, all lines and unexpected planes, with nothing overemphasized and nothing underemphasized, with a big nose, a big mouth and two deep-set eyes hidden like two precious aquamarines beneath the thickets of his eyelashes. They were gleaming, watchful and ironic, with the flash of oxyhydrogen flames.

"Yes, dat iss me. How iss your laty frient?"

You couldn't lie to those eyes. I didn't know what to say. He answered for me.

"I understant. She playt the trumpet divinely."

Then he laughed. And it was as if I'd never heard a German laugh before. It was like suddenly making peace with an enemy you've been hunting for more than twenty years, whom you don't forgive, whom you don't want to forgive, but then here he is holding out his hand to you, saying: Let's have a rest, let's at least call a truce, and then you give him your hand, you laugh with him. Well, Father, deep in your heart you are stung with remorse, don't cast aside your rancor, you think, you swore never to cast it aside, to remain faithful to your hatred, to answer whiplash with whiplash, shot with shot, not to be weak, diverted, not to be Christian. But as well as the remorse a new thought is taking hold, and you think maybe he'd also sworn the same things about you, maybe he too doesn't want to cast aside his rancor, maybe he too had a brother killed by your brother, yet he came to meet you, and he's waited more than an hour for you although he has so much to do, he has to construct the spacecraft for Mars, for example, and he's made a reservation for you at a motel and look, he's even stooping to pick up your suitcase, which is a weight, and then he laughs!

"She also played the double-bass well, Dr. Stuhlinger."

"Not the piano?"

"That too."

"And the clarinet? How did she play the clarinet?"

"Like an angel."

I no longer even heard his wrong consonants, I would never hear them again. I saw only a witty and kind man who picked up my suitcase himself, refusing the porter, and went up to his car saying he was sorry it was only a Volkswagen, so uncomfortable for anyone used to big cars, now we'd drop the suitcase off at the motel, where I could change, then we'd go home, it wouldn't be a great dinner, I'd have to take pot-luck: yes, of course, Dr. Stuhlinger. He didn't emanate the sad scent of lemon, not at all.

"And your bicycle, Dr. Stuhlinger?"

"It's at home. I'd have come on it, but I remembered there was the luggage."

"Then you really do ride it."

"Certainly I do. Sometimes I even go to the office on it." A pause. "When I was young I used to go to Italy on my bicycle every summer. I used to go from Tübingen, where I lived, and through Innsbruck down to Milan, from Milan to the Riviera: Santa Margherita, Bordighera, Rapallo. I used to travel with my things in a knapsack and I would often meet those young racing cyclists in colored sweaters, we'd have contests for fun and maybe I'd win with my knapsack. After Rapallo I always went to Florence or Venice—Giotto and Masaccio, Titian and Raphael. I used to stand for hours looking at those frescoes, those paintings, and they were wonderful summers. Giotto and Masaccio, Titian and Raphael . . . Then the war broke out and . . . I never went again." Another pause. "I missed them for many years, you know that? We have other things, we have Bach and Brahms and Beethoven, but we don't have Giotto and Masaccio, Titian and Raphael. You're from Florence, aren't you? Are the Giottos and Masaccios still there? Is everything all right now?"

"Yes, Dr. Stuhlinger, now everything's . . . all right."

"I must see them again sooner or later. It's that I don't have the time. This journey to the Moon takes up all one's time. After the Moon it'll be Mars and so . . ."

We reached the motel. I left my suitcase, hastily changed my clothes, and we left again immediately in his Volkswagen.

"Speaking of the Moon: I promised some kids who go to school with my kids that I'd show them the Moon through a telescope this evening and I haven't been able to put it off. So after dinner I shall have to slip away to the telescope, but it won't take more than an hour. Have you ever seen the Moon close up?"

"No, Dr. Stuhlinger."

"Then perhaps you wouldn't mind coming to see her."

You should have heard him. It was as if he'd been talking about a visit to take tea with a lady.

"Naturally I'd prefer you to see Mars; it's disappointing through the telescope, though. Just a small gleaming ball. On the other hand, the Moon is interesting through the telescope."

"Only through the telescope?"

"I've never thought about the Moon, I've always thought about Mars. Going to Mars was in my head when I was studying cosmic rays in Berlin, going to Mars was in my head when I was working in Peenemünde, and von Braun used to think the same way. Obviously on our way to Mars we shall stop to have a look at the Moon, he used to say, but now he's got fond of the idea of the Moon and I'm the only one who still dreams of Mars."

"Yes, Dr. Stuhlinger, I know."

We took a long winding road that climbed upward between walls of trees. He pointed at some woods higher up.

"That's Monte Sano. We've all lived there since 1954." He glanced at me. "I mean myself, von Braun, the other Germans."

"Yes, Dr. Stuhlinger, I know."

"It was I who found the spot. But we were all friends, fellow countrymen, so we thought we'd stay together."

"Yes, Dr. Stuhlinger, I know."

I glanced back at him. I liked this getting things straight, this repeating to me, listen, I'm one of them too, one of the men from Peenemünde. Giotto yes, Masaccio yes, Raphael yes, Titian yes, but I too used to make the V2's.

"As soon as we were transferred to Huntsville I took an airplane, a Piper, and flew with my wife over these mountains, picked out a big oak and said: here, I want to build the house here. Ten years ago the zone was uninhabited: only snakes and squirrels. Now it's a residential district. I drew up the plans myself, built the walls with the help of two or three laborers. Irmgard, my wife, gave a hand with cutting down the trees. We didn't cut down many, just enough to make room. The big oak, naturally, is still standing. I like trees. One reason why I'd rather go to Mars than the Moon is that I hope to find trees on Mars and I know that there are none on the Moon."

He drove without hurry as if he would like to take time. He turned into a gravel drive at the end of which there was a lawn and a fine bungalow. He slowed down a little to say what he wanted to say before we reached the bungalow.

"Von Braun doesn't think there are trees on Mars—odd how we can't agree with each other about this. Over everything else we have much in common. The way we've each started a new life, for example. The way we were each married. Almost at the same time. When we made our decision, at El Paso, he was thirty-seven and I was thirty-six. He chose his cousin Maria, I chose a childhood friend. Irmgard used to live not far from me in Tübingen, her parents knew mine, her father was a friend of my uncle's, they both taught geology and Irmgard has a degree in geology. Irmgard's father often used to come and see us with this shy brown-haired little girl, and I was a young man and I used to say jokingly: as soon as you grow up I'll marry you. I wrote to her from El Paso, then I asked for a week's leave and I went to Germany to see her. I didn't even recognize her, she'd become a woman. Three hours after seeing her again, I asked her if she felt she would like to create a family with me. She was surprised and said she'd have to think it over. I told her there wasn't time to think it over and we were married. Then I came back to El Paso and Irmgard joined me later. There's Irmgard," he concluded, pointing to a woman in a flowered dress standing on the edge of the lawn. "And there are my children."

Mrs. Stuhlinger came toward us and seemed to be very shy. She went through her words of greeting with a sort of diffidence and said that this was Susan, aged twelve, this was Til, aged eight, this was Chris, aged four and a half. This ceremony over, she took me into the house and for the first time in my entire journey I found myself in the family of a man involved in the Great Venture. For months I had been plagued with a certain curiosity; however naïve it may seem, I had never understood how it was possible for a man to prepare for a journey to Mars and at the same time listen to his wife saying Til has a tummy ache, Chris won't go to sleep, heavens, the price of eggs has gone up. Mozart had such problems, so did Marx, so did Tolstoy, all men burdened with wives and children, but to reconcile a great task with such terrestrial realities has always seemed to me quite heroic. It isn't a question of living together, bills to be paid, noise, it's a question of inner solitude, of inner silence. What did Stuhlinger think about in the morning as he brushed his teeth? Did he think we must buy some new shoes for Susan or did he think the evaporation of ionized atoms should generate sufficient speed to orbit Venus and then head for Mars? Did he think Irmgard has a gray hair on her left temple, poor Irmgard's getting older too, or did he think about the cubic root of alpha over gamma multiplied by epsilon? Or did he think about both things at once?

"Ernst, dear, there's something important I have to tell you," said Irmgard, blushing.

"Yes, Irmgard," Stuhlinger replied and immediately vanished into his study.

"He always does that," Irmgard murmured, clasping her hands. "He says 'Yes, Irmgard,' and then he melts away into his study. You can never tell him anything, his head's full of Mars and nothing else."

"Yes, Irmgard," Stuhlinger replied when he reappeared carrying a photograph of a very mysterious object. But instead of turning to Irmgard, he came over to me, brandishing the photograph. "Here she is, here's my spacecraft for Mars."

"Ernst, dear, I couldn't find any watercress," murmured Irmgard, and she blushed again.

"What you can't tell from this is the size of the spacecraft," Stuhlinger remarked. "From one end to the other, including the centrifuge blades, it's a good five hundred feet."

"Ernst, are you listening to me?" Irmgard repeated.

"Yes, dear. I'm listening. The weight is obviously enormous. It's clear that a spacecraft of this kind can't lift off by chemical propulsion."

"The watercress, Ernst."

"The what?" asked Stuhlinger, looking at his wife as if she'd sprung up out of nowhere.

"The watercress," Irmgard stammered. "Today you said you wanted the watercress because it's the typical Huntsville vegetable and Miss Fallaci would like to try the typical Huntsville vegetable."

"Oh! Ah! Uh! Watercress. Before we came to Huntsville all that grew here was watercress. Cotton and watercress," he told me.

"There wasn't any, Ernst. It's out of season."

"Ah!"

"So I got peas," Irmgard concluded, at the end of her strength. Dear Irmgard, what use was her geology degree now? What use those studies to trace the origins of a rock if now she had to drive herself around the bend looking for watercress for me? That's another thing I've never understood, why one should spend the best years of her life studying the origins of a rock or a river and then have to spend her time worrying about peas and watercress.

"You did very well, Irmgard," Stuhlinger declared as if in the desperate hope that she would go away. Then he turned back to address me. "It is my conviction that such a heavy spacecraft cannot lift off by nuclear propulsion either and so I am firmly convinced that the other method, the one for which I've been fighting for years, the electric propulsion method, is the only one that's suitable. The Americans never stop complaining because the Russians have a better fuel, even von Braun is always saying: but the Russians have a better fuel. Agreed, so why don't we use electric propulsion? I—"

"Fa-a-ther!" shouted Til. "Mother says it's ready!"

"Who's ready?" said Stuhlinger, almost in alarm.

"Dinner, Father!"

"Oh! Yes, of course, dinner. We must eat."

"Certainly if it was up to him he'd even forget to eat," Irmgard complained.

"He says all he needs is a banana!" yelled Til.

"But he gets hungry in the night and eats up all the best things in the refrigerator!" Susan revealed.

"Children!" Mrs. Stuhlinger protested. Then she took us into the garden, the table was laid on the terrace. When we were all seated she sat down too. A puff of wind fluttered a gray hair on her left temple.

"Why don't we adopt electric propulsion? I answer, and they say it's expensive. Of course it's expensive, but we can't delude ourselves that the cost of going to Mars will be moderate. I've been saying so ever since the days of Fort Bliss: it was at Fort Bliss that I got the idea of the electric method of propulsion. I talked about it to von Braun and—"

"Eat up, dear," Irmgard begged.

"E-e-eat, Faather!" yelled Til.

"—we found ourselves in immediate agreement: apart from the fact of it's being too expensive. Von Braun and I were already looking for a method of this kind back in Peenemünde. But we couldn't work on it: there we were on the V2. Then we had to give up work on those too, the Allies were advancing, but this didn't give us any more time or any more desire to work on the journey to Mars. We went around without hope, we let ourselves drift along like a boat without oars, blown hither and thither, and at one point I found myself separated from von

Braun. When the Allies came, I took refuge in Tübingen, my parents
were there, my university—"

"Eat, Faather!" yelled Til.

"Hush, Til!" Irmgard whispered.

"You said it first. You said: Eat, Ernst. Now I say it and you tell
me to hush," Til protested with logic.

"Will you shut up, Til!"

"All right, I'll shut up!"

Susan didn't say anything. She might or might not have been
listening: for her, Peenemünde was more distant than the Punic Wars.
Chris, on the other hand, kept his innocent blue eyes glued to his
father.

"You see, Miss Fallaci, there were people who didn't understand
and still don't understand why we agreed to come here, to become U.S.
citizens etcetera. I'm talking of the most ardent nationalists. Others,
like you, clearly anti-Nazi, don't understand why we stayed at Peenemünde, and they think badly of us for it."

"Yes, Dr. Stuhlinger."

"Yes. But, you see, we stayed at Peenemünde for the same reason
we came to America, where we're no longer Germans but Americans.
Peenemünde and America were—are—both instruments for realizing
our dream of reaching Mars, other planets. At least for me that's how it
is. I didn't know Peenemünde existed, I didn't even know von Braun
when they removed me from the Russian front and took me there. I
didn't even know why they'd picked me, I thought they were recruiting
men with physics degrees and that they knew of my studies on cosmic
rays. But as soon as I got there I said to myself: this is the place for
me. It was the same thing at the end of the war when that American
officer came to Tübingen and asked if I wanted to place myself at the
service of the United States. I couldn't make head or tail of what he
said, but one thing I knew: that I'd be able to go on with my work again
in the United States. The Americans are adventurous, curious, they
wouldn't think us mad for saying we wanted to go to the Moon, to Mars,
to Venus. The Americans wanted to use the V2 for military purposes,
but I knew that the V2 could serve for something else too: for going up
there. Oh, Miss Fallaci! My dream came to life again while that officer
was talking! I—"

"Eat, dear," Irmgard begged once more.

"You see? First I said it and you told me to shut up. Now you say
it and you're only saying what I said already," Til said.

"Til! Silence!"

"He's quite right," Susan said.

"Silence, both of you!"

Stuhlinger conciliatingly put something in his mouth, I went on asking.

"But do you really think we'll be able to settle Mars, Dr. Stuhlinger? Willy Ley says—"

"Not like Willy Ley says. Yes, I know Willy Ley well. Let's be clear about it, what Willy says will come about: but not so soon. By 'settle Mars' I mean 'survive on Mars.' To live, that is to say, as we live at the South Pole: a thousand people in the summer and no more than a hundred in the winter. People who are skilled, trained . . ."

"And does it hurt you to think that you cannot be one of that thousand, that hundred?"

Stuhlinger looked toward his wife, who was on her way to the kitchen, and assured himself that she couldn't hear. Then he looked at the children, who, with the exception of Chris, had their attention absorbed by a squirrel. Prudently he lowered his voice until it was a mere whisper. He smiled.

"But I shall, Miss Fallaci. I'm telling you now while Irmgard can't hear or else she'd get angry. One day she realized I was thinking of going and she was angry, she was really angry. I'm telling you now: no, not to Mars, I'd never make it, unfortunately. I'll be over seventy and you know how it is. But I'll certainly go to the Moon. I'm forty-nine now, in ten years I'll be fifty-nine. That's not too old, providing I keep fit, keep on riding my bicycle and so on. In ten years it won't be necessary to be an astronaut, you know, in order to go to the Moon. In ten years you'll be going yourself."

"Me?"

"Yes, you. Don't you want to go to the Moon?"

"I'd like to, but there won't be room for someone who's no technician, Dr. Stuhlinger: that's the hard thing about these times. There's no room for those of us who use words instead of numbers."

"That's what you say. The world has always been in the hands of the technicians—the politicians and the technicians. Never in the hands of those who write poetry, never in the hands of those who protest. And yet the world has always needed those who write poetry and those who protest. And you know why? Because they're the only people who can explain things. I, a man without doubts, cannot explain why it is right to go to Mars. Or to the Moon. Or to Alpha Centauri. But you, who probably have doubts, could explain it. The technician's job . . ."

Irmgard returned with a strawberry shortcake and began to distribute it. Susan and Til promptly forgot the squirrel and flung themselves voraciously on the shortcake. But Chris didn't even glance at it; his eyes still glued to his father, he broke the silence he had maintained throughout the entire evening. He had a high voice that sounded like the peeping of a chick.

"Daddy, what job do you do?"

"What a bore!" grumbled Susan with her mouth full of strawberries. "You asked me the same thing yesterday and I told you that Father is constructing the spacecraft to go to Mars."

As far as Chris was concerned, she could have said that the dialectic synthesis of Hegelian metaphysics leads one to the conclusion that historical romanticism is a verified and verifiable reality. He repeated his question.

"Daddy, what job do you do?"

"I'm in the transport industry, Chris," Stuhlinger replied.

"Like the driver of the bus that takes us to school?" asked Chris.

"More or less," said Stuhlinger.

"What do you mean, 'more or less,' Daddy?"

"It's like this, Chris: you could say that my job is making the bus," said Stuhlinger.

"Is that important, Daddy?"

"Certainly it is," said Stuhlinger.

"Why?"

Stuhlinger took Chris on his lap.

"You see, Chris, the question of transport has always been man's chief problem."

"Only for men, Daddy?"

"For men, women and children. But it was a long time before they invented the bus. Let me tell you, for the first five hundred thousand years men, women and children had only their own legs to take them from one place to another."

"How many years are five-five-dred thousand, Daddy?"

"Many, Chris. Very many. More than ten thousand. And it was only ten thousand years ago that men, women and children discovered they could use the horse to take them around. The horse, the donkey, the camel, the elephant—good animals, in short. Do you follow me, Chris? Well. At about the same time the men and women and children discovered that they could sail across the sea in a boat. A boat, a raft, a ship—that kind of thing. Do you follow me, Chris? Then something happened, seven thousand years ago. What happened was that the men, women and children invented the wheel and so they discovered that they could also travel in a horse-drawn carriage."

Chris gazed at his father in bewilderment.

"Daddy! What's a horse-drawn carriage, Daddy?"

"A horse-drawn carriage," said Stuhlinger, "is a kind of automobile pulled by a horse."

"I never saw one," said Chris.

"You've never seen a horse and carriage, Chris?" I cried.

"Neither have I," said Til.

"Neither have I," said Susan. "But Daddy's promised to take me to New Orleans, where they've got them. Say, what are they like, the carriages in New Orleans? Mummy says you've just been to New Orleans."

"They're beautiful," I said. "They're drawn by a horse and they have a canopy with fringes, all white. When the horse goes, the fringes tremble like leaves and the horse's hoofs go clop! clop! clop!"

My God, Father! Do you realize? I was telling a fairy tale. A carriage drawn by a horse was already a fairy tale. And Chris didn't even understand. He couldn't even imagine what I was talking about. One day, when he was older, he would see a carriage in some museum and he would look at it with the same expression he had now, as if saying to me: what on Earth do you think you're talking about? He turned back to his father.

"Go on, Daddy!"

Stuhlinger threw me a glance that I couldn't interpret.

"Then suddenly, seven thousand years after the horse-drawn carriage, the men, women and children discovered the engine and so the train was born. After the train came the automobile and—"

"Say, Daddy," Susan broke in, "how did they manage to live without automobiles?"

"They managed very well," said Stuhlinger. "Exactly as they do today in many countries that aren't America. There are lots of people in the world who don't have cars."

"You're trying to be funny," Susan laughed. "Don't tell me tall stories, Daddy. Nobody can live without a car."

Again Stuhlinger threw me a glance. Then he continued to give his attention to Chris, who was following his sister's words as if he quite agreed.

". . . and from that moment, as I was saying, everything happened very quickly. Very, very quickly. They immediately invented the airplane, Chris: that happened only fifty years ago. Think, Chris, only fifty years ago. And after the airplane they immediately invented the rocket. That happened only twenty years ago, Chris. Do you know what a rocket is, Chris?"

"A rocket is an airplane without wings!" Chris piped up.

"You're a silly fool!" said Til.

"Silly fool!" Susan echoed.

Chris began to cry.

"Mummy told me a rocket is an airplane without wings!"

Mrs. Stuhlinger squirmed on her chair in embarrassment. Susan and Til glared at her.

"Mummy! Oh, Mummy! At four and a half he ought to know that a rocket is nothing like an airplane! Mummy! An airplane flies in the atmosphere, a rocket flies in the stratosphere!" Susan explained, appalled. Then she turned to Chris, who was listening in frustration.

"So much so that a rocket carries a spacecraft! Now, don't tell me you don't know what a spacecraft is! Idiot!"

"A spacecraft is what Glenn went in," sighed Chris, humiliated. "It's pointed like my pencil-sharpener and it's so small that Glenn was all doubled up inside."

"A spacecraft can have thousands of different shapes and it can be very big, like Daddy's," said Til. Then he got up, took the photograph that Stuhlinger had been trying to explain to me when we'd had the watercress episode and handed it to his father. "Show it to him, Daddy."

Stuhlinger proudly showed it to his Chris.

"Look, Chris. Daddy's constructing this one, little by little. You can't tell from the photograph, but this one's very big: as big as our house, but two stories high . . ."

Chris bent over to look. Then he lighted up and shrilled: "It's a pinwheel!"

"No, Chris, it's not a pinwheel," replied Stuhlinger. "It's a spacecraft for going to Mars."

"To where, Daddy?"

"To the Moon," Stuhlinger lied.

"Will you go to the Moon, Daddy?"

Stuhlinger glanced at his wife, who was telling Til off for something and so her attention was elsewhere. Then he bent swiftly down to Chris.

"Yes, Chris. I'll be going."

Chris frowned.

"Why, Daddy?"

"What do you mean, why?" said Stuhlinger.

"Why do you want to go to the Moon?"

Mrs. Stuhlinger looked up, forgetting Til and his misdemeanors.

"What were you saying?!"

"We were just talking in general," said Stuhlinger. And he seemed dismayed, I don't know whether on account of his wife or his son. But I'd say rather on account of his son. Tell me, how do you answer a child of four and a half when he asks you: why are you going to the Moon?

"Oh, Chris! Don't you start too, my boy!"

Chris insisted.

"Why do you want to go to the Moon, Daddy?"

"Oh, heavens! And why do you want to go out on the lawn when you do?" Stuhlinger was getting cross.

The child was silent for a while, thinking. Then his eyes shone.

"Because it's there, Daddy!"

There was a moment's silence. Then Stuhlinger's eyes shone too.

"There you are, Chris. I want to go to the Moon for the same reason you want to go out on the lawn. Because it's there."

"I don't get it," Chris concluded as he climbed down from his father's knee and went to eat his strawberry shortcake.

"That's a good answer," I remarked. "Somebody once said it of Everest, I believe. Now tell me, Dr. Stuhlinger: when other people ask the same question as Chris, what do you tell them?"

"It depends," he replied reflectively. "It depends on who asks me. There are so many reasons you could give, von Braun's right when he says it's less tiring to construct the rockets than to explain your reasons for constructing them. Listen: to start with, there's the economists' reason. The reason you'll be given by the director of NASA, who's neither a technologist nor a dreamer, I think. My chief aim, he says, is to establish a new economic entity in American industry, and space technology is establishing this entity . . ."

"Yes, but that doesn't seem a good reason."

"It's a good reason for some."

"A good reason, not *the* reason."

"Agreed. Then there's the politicians' reason—at least of those who believe in peace. The armaments race, they say, employed hundreds of thousands of Americans in making bombs, guns, military aircraft. With armaments halved, at least half of those Americans were directed into space industry . . ."

"That's a good reason. An excellent reason. But it's not *the* reason."

"Exactly. Then there's the reason given by the pure scientists, those who talk in exclusively scientific terms and say that going to the Moon means learning more about the origins and structure of the universe, about the origins and structure of the Earth."

"That's a good reason too, but not *the* reason."

"And lastly there's the reason given by the adventurous ones, the romantics, the madmen like myself who want to go where others have never been before or go again to where others have had to suffer to go: and they want to for the same reason as those who want to climb to the peak of Everest, for the same reason as those who climb mountains and risk a fall with every piton, for the same reason as those who lower themselves to the bottom of the sea or down into underground caves, even if they don't know how it'll end, maybe in disaster, but they have to go all the same because the spirit of adventure is in our blood, and the destiny of human beings is to go as far as possible, to expand, as gas emerging from its container expands as far as possible . . . And this is the reason for me. The real reason. My reason, and your reason too when you've freed yourself of all doubts. It's the reason that makes us tolerate so many things we don't like, so many people we don't like, the reason for which you forgive von Braun and me for having made the V2 and I forgive you for forgiving von Braun and me for having made the V2 . . ."

"Ernst, dear, you're going to be late if you want to see the Moon," said Irmgard.

Stuhlinger looked at his watch, quickly got to his feet.

"Come on, let's go, children, or else we'll miss the Moon. Come on, Susan."

Susan shrugged her shoulders.

"I've seen the Moon so many times, Daddy. I know it by heart. Take Til to see it."

Til shrugged his shoulders too.

"I know it by heart too," he said. "Take Chris."

We took Chris with us. The night air was soft and Chris was happy. I was happy too to be going to see the Moon, and Stuhlinger also was happy as he drove along a road hedged with pine trees and then the headlights picked out a wire stretched across the road to block it and around the wire there were nine children, three or four parents, a pregnant woman. Stuhlinger got out, removed the wire and gave a lift to the pregnant woman, who was very pretty and said she wanted to see the Moon because the full Moon is good for pregnant women. The others followed on foot and after a few minutes we all met in a clearing in the middle of which stood a kind of concrete hut surmounted by a big dome: the telescope. He, von Braun and a few others had built the telescope themselves, Stuhlinger told me, piece by piece, and Irmgard had painted the door. Then he opened the door and took the children into a very small room with a wooden staircase. The steps were broken and the pregnant woman started making a great fuss, the broken steps scared her, if she got scared she'd lose the baby, if she lost the baby there'd be no point in seeing the Moon because the full Moon is only good for pregnant women, etcetera. So we all hoped she wouldn't go up, but she went up, worse luck, and we were stuck with her: while Chris helped his father to arrange everybody and everything. Chris had been to the telescope before and he knew what to do. In a very grown-up way he climbed onto a stool, pulled some wires, turned a handle and opened the dome; it was curious to watch this child who couldn't even picture a horse-drawn carriage and so casually handled the trappings of a telescope. At last, when everything was ready, Stuhlinger assembled old and young together and gave them a little lecture about the Moon.

"When you are thirty or forty years old, children, men will already have landed on Mars. So going to the Moon will be very easy and you'll laugh a little when you think back to the first landing. But you shouldn't laugh because you should remember that at that time going to the Moon was very perilous, very difficult, and our astronauts knew it would maybe cost them their lives. Will you remember that, children?"

"I'll remember," said Chris gravely.

"I'll remember too," said another child. "And then I'm going to be an astronaut."

"I'm going to be an astronaut too," said a little girl.

"Uh, are we going to look at this Moon or not?" said the pregnant woman. "I don't feel so good, I need to look at the Moon."

Stuhlinger threw me one of his meaningful glances. Then he asked me how I felt. I felt the way I had the day Mother took me to see the sea.

"Dr. Stuhlinger, what does it feel like, looking at it?"

"I don't know," he said. "I've never been able to make it out. I once asked von Braun what he felt when he looked at it. And his answer was also: I don't know, I've never been able to make it out. But both of us agreed that parting from the telescope fills us with great regret."

Then he turned to his public.

"Are we ready? Go! First the children."

"Then pregnant women," yelped the pregnant woman.

"Then the fathers and mothers," declared the children's fathers and mothers.

"And at the very last the madmen, the adventurous ones and the romantics," concluded Stuhlinger. And he told us that naturally we wouldn't see the whole Moon but only a part of the Moon because when you look at a thing through a telescope you see it very much bigger but you can't see the whole of it because the whole thing wouldn't fit in the telescope. "Agreed?"

"Agreed," the children chorused.

And they began each taking a good look at the Moon: little needles to torment my patience. Once they'd got their eye to the telescope, there was no getting them away and Stuhlinger kept saying: That's enough, come along, that's enough, but they would cling to some protruding bit of metal, digging their toes in, and we had to give them a little longer. At last they would draw aside, frowning in adult perplexity, and stand silent in a corner. I called Chris.

"Chris, you've seen it, haven't you?"

"Yes."

"Tell me, Chris, what's it like close-up?"

"It's beautiful. It's very beautiful," said Chris.

"Yes. And what else?"

"What do you mean, what else?" said Chris.

What do you mean, what else? That was how Mother had answered too the day she took me to see the sea and we were getting on the train to Viareggio, Father. "Mother, you've seen it before, haven't you?" I kept asking. "Yes." "Tell me, Mother what's it like close-up?" "It's beautiful. It's very beautiful." "Yes. And what else?" "What do you mean, what else?" The train never seemed to be getting there. Every few minutes it stopped at some station and we had to wait ages for it to start again, because somebody wanted to buy ice cream, somebody else wanted to buy a newspaper, and I was fuming, I'd have liked to wring it in my hands, that train. "Mother, when will we get there?" And Mother: "Don't be such a nuisance!" At last we arrived, but the station wasn't by the sea and you couldn't see the sea. You could only hear the sound of it, like a roar, and to save time Mother called a carriage. The carriage smelled of hay and the horse's hoofbeats were hammering in my ears, but the roar of the sea grew louder and louder, with every turn of the wheels it overpowered the hammering, I was getting impatient, in my impatience we were hastening down a street, then another street, then yet another, at last we were in a wide avenue, and on the other side of the avenue there was the sea, the sea was suddenly right before us: like a slap in the eyes. Gray, infinite, smooth as smooth. A sky fallen to earth.

"Your turn, ma'am," said Stuhlinger, leading the pregnant woman to the telescope.

"Wait a moment, wait a moment, I must put my glasses on!" yelped the pregnant girl. "My Johnny says I must put my glasses on!"

I lowered my head when I saw that sky fallen on the earth. It was so disconcerting that the sky had fallen on the earth. Then Mother held out her hand and said: "Get down, we'll go and see it really close." We left the carriage and walked across the beach, just the two of us, holding hands. The beach was large and deserted because it was October and nobody stays at the seaside in October, Mother kept saying, it's cold and nobody comes. I'd never seen the beach either, you know, because I'd never seen the sea, and I couldn't manage to walk on it and I was having great difficulty because the sand kept getting into my shoes and my shoes were heavy. So Mother took off my shoes and I went on without shoes, but I still didn't raise my head, I still didn't look at the sea, because the sea frightened me, instead of looking at the sea I looked at my feet that were sinking less and less into the sand, in fact the sand was becoming increasingly damp and hard, and as it became hard it was changing color and now it was gray, gray that grew darker and darker, and when it was very dark the sand became kind of soft again and my feet made little puddles of water that disappeared immediately in a soundless gurgle.

"Oh!" yelped the pregnant girl. "Is that the Moon?"

"Yes, ma'am. That's the Moon," said Stuhlinger very patiently.

"It looks as if it's made of plastic!"

"What did you say, ma'am?"

"I said it looks as if it's made of plastic. Will it do me good all the same?"

"Plastic never does any harm, ma'am," said Stuhlinger. Then he called me. "Your turn, Miss Fallaci."

Suddenly, though, they no longer disappeared, those puddles of water, because my feet were in water, in the water of the sea. The sea water was clean, and it came toward my feet as if it were asking a question, as if it wanted to taste them, and when it had tasted them it withdrew in fear, as if my feet burned it, and around them there remained a little whirlpool, then not even that. And so I gathered courage, I finally raised my eyes and looked at the sea, the sea that was running away from me and . . . I don't remember how long I stood there looking at it, I must have stayed there for a long time because every now and then Mother would touch my shoulder and with Stuhlinger's voice she would say: "Come along, that's enough, that's enough now." But I didn't obey it, and I didn't obey because it was the second time that I was seeing the sea for the first time, and I didn't want it to run away from me again. What I felt while I looked at it I don't know, I couldn't make it out, I still can't make it out, Father. Stuhlinger was right, von Braun was right too, I can only tell you what I saw, and what I saw was the sea. Gray, infinite, smooth except for the round craters, so perfectly round that they seemed to have been made with a compass, and they reminded me of the holes you make for an instant when you throw a stone into water. But there was one thing about that sea, one terrible thing: it was a motionless sea. A sea that didn't move forward, that didn't move backward, that did nothing at all: a sea without sea. I'd say it was more like a beach than the sea, a gleaming beach, a hard dry enameled beach. It was gray—but a gray so gray that it wasn't even gray. It was death. And it wasn't even death. It was nothing.

"Come along, that's enough. That's enough now," Stuhlinger was gently repeating.

I tore myself regretfully away from the nothing.

"What's it like?" asked Stuhlinger.

"It's gray," I replied. "I thought it was white, but it's gray."

"No," said Stuhlinger. "It isn't gray. The gray is an optical illusion, a trick of light."

"Oh! It's really white?"

"No," said Stuhlinger. "It's black. As black as the blackest black you can imagine. As black as the darkest darkness, as . . . I don't know. Try to imagine the blackest of blacks. And that's the Moon."

Tell me, doesn't that revelation upset you, Father? It upset me so much. The white Moon. White as the Moon. Pale as the Moon. And it was black. Black as the blackest black; try to imagine the blackest of blacks and that's the Moon. I was very upset. I thought—do you find it funny?—that I'd never again be able to read Sappho or Leopardi without thinking why say it's white when it's black? I thought that it's sometimes better not to know things, to remain ignorant, since there's always something sad behind the truth.

"You're quite right, Dr. Stuhlinger, to aim at Mars instead of the Moon."

Stuhlinger spread his arms, stayed silent for a moment, then poured himself some coffee. We had gone back to the house and were sitting drinking coffee with Irmgard on the veranda. The children were asleep.

"Of course! Mars is more interesting from every point of view. If it were up to me, I'd aim for Mars instead of the Moon. Without hesitation. In any case, think: the Moon will be an abandoned station in fifty years, people will go and look at it as they go to look at the Colosseum. We've even calculated how much it will cost a private individual to visit the Moon in 1980: there and back, twenty thousand dollars, the price of a prefabricated house. But they insist: let's go to the Moon—and I shrug my shoulders."

"And what if that's a disappointment too?"

"We've already had the only disappointment we could have: atmospheric pressure on Mars is very low, one percent of what it is on Earth. We had hoped to find it was twenty percent: that's to say, the rarefied atmosphere you get here on very high mountains. We had hoped we'd be able to walk on Mars without pressurized spacesuits, without oxygen cylinders. Instead we won't even be able to expose our skin because our blood would begin to boil as on the Moon, or almost. If our calculations are not wrong."

"And if they're wrong?"

"In that case Mars would not be so inhospitable. There's water, although not much. Its poles are covered with thin layers of snow. There's oxygen, although not much. The temperature at the equator is twenty-two degrees below zero at night but fifty or sixty degrees above zero during the day."

"But no life, no little green men, von Braun says. Only scrub that might be covering the remains of a very ancient civilization."

"I too believe in the remains of a very ancient civilization. Mars is a very much older planet than Earth. When I say older I don't mean that it was formed earlier than the Earth—all the planets in our solar system were formed more or less contemporaneously. What I mean is that it's grown old faster than the Earth. Take, for example, a dog and a man who are born the same day. The dog will live for fourteen years at the most, the man can live for a hundred years and more: the dog grows old faster than the man. And since that planet has grown faster, its civilization came to an end faster. Life means energy and energy means movement. There are no signs of movement on Mars, apart from the growth of vegetation in spring and its withering in autumn. If cities existed, for example, in one way or another they would be illuminated, so we would see them. Unless they are underground cities —a hypothesis that is far from nonsensical. But there are plants and, according to our conception of life, where there are plants there are animals that eat the plants. And where there are animals that eat plants . . . Miss Fallaci, one has to be very prudent when speaking of such things. One is in danger of entering the realm of fantasy and being considered mad or visionary."

"I don't consider you mad or visionary, Dr. Stuhlinger."

"You don't. But others will."

"Please, go on all the same."

"All right, then. I was going to say this. Life as we conceive it can exist only through two chemical cycles: our own and that of the plants. Our own feeds on oxygen and gives out carbon dioxide, that of the plants feeds on carbon dioxide and gives out oxygen. Agreed? But if Mars has little oxygen and therefore little carbon dioxide, how do plants live there? Certainly not on nothing: energy can't be created from nothing, nothing can be created from nothing, and this principle is valid for the whole universe. Martian plants could therefore live by themselves, heating their own atmosphere within an involucre: an involucre that must be transparent so they can get the light, a kind of soap bubble, a glass egg. But . . . but if this hypothesis is acceptable as far as plants are concerned, then it's also acceptable for animal life. And if animals do exist on Mars, then it's probable that there exist also . . . also intelligent animals."

"Oh, Jesus! Men inside eggs?"

Eggs, eggs, eggs! You always wind up talking about eggs with these space people. You'd think they were persecuted by the idea of the egg, the shape of the egg, and that they live in a round egg-shaped nightmare, in an egg. Why?

"Men, no. Or not men exactly. Or anyway not men with our kind of skin, our blood circulation, our form . . . In twenty years we'll know. Von Braun says we won't go to Mars before 1990, but I've bet we'll go by 1986. Good years for going to Mars, the years when Mars will be closest to Earth, that is, are 1971, 1986, 1990. We'll be able to make it in 1986. The only trouble is that everyone, in America at least, is taken up with going to the Moon, and Mars is getting pushed aside. NASA doesn't even have a precise Mars project: all that they've done is take under consideration my method of electric propulsion. You've grasped what that entails, haven't you?"

"No," I said candidly. "No, not really."

"Then I'll explain it to you: by evaporating ionized atoms—"

"It doesn't matter, please don't trouble."

"No, no, I'll explain it to you."

He saw the expression on my face, burst out laughing and, thank God, gave up. Then he asked Irmgard if the children were really asleep and went to get the little model of his spacecraft, by day in danger from the curiosity of Chris, Til and Susan. Through the windows of his study we saw him open a cupboard, then glance around suspiciously and grab a toy. When he had hold of it he switched off the light and came tiptoeing back to us, moving silently as a cat, his toy clasped to his heart.

"There," said Stuhlinger, setting the spacecraft down next to the coffee pot. "With this we'll go to Mars. Look at it closely, please."

I looked and I must say first that Chris was right: it looks more or less like a pinwheel. In fact, it consists of two very tapering wings, joined together at the base, and surmounted by an object placed on a perpendicular tube in the middle. The object is the actual rocket—that is, the rocket that will take the spacecraft to Mars by an electric propulsion method. The tapering wings are a gigantic centrifuge which, as it whirls around, creates in space a force of gravity equal to that on Earth. The spacecraft, similar to a Coca-Cola bottle, is latched on to the tip of one wing in horizontal position: like the sidecar on the end of the arm of the centrifuge wheel in San Antonio. Rocket and pinwheel operate simultaneously—which calls to mind the flying saucers that, according to von Braun, do not and cannot exist.

"With my spacecraft the journey to Mars can be accomplished in five hundred and seventy days: two hundred and eighty-five to go and two hundred and eighty-five to come back."

"Yes . . ."

"The time to be spent on Mars has obviously not been allowed for. It might be a month or it might be two years. Two years if the astronauts miss the coincidence with the Earth: coincidence occurs precisely every two years, at times every six. And now that's why it's constructed like this: we know that the human body cannot float weightless for five hundred and seventy days, more than a year and a half. The astronauts must live in a normal way and possess weight as if they were on Earth. This part that Chris calls a pinwheel serves precisely to restore terrestrial weight. The spacecraft is on two floors: apart from the control cabin, the laboratory, the storeroom, etcetera. The amount of room reserved for the men is the same as this house. That is, three bedrooms with bath, a kitchen, a living room, a gymnasium. Each room contains television and telephone, the living room also has a movie projector. I think that should be enough."

"I don't," said Irmgard. "If it's the same as this house, I really don't. I'm always telling you we need an extra room in this house. You'll see, those poor things will need an extra room too."

"There are five of us and there'll be three of them," Stuhlinger replied in the tone of one who had already heard that observation many times. Then he turned to me: "If anything happens, there'll be too much room for only three people: they have very much less room in submarines. The rooms are big—I've made them big so that in case of accidents every spacecraft will be able to take in extra men. Five, say, or ten, or fifteen—"

"So then you need an extra room. Now do you see you'll need one?" Irmgard repeated.

Stuhlinger sighed.

"The fleet will consist of five spacecraft, each spacecraft containing three men, which makes a total of fifteen. Statistically it is very unlikely that all five spacecraft will have accidents or be destroyed. One of them at least ought to remain intact. And in that event it would be up to the remaining one to take on board the survivors. If four spacecraft are destroyed but the twelve men survive, the fifth spacecraft will have room for them as well as its own three." He broke off at the first signs of a gesture from Irmgard. "Irmgard, don't start again. One of them can sleep on the sofa, for goodness sakes!"

"It's the food, the drink," Irmgard insisted.

"Every spacecraft carries enough for fifteen men!" Stuhlinger sighed.

"All right, Ernst, all right. Because they might have room to sleep, the poor things, and then suffer from hunger, thirst."

"They won't suffer from anything."

"They'll suffer from being shut up all the time," I ventured. "Two years or thereabouts is a long time."

"They'll go out," Stuhlinger explained. "When they wear their pressurized suits they'll be able to move about in the void, go from one spacecraft to another. The method of egress is identical to that in submarines: they go through a chamber into an antechamber, through that into another one, and then they can get out. Once outside they'll use rocket belts. I don't know whether you've seen them."

"Yes," I said, "I've seen them."

"Cute, aren't they?"

"Yes, very cute."

"I personally think rocket belts are more convenient than space taxis, and also less expensive. However, we're also going to make space taxis, which shows you that it's really no problem getting about in space outside the spacecraft. So I could go . . ."

"Here again! To go! He wants to go! To go!" grumbled Irmgard. "Everyone in this family wants to go. He wants to go, Til wants to go, Chris wants to go, even Susan wants to go. To hell with Mars!"

"Don't say to hell with Mars!" said Stuhlinger.

"To hell with Venus, then."

"Don't say to hell with Venus," said Stuhlinger.

"To hell with the Moon," Irmgard concluded.

"Bah!" was Stuhlinger's comment as he shrugged his shoulders.

We stayed on that veranda until two in the morning, beside the toy that Susan, Til and Chris were always threatening to steal from Daddy. We talked about the astronauts—Stuhlinger knows them well—and about distant things such as journeys to other solar systems. Stuhlinger didn't share Willy Ley's optimism: to travel at the speed of light, he said, is almost impossible. Scientists never totally exclude a possibility, never use the adjective impossible, but in a case like this one could use the adjective impossible. Even using the electric propulsion method it would take ten thousand years to reach Alpha Centauri: which is to say no fewer than three hundred generations. It is possible to construct spacecraft that would last for ten thousand years. It is also possible to procreate inside spacecraft for three hundred generations: but who can be sure that the three-hundredth generation will have souls like ours? Who can be sure that they will have souls at all, any kind of soul? Here was the paradox: we knew a heap of things about the cosmos, about the distant worlds, and we knew nothing about that little world at our elbow, that world called mind.

So we stood up, we who wanted to go into the cosmos but knew nothing about our minds, and Stuhlinger said he'd take me back to my motel. But first he wanted to show me something, so he led me into his study: a writing desk, a chair, a divan, some shelves of scientific books, lastly a low round table covered with brown velvet.

"Something very beautiful," said Stuhlinger, making ready to raise the velvet.

"Something found in the sky?" I asked.

"No."

"Something from another planet?"

"No."

"Something that grows on Earth?"

"Not exactly."

"Then where?"

"In the sea," he replied, sweeping off the velvet like a conjuror. Beneath the velvet there was a little display case covered with glass. Beneath the glass, shells. Round shells, flat ones, spiral-shaped, button-shaped, transparent, phosphorescent, yellow as sunflower petals, pink as a baby's fingernails, blue as scraps of sky, seahorses, coral . . .

"They're his passion," said Irmgard. "When he takes us to the beach he never spends any time with us, he's always with his shells. Or else he makes us look for shells. And he's so possessive about them. More possessive about his shells than he is about his spacecraft."

Stuhlinger dwelt fondly on them with his eyes.

"How beautiful they are. Beautiful like the sea. The velvet is to keep them in darkness so they'll retain the colors they had down under the sea. From time to time, though, I take it off and have a look at them."

He moved the glass, and picked up one that looked like a porcelain flower. He held it up to his big nose.

"What a scent. It still smells of the sea. And inside it there's a singing mermaid. Listen."

I listened. The mermaid was singing.

"She's really singing."

"Yes, every night. During the day she's silent."

"Dear, put it back, dear. It'll get broken," said Irmgard.

Stuhlinger did as his wife said. He replaced the glass, covered it again with the brown velvet, then went toward the door with determination.

"Come on, let's get going. It'll soon be three in the morning."

I thanked Irmgard, climbed into the Volkswagen. Very gradually the night was beginning to fade into blue and the Moon was white, white, white. In silence we drove down the twisting road, passed von Braun's house, a big house, took the freeway to the motel, and at this point I realized that I was sorry to be leaving this German who wants to go to Mars and collects seashells. Whether miraculously or by sorcery, a friend had got through the impenetrable barrier of my rancor. Truly, Father. And I felt sad that we were at the motel already, that the Volkswagen was drawing up. The Volkswagen drew up. I got out and Stuhlinger got out too. I held out my hand to him. And then I felt between my palm and his palm something smooth, like a porcelain flower. I opened my hand and there was the shell.

A shell is only a shell. I was to find many, weeks later, on the beach at Cape Kennedy. But Stuhlinger's shell, oh, Father, it is really another shell. It is the shell from the man who for the second time showed me the sea for the first time, and upset me by saying that the Moon isn't white but black, and made me forget the rancor.

"Thank you," I said to him.

"Iss just a little memento," he replied.

He started up the Volkswagen and vanished.

22.

"But there's no light in this room!"

"No, there isn't."

"It's completely dark, you bump into things."

"Yes, you do."

"But where are the lights?"

"The bulbs are broken."

"Broken!"

"Yes, broken."

"Why?"

"Because they need fixing."

"Then fix them!"

"I'm the porter. A porter doesn't fix light bulbs."

"Take the bags back."

"I'm not taking anything back."

"Why not?"

"Because the manager said Number 203."

"Pick up the bags again!"

He picked up the bags and the light from the road illuminated his black hostile face. He dragged his feet as he walked, his shoulders bent. Oh, why was I making him carry the bags back to the entrance, why? Who needs lights at night? At night you sleep. Was this a room for sleeping in or wasn't it? I was shouting at him because he was black, that's why. They arrive full of arrogance, these whites, and immediately start making you go up and down the stairs with their bags. With a great sigh he put the bags on the floor in front of the manager of the motel. The manager was a woman, about forty years old, ugly, dressed in blue. She was bent over a sheet of paper, writing down numbers.

"Excuse me, there's no light in my room."

Silence.

"My room's in complete darkness. All the bulbs are broken."

Silence.

"Are you listening to me?"

She moved her lips and went on writing numbers.

"Yes?"

"I was saying that there's no light in my room."

"Yes."

"It's completely dark."

"Yes."

"What do you mean, yes?"

"Yes."

I clenched my fists, resisted the urge to slap her, hoped ardently that she might be deaf, began again from the start.

"Eight days ago I reserved a room in this motel. I know it's a very bad motel because I stayed here once before. Nevertheless I reserved a room all the same. I phoned from New York."

"Yes."

"By room I mean one complete with light bulbs."

"Yes."

"Do you understand my English?"

"Yes."

"You understand that I want a room with bulbs that give light when you switch them on?"

"Yes."

"Then change the bulbs, for God's sake! Or give me another roooom!"

"There's no other room."

"But there must be, because I reserved a room."

"You have a room."

"It's a room without light and therefore it isn't a room."

"It is a room."

"I want a room with light."

A man stepped forward hesitantly: another client.

"It seems to me that the young lady's not in the wrong. It seems to me she's making a perfectly reasonable request."

Silence.

"If there aren't any other rooms, then change the bulbs in that one."

Silence.

"When you rent a room, the light is included."

"This is none of your business," said the woman and went on writing down numbers.

The man withdrew, red in the face. I continued.

"Look, it's one o'clock in the morning. I've come straight from the airport and I'm tired. I need a room, and a room with a light."

"Go to another motel."

"Look, I've no intention of looking for another motel at one in the morning. This motel is a disgrace, and you, madam, are a daughter of a bitch. The most stupid daughter of a bitch I've ever met. But I still want a room because I've paid for one and I have a right to one."

The woman finally forgot her numbers and raised an ugly greedy face full of pimples. Then she started sniggering. She didn't seem in the least offended, my insults ran off her like water off a duck's back. Incredulous, I stood staring at her. Then I looked around for help and through the clouds of my despair emerged a man: another guest. He looked kind, well-bred. He smiled at me, I smiled at him. He bowed, I bowed.

"Shall we sleep together?" he suggested, leering.

The taxi was a long time coming because the motel was a long way from the city, and when it came it was nearly two in the morning. I explained the situation to the taxi driver, the taxi driver observed that it was nothing unusual, people couldn't care less these days, and so on, and finally he asked me which part of Houston I was visiting, so that he could find me a motel relatively nearby. NASA, I told him. NASA? But then the motel I had chosen was no good, he said. What did he mean, NASA was only a stone's throw. A stone's throw from here? How long was it since my last visit? Only four months. Oh, four months is a long time. Long? Yes, long, very long, NASA had moved, now NASA was at Clear Lake City. And where was he taking me now? He was taking me to Clear Lake City. Far? No, very near—forty-five minutes along the freeway. But it'll be three by the time we get there! Uh, yes, we'll get there at three. But it's a different town, then! No, it isn't a different town, it's a suburb of Houston, a fine suburb, what's more, there's nothing except NASA and a motel. Which motel? The King's Inn. With light bulbs that give light when you switch them on? Yes, of course. And a human being as manager? Yes, of course.

The manager of the King's Inn offered me a smile and a key. I rushed to my room and, without checking whether the light bulbs gave light when you switched them on, I fell on the bed. I was going to sleep when I suddenly thought of the other unmentionable motel, remembered that I'd left my cosmetic case there with perfume, bath salts, all the useless things women carry around. In great vexation I telephoned, the receptionist replied that I'd left nothing behind at all. But no, miss, look, it must have got left on the bed in the dark, I remember putting it down there when I was looking for the light, you can even keep the perfume if you want, but the bath salts are French bath salts and . . . Silence. Hello, Miss? Are you there, Miss? Silence. Miss! You dirty whore! Silence. Well, Father, once in Jerusalem—I don't know if I ever told you this, Father—I saw a very fat woman who was going to Paradise by squeezing herself through a corridor of columns no more than a foot apart. Her religion said that whoever managed to get through those columns would go to Paradise, and she, don't ask me how, was squeezing herself through: becoming immediately imprisoned by them. She could go neither forward nor backward, and besides going back would have meant accepting Hell forever. So she didn't go back, she didn't even try, she stood there, compressed by those columns that gripped her more and more, like a vise, her stomach seemed to be splitting in two, a column was cutting it right down the middle, the woman was yelling with pain and weeping, while kissing the columns and saying columns I beg you, let me through, columns, I want to go to Paradise, columns, and the columns silently crushed her even harder. Everyone was silent. I wanted to shout to her why do you want to go to Paradise, woman, can't you see that Paradise hurts, go back to Hell, woman, Hell is more comfortable, and instead I was silent like the others. I watched, full of respect and of pity, and suddenly the woman let forth a cry that wasn't pain but joy and she managed to free her shoulders; after her shoulders she managed to free her stomach, and she offered it up to another column that cut it down the middle again, and then slowly, and painfully, so very painfully, kissing, weeping, praying, she reached the last column, the end of the corridor, and fell exhausted to the ground and was in Paradise. Yes, there are many ways of going to Paradise. I, for example, was getting a little nearer every time I came to Houston, Texas. This was Houston comma Texas.

———————

And this was NASA, Clear Lake City: a city that had been shifted forty miles in the course of four months, the way you'd shift a bundle from one table to another. If you didn't know it, you wouldn't even realize that it wasn't in the same place. The only difference was the whiteness. Like a mirage, an absurdity, NASA now stood on a stretch of unbroken calcareous whiteness.

"But it's not possible, Paul!"

"It is possible, though, we've done it."

"And all that white, Paul, what is it?"

"Shells. We bring them from the Gulf of Mexico, we use them as building material instead of gravel. All the walls here are mixed with shells."

"Mixed with shells?"

"Yes. We crush them to powder first. For the astronauts' building we crushed nine tons of shells. Look how many are still on the ground."

I bent down and picked up a shell, thinking of Stuhlinger.

"But they're beautiful! Look what a lovely shape, see how delicate this is."

"Yes, they're beautiful."

"And you crush them."

"Yes, we crush them."

Paul Haney was laughing proudly, not in the least annoyed at my indignation. Americans ask only one thing to make them happy: that you should be amazed or indignant, never indifferent. And Paul is so American—remember the half-serious, half-joking interrogation he'd subjected me to the first time? Standing there tall and big, he pointed out the nightmare of those huge monstrous buildings, his columns of Paradise, and all my amazement, indignation, took him a little further away from Hell.

"You see that big round building? It's the triple centrifuge: it takes three men instead of one. The three men for the Apollo capsule. Now look at the motor, the most powerful on Earth, and the heaviest. Once it was put together, we couldn't even move it. We tried with trucks: they broke like matchsticks. We tried with cranes: they snapped like toothpicks. Nothing seemed strong enough to raise it, to drag it, nothing!"

The most powerful and heaviest motor on Earth, like a great steel vat, so like a vat that you felt like tipping baskets of grapes into it, stood on rollers, ready to be lowered into the hole in the middle of the round room containing the centrifuge.

"And so then what, Paul? Who dragged it here?"

"An incredible business. It was one of the laborers who suggested it. He said: why don't you try rollers? You lay a carpet of rollers, then you turn the rollers and they carry the motor along. Brilliant. Our engineers tried it and they said it was brilliant . . . What are you laughing at?"

"Oh, Paul! Oh!"

"I don't see anything funny about it."

"But Paul! But that's how they built the Pyramids!"

"There you go again! You and your past!"

And for a moment I seemed to see him squashed between two columns that were crushing his rib cage. But he wriggled skillfully out of it—"If it was up to people like you, we'd still go around on bicycles or on foot"—and in penance I continued my pilgrimage to Jerusalem: greeted by one and all like a prodigal son come to ask forgiveness, or, better, a sick person come to seek healing. As relatives or doctors the people I knew issued gaily forth from offices and it goes without saying that they seemed to be the sick ones, not me: in four months they had aged four years. Because of worries, boredom? Who knows, Father? Even their voices were old. Remember me? I'm Jack Riley. Remember me? I'm Ben Gallespie. Remember me? I'm Katherine, I'm Howard Gibbons. Remember Howard Gibbons? Gibbons no longer showed the irascibility of a sergeant who's lost his hat, if he made an effort he could just about manage to lift his lips into something like a smile, and with that kind of smile he said he had a surprise for me: Bob Button was here, transferred from California. The door right next to me, yes. I flung open the door.

"Bob! How lovely to see you again, Bob!"

"Yeah," Bob muttered without moving.

"Bob! How are you, dear Bob?"

"Uhm."

"Bob! Don't you recognize me, Bob?"

"Yes, sure, hello."

"Hello? Is that all you've got to say?"

"Welcome."

He too seemed somehow withered: a leaf fallen from the tree and shriveled by the sun. Apathetically he held out his hand, and his fingers had less life in them than his mustache. His mustache had grown sparse, the hairs seemed about to drop out, one by one, forever.

"Oh, Bob! But what have they done to you, Bob?"

"Eh?"

"Bob! How long have you been here?"

"Three months."

"I see."

"Eh?"

"Bob, you'll help me—I hope. I've come back on account of the book and I'll need help badly."

"Uhm."

"Are you listening, Bob? I'm telling you I need help."

"Howard Gibbons is the chief here. Over him there's Ben Gallespie. And over everyone there's Paul Haney."

"But what's got into you, Bob?"

"Nothing's got into me."

"If that's how it is, so long."

I stood up. I went toward the door, in anger. I was stopped by his humiliated face.

"Oriana . . ."

"Yes?"

"I hope you understand . . ."

"Understand what?"

"I hope you understand that it would be hard for me here in Houston to reconcile my friendship for you with loyalty toward my superiors."

"Reconcile? Friendship? Loyalty?"

"My new job means a lot to me, and duty obliges me to—"

"Go to Hell, Bob!"

I slammed the door as I went out and everyone quickly bent their heads over their papers, pretending not to have heard or seen. Everyone except her. So I was astonished that I hadn't noticed her when I arrived and astonished that Paul hadn't introduced us before going off. A glance, in fact, was enough to show that here was someone who didn't run to type. First, because of her eyes: perfidious, intelligent, green of an emerald green. Then for the face: bony, and hard, crowned with hair as red as carrots. Finally the smile that lightly curved two thin lips, scornful, ironical, a smile, I would say, that commented in coldness and excluded all softness, all acquiescence to that kind of world. She offered her hand, she said her name. The name was a common name, Sally Gates, but for me it will always be an important name because I would not have understood many things if Sally had not offered me that hand and spoken and taken me out, on the pretext of lunch, to the NASA cafeteria, where she told me at once, out of pride, that she had lived in Europe for years, had been born in Philadelphia and brought up in San Francisco, where she'd married a general.

"But why are you here with these people, Sally? Born in Philadelphia, brought up in San Francisco, married to a general: why do you work for NASA, why do you live in Houston?"

"So that when I'm old I'll be able to say I was there, I had a share in the thing."

"That's what they all say."

"That's why they all stay here."

"Bob too?"

"Bob too."

"Howard too?"

"Howard too."

"Then why do they look so discontented, so sick, so frightened?"

Sally's wicked eyes flashed.

"Dear! Here youth is something that's over at twenty. They feel old and so they are old and they act as if they're old. And then they are afraid. Afraid of committing themselves, afraid of doing too much or too little, afraid of going beyond the limits of their job. Their job exacts discipline. Nothing more. And they give nothing more. Why should they? The Moon, my dear, isn't the romantic adventure you think it is: the Moon is a big industrial enterprise."

"An industrial enterprise?"

"Why are you shocked? It doesn't make it any less fascinating. But, being an industrial enterprise, it depends more on discipline than enthusiasm, and wherever you find discipline you find . . . well, let's say apprehension. This goes for me, for Bob, for Howard, for the astronauts, for everyone. Away from Houston we're all gayer and more alive. We can laugh, we can throw our hats in the air if we meet a friend. In Houston we stiffen up like boys in school. We watch each other, we spy on each other, and we're in terror of being thrown out. We'd feel naked, like Adam and Eve, if they threw us out of this fearsome Terrestrial Paradise, because we'd no longer have a share in the Thing. Of course there are exceptions, but such exceptions are rare and—"

"Talking about me, Sally?" a cheerful voice broke in behind us. Then that husky laughter.

"Wally! Oh, Wally! Sure, I was talking about you. Who else would I be talking about?"

Sally was flooded with such a blush that you couldn't tell where her face finished and her red hair began. She'd turned into, that's it, a carrot, with her eyes two little green leaves.

"Wally, let me introduce a friend . . ."

"We know each other already," said the cheerful voice. And the smile that was full of the same kindness and indulgence, amusement and curiosity, spread across his cheeks, his forehead, his eyes that were piercing me like two needle points.

"Well, how are you? Still arguing about courage, and fear?"

He hadn't changed, I thought. If anything, he was thinner. His cheeks were less round and his hips were less heavy. This made him handsomer without detracting from his weight, the feeling of comfort, confidence, surrender that you derived from his weight, and the memory of that extraordinary talk at Cape Kennedy when he had disappeared so swiftly, calm, erect, a victorious bullfighter leaving the ring with the bull's ears, the bull's tail, and it's a sunny Sunday, the people are throwing their hats into the ruedo, the tinkling horses are dragging out the bull that is dead, in a long gush of blood.

"Fine, thank you. My tail has grown again and so have my ears."

"So I see. I'm glad."

"What on earth are you talking about?" Sally said, a little offended.

Again that husky laughter.

"About corridas. About her notion that a new race is being born and going to kill the old one. She's convinced we want to kill her."

No, it wasn't true that he hadn't changed. He had—how shall I say it?—aged. He too. The lines that scored his skin with tiny iron scars had aged, and his swift loss of interest in others had aged, now somehow spoiled by a certain impatience. I spontaneously calculated how old he was: forty-one that year. God! Only?

"However, I came back." I answered.

"So I see. I'm glad."

But no, age didn't come into it. It was more a kind of anxiety, a waiting that was consuming him. And it was taking him back further than to an island that nobody would dare to approach, not even to pay him homage or ask him for help. In short, he had grown distant and frozen. So maybe, Father, the possible bridge flung from his shore to ours had fallen down. For a while or forever.

"What gives?" said another voice behind me, this one familiar too. It was Shepard. With his chest flung out, his nose raised to catch God knows what smells, what regrets.

I greeted him gaily because he released me from a kind of disillusionment, defeat.

"What gives is that my father wants the cow."

"Buy it."

"But my mother wants the horse."

"Buy it."

"And they both maintain it would be nice of you to give them to us."

"Do they think I'm crazy? They're worth a lot, you know."

"But what are you talking about?" Sally said again.

"Business."

Yet he too wasn't exactly the same, Father. He seemed tired, resigned, reluctant to joke. The carnivorous plant had somehow become vegetarian: mosquitoes, ants, animals of any size could have fallen into it without danger of being devoured, digested. And this made him acceptable, likable, finally a next-door man: with a cloud of sadness, though. Quickly I calculated how old he was: forty that year. God! Only?

"So long, girls."

"So long, Al."

"Bye to all."

"Bye, Wally."

They went. Nonchalantly, distractedly. Perhaps they had had a bad day. A bad day?

I turned to Sally.

"Sally! Is it possible that nothing, nobody here can stay the same? But how long is a month here, a year, a minute?"

Sally smiled strangely.

"Short, very short. Whom have you asked to talk to today?"

"Slayton. I want to see him again."

"Ah! You'll certainly find him changed."

"Him too?"

"He's one of the most important men in Houston. He's the one who controls the astronauts, their timetable, their movements, everything. No one can so much as raise a little finger these days without Deke's permission."

"And this has changed him?"

"No, not that." Sally sounded odd. It was as if, I don't know, she disliked the idea of my appointment or was scared by it and yet . . . "What time's your appointment?"

"In ten minutes."

"Well, what are you waiting for? Do you want to keep him waiting? What do you expect? Do you think he can wait for you? Come on, hurry. Come on, get going!"

She grabbed me by the arm and as if I were a child who's late for school she dragged me to the astronauts' building, handed me over to an escort named Don Green. Through corridors, up elevators, more corridors, more elevators, he took me to the Chief's office. And no, we should never, never try to see again someone who has meant something to us, Father. We should never try to repeat something that has meant something to us. It's a mistake, isn't it, Father? We two know it is because I've already made that mistake once: with the heroes of my childhood.

My childhood, you know it well, Father, is full of heroes because I had the privilege of being a child at a time of glory. I associated with heroes as other children collect stamps, I played with them as other little girls play with dolls. Eleven months of my life were filled to the brim with heroes, or with those who seemed heroes to me—the eleven months from September 8, 1943, to August 11, 1944, the German occupation of Florence. That was the time, I think, when I developed my veneration for courage, my worship of sacrifice, my fear of fear. You fought with them, Father, you and they used me to help in little ways, such as carrying newspapers and messages, munitions, and so I used to meet my heroes every day, at home, in the street, in the country. I was a child without any illusions at that time, a hard and fully aware child, nothing was kept from me and nothing was minimized for me: every time I met them, my heroes, I knew it might be for the last time. And for this reason I loved them so much that I'd have been ready to die for any of them, without waiting for the arrival of the Allies, for white bread and chocolate. I respected them so deeply that when the war was over they remained within me like a precious jewel—or a drug. A drug. Whatever I did or saw or heard, I measured by that yardstick: even love, my God! When I became a woman I wasted my best years comparing the men who came my way with my heroes: rejecting them because they weren't at all like my heroes. Very few people, I suspect, have been persecuted by a memory or a misunderstanding as much as I was. Then, seventeen years after that far-off August, I thought of writing a book about my heroes. And I made that mistake: I went to look for them. One by one, those who were still alive . . . Well: I haven't yet written that book, Father, you know I haven't. I haven't written it yet and I wonder if I ever will. The book is here, clear in my mind, clearer than many other things in my life, but I haven't the courage to put it into words. Words are heavier than stones, and heroes go bad. If they don't go bad, they get fat. If they don't get fat, they get old. And it hurts to find it out, Father, to write it down hurts doubly, revolts you. When it doesn't hurt you it moves you and that is even more dangerous because being hurt is a sickness and being moved is a feeling. Sickness can be cured, but feelings can't. Shall we get back to my brand-new heroes?

Sally was right. The Chief had certainly become a very important person. His office was on the top floor (important people in America always have their offices on the top floor), guarded by two charming secretaries (important people in America always have charming secretaries to guard their offices), furnished with a handsome wall-to-wall carpet, four telephones, a conference table (important people in America all have a handsome wall-to-wall carpet, four telephones and a conference table in their offices). Going into it was like going into something gone bad, fat and . . . Well, perhaps he hadn't gone bad and he hadn't grown fat. The heroes we choose when we're adults don't flake so easily, we pass them through a sieve before accepting them, we filter them through our cynicism. Yet, even so, he was no longer my brand-new hero; he had aged badly. In a world where things happen in twenty-four hours that would take a month anywhere else, four months had passed over him and wrought as much devastation as four years. His body seemed tired, his shoulders seemed bowed beneath a sack of lead, his eyes, formerly full of irony and sadness, had lost all irony and retained only the sadness. Even the way he held out his hand had changed, no longer openly but with reluctance, as if he didn't trust you. And his handshake was no longer as firm: it was the handshake of a man who no longer cares about establishing friendship, trust, hope, respect, things like that.

"Welcome back."

"Thank you . . ."

"Hot, isn't it?"

"Yes, it's hot . . ."

"It's cooler in here, though."

"Yes, it's cooler in here. It's a fine office . . ."

"So they say."

He looked around absently and it was clear that he couldn't care less about being on the top floor, about the wall-to-wall carpet, the big table, the telephones and maybe—who knows?—not even about the charming secretaries. Or, better, only about them.

"Many things have changed here . . ."

He stood up, went over to his desk, pressed a button, lowered his mouth to a microphone: "Tell Grissom to be here in ten minutes. I'm busy for the next ten minutes." Grissom, not Gus. And he'd got his secretary to tell him. Four months ago he'd have called up his friend himself: "Say, Gus, I'll be busy for ten minutes or so, hold off for ten minutes, O.K.?"

At that time Grissom was the next to go up with Project Gemini. I thought spontaneously of Stig and Bjorn in Stockholm: "Have you seen? At the end of the year they're starting Project Gemini. This time Slayton's going up. We've got the cover page ready. In color." It was a beautiful cover page: Slayton was shown against a background of white clouds looking up at the sky, and Bjorn had cheerfully brandished it under my nose: "Look at your hero." He pressed the button again, left his desk and turned to me. He looked at me as much as to say: go on, shoot. I shot.

"So it's Grissom who's going up."

"Yes. Grissom."

"We were all surprised. We all thought you'd be going. We were sorry."

"Thank you."

"But isn't it you who picks the astronauts who are to go up?"

"I'm one of the people who pick them."

"Couldn't you pick yourself?"

"It doesn't do any good. The final decision rests with Washington."

He gave a sudden flash of boredom, irritation.

"Nothing has changed. You go on talking, negotiating, and they always answer no. You go to see others, you ask their damn opinions, and they reply with the same damn prudence. Better not. Why take risks? Why gamble? It's an unknown field. We know everything and we know nothing. The fact that there are two of them isn't enough. What if he dies in mid-air? How will that make us look? Super-conservatism! Super-prudence! Super-idiocy! Before, it was just the Air Force doctors, now it's the politicians too. Someone high up must have whispered the same old story in their ears. Better not. The hell with it, I'm fine, I tell you. I'm perfectly well."

He held out his wrist. It was very white beneath the brown hairs. You'd have said it hadn't been in the sun for a long while. It had spent too long in the office. I tried to imagine the sound of the artery. Dum-dum. Dum-dum. Dum-dum. All the disappointment in the world in that pulse, in that artery. Like Mother.

"It's going well, I'm sure."

He put his finger on the wrist: a frown on his forehead.

"It's going very well. But what do they care? It's so easy to say no and remain an expert. You know that philosophy?"

"I know it."

"It's so difficult, on the other hand, to take risks. Sometimes you lose your job through taking risks!"

"Yes. But why do you stay in here? Why aren't you out training with the others?"

"I do train, now and then. I do this and the rest too. Of course I spend a little less time on the rest. There just isn't the time. And it gets a little worse with every day that passes. Glenn's left, but there are still twenty-nine of us, others to come. When they all sit around that table for the damn meetings . . . They all have proposals, protests, problems. And I have to sort them out. So finding time for training becomes more and more difficult."

"That's what I thought." I was also thinking: You've let yourself be taken in, Major; you've got yourself put here, with your telephones and your fine wall-to-wall carpet, your charming secretaries, and now who's going to get you out of it?

"Besides, somebody's got to do the job of listening to them, directing them. We're no longer a little group of friends, we're a big group, a college. There are so many new ones. Soon there'll be fifty of us."

As he spoke he continued to handle his pulse, counting the beats, I think. I don't know how he managed to count and talk at the same time, but he did. And he was looking at his shoes. Yes, this man who used to look you in the eye as if he was reading your mind. The same thing had happened to Rio, one of my heroes. Rio had a way of looking you in the eye as if he was reading your mind, but when I found him again, that day seventeen years later, he nearly always looked at his shoes. Rio hadn't gone bad either, no. He hadn't got fat, he hadn't betrayed. But old age had come upon him like a cloudburst, completely drenching him, altogether diluting him into regrets, bitterness, rancor. And when he spoke he almost always looked at his shoes. Remember, Father?

"I must meet some of the new ones. That's why I came back."

"Aha! It jumped a bit then. But so little you could hardly notice it."

"What are the new ones like?"

"Now it's back to normal. The new ones? I like them. Good boys. Perhaps, compared with us, they have less flying experience. On the other hand, they're better educated. They had more schooling than we did, they didn't lose time with the war and so on. And they're the kind of men we need."

"Men who weren't in the war, you mean?"

"Young men, whether they were in the war or not. What's the use of having been in the war? No use at all. But schooling, that's of some use. Two of the new ones come from M.I.T., Schweickart and Scott. Schweickart is thirty, he got his degree with a thesis on stratospheric radiation. Scott is thirty-two, he got his degree with a thesis on interplanetary navigation. They're young, healthy, intelligent. They're what we need. Having studied interplanetary navigation is more use than having bombed children, don't you think?"

He looked me in the eye, smiled, and for a moment I could see again that extraordinary carved face. Then one of the secretaries knocked on the door, peered in and announced that Grissom was there.

"One moment," he replied curtly.

I stood up. Grissom who had taken away his hope. Grissom who had given him the papers of lost hope to sign.

"I'm in your way. I'd better go."

"You're not in the way at all. Sit down."

"Then I'll ask you one thing."

"Ask it."

"How long will this go on? This tug of war, I mean. This waiting that leads to disappointment every time."

"I don't know. We just go on waiting, and hoping it'll come."

"What?"

"A reply in the affirmative."

"And if it never comes?"

He was silent for a long time. Then he looked at his shoes. Then he looked at the wall-to-wall carpet, then he looked at the telephones, in a silence that knew the answer would never come. Then he spoke.

"If it never comes, if the yes never comes, I'll go on doing what I do now. Staying here."

"I understand."

"This is very interesting too, you know? And nobody raises a hand, nobody changes his job because of a little bad luck. Nobody left the program because Glenn went up instead of another."

"I understand."

I stood up again and this time he stood up too, wearily escorting me to the door. Oh, Father, we should never repeat something that's meant something to us, we should never. It hurts. It hurts to discover, over and over again, that you pay such a price for moral courage, doesn't it, Father? You pay more for it than for the rest, and at a certain point those who stand and watch must pay for it too. Which is why we always end by suffering, just looking on.

"So long, then. And thank you."

"So long."

"I hope I'll see you again."

"Certainly."

He opened the door for me. Outside the door stood Grissom. Small, suntanned and happy. He was joking with the secretaries and jumping around, full of mischief. He suddenly stopped when he heard the Chief's voice: solemn, resigned, containing just a hint of reproof.

"Come in, Grissom."

23.

Sally was listening like someone who knows it all already and so isn't surprised. With raised eyebrows she was shaking her head and her dangling earrings were going clink-clink. In the intervals between one clink-clink and the next she was drinking. She's a great drinker, Sally.

"I didn't tell you because I didn't want to influence you. Deke despises the role of a pathetic character. His self-respect won't allow him to accept a pathetic role, so you're wrong to compare him with your heroes. Your heroes no longer had any self-respect, Deke has twice as much as he did before. Your heroes were ex-heroes, Deke's beginning to be a hero now, he's beginning now to show he's the best of them all. I don't know how many others would have been able to bear defeat with Deke's courage. I don't know how many others would have been able to shut themselves in their office and sign permits for companions who are stealing their place. By God! For twenty-five years Deke made his living as a test pilot, risking his life in planes, and now that he could die gloriously they tie him to a chair so he can die of heartbreak. Remember when I told you that the Moon is a big industrial enterprise? Well, that's just it. More than a romantic adventure, more than political speculation, the Moon is a big industrial enterprise, and industrial enterprises have to bear the public in mind. If Deke went up and died of a heart attack, NASA would become unpopular and the firms that supply them would stop accepting orders. What firm would dare to defy the outcry of a pious public? You're building machines that kill them, they'd say. Every year dozens of test pilots die in America, but this doesn't prevent the manufacture of planes. If an astronaut were to die, the whole world would know about it, his death throes would be followed minute by minute, and the journey to the Moon would be compromised as a result. On account of money. Don't buy television sets from the Douglas Company, the North American Company, the Garrett Company, the firms that murdered Donald K. Slayton! Deke knows this and he's held back by disgust. My God! I'd give everything I've got so that he could go up to see what there is up there, even if it meant he could never come down again. I'd still be doing him a favor.

Bartender, give me another Martini, make it a double."

Sally drank it in silence. I was silent too and the only sound was the clink-clink of her dangling earrings. There was nobody in the restaurant yet. The restaurant was Flintlock Inn, a pretty place, full of guns and stags' heads, on Freeway 528, not far from NASA. But at that hour in the afternoon the place was deserted except for ourselves and the bartender, who also kept quiet.

"I'd certainly pay to know what there is up there, what it is they spend their lives regretting once they've been there." She shrugged. "Do you realize they grow old in the fear of not going back? What do you think Shepard's behavior indicates? Arrogance? No. It's anguish that he was the first to go and made such a short flight, too short for him to see what the others have seen. Gus shared the same anguish before he was picked for Project Gemini: in two years he'd turned into a little grandfather. When he heard he was going back he immediately grew younger, his eyes were bright again, his voice became vigorous. Obviously Deke follows Gus's work, and so day by day he watches his rejuvenation, Gus who has already had and is about to have once more something that Deke will never have, or probably never. He's aged, you say. He's turned gray, you mean. You should have known him the day the Seven were presented to the press. They came in one by one and each time it was like receiving a blow in the stomach. A woman shouted: 'Lord God, what a parade of stallions!' They were the flower of the flower of the population, the best of the best, and he was the best of them all. Listen, compared with what he was then, he looks like his own father."

Then Sally asked for her fifth Martini, and if you figure that the one before was a double, it was her sixth. She forgot about Deke Slayton and became more cheerful. The next day I was to see the new astronauts, some from the second and some from the third group. Waving her arms and her earrings about, Sally shouted that she wouldn't be in my shoes for anything in the world. The escort allotted to me wasn't a friend, the new astronauts didn't have the self-possession of the older ones, getting something good out of them would be difficult unless I found some Turtles among them. Turtles were people who knew how to give the cleanest answers to the dirtiest questions, people who were witty and civilized. So anyone who gave a dirty answer to a dirty question wasn't a Turtle, he was an Ass. And anyone who was an Ass wasn't a man. From which it followed that Turtles were fundamentally men. Naturally a woman could be a Turtle, but, as far as she knew, the only woman Turtle in America was herself, Sally Gates. Imperial Turtle, what's more, empowered to enroll Turtles, submit them to examination, sign their certificates. This was the certificate. Sally opened her handbag and took out a card printed: *International Association of Turtles*. And at the top of her voice she put me through the examination. Not that I consider myself a candidate for laurel crowns, but without immodesty I swear that no Turtle ever deserved to be enrolled more than I did that evening. Flintlock Inn had meanwhile become crowded with quiet fathers of families, chaste engaged couples, untouched virgins, and that demon of a Sally was now shouting questions that I report only with some reluctance.

"What are the things that a cow has four of and a woman only two?"

The sound of forks on plates ceased immediately, bursts of coughing broke the sudden silence, a Coca-Cola fell to the floor and exploded like a bomb.

"Legs, Sally."

"What is it that a woman does sitting down, a man standing up and a dog on three legs?"

This time the whole Flintlock Inn, stiffening with cold like the South Pole, seemed seized with broncho-pneumonia and bursts of coughing.

"Shaking hands, Sally."

And here I must stop because even Turtles have shame and the memory of Flintlock Inn still makes me uncomfortable. I will only add, without wishing to boast, that I gave clean answers to all Sally's provoking questions, fully understanding that her brutal game had a very serious meaning: it concealed a certain attitude adopted in the face of the most hypocritical conformism of the overwhelming majority of Asses. In a society where distinguishing oneself by being better or worse than others is a deadly sin and the most grim puritanism is the standard for living, screeching such things was something like yelling Viva la Libertad while Generalissimo Franco is passing by. In other words, the game was due not to vulgarity or arrogance but to heresy and courage. It was, in fact, necessary to make some effort not to give the reply of the Asses: that is, the first that came to mind. Finally, as a test it was far more ingenious than the ones the psychologists at San Antonio use, and too bad if its tenor was so oversimple and infantile. Truth doesn't need to be decadent in order to be true.

So Sally gave voice to shouts of glee and hastened to sign my certificate, to inform our audience that I was now an official Turtle and would remain one so long as I kept a secret: the Turtle password. The password could be shouted aloud if you wanted, but only in the presence of another Turtle, and to request it was easy. You only had to ask your suspect: Are you a Turtle? As for the rest, Sally added with a wicked emerald glance, it was clear that with my certificate I officially entered a world that I had formerly half-rejected: the first seven astronauts were all Turtles or Imperial Turtles, a great many scientists and NASA officials were Turtles too. O.K., and among the new astronauts I was to meet, which were Turtles?

"That's something you'll have to discover for yourself," said Sally. "And you won't find it easy."

And she was right.

———————

The bureaucrat who escorted me was so bureaucratic that I can't think of any other name to give him than Bureaucrat. The first thing he said was this: "I don't understand why anyone spends time and money coming here when they could write down their questions and have the answers sent back for the price of a few postage stamps." The second thing he said was: "Do you do your books with a dictaphone or a secretary?" The third thing he said was: "I'd die without television." I don't know how to describe him physically: he had two round very bureaucrat eyes, and a dark brown mustache, a bureaucrat mustache. He had a hoarse voice and a bow tie. His devotion to NASA was comparable to the devotion displayed by the Black Shirts for fascism. He took me straight to the astronauts' building and began giving me forms to fill up: who was I, whom did I represent, where did I come from, why had I come, at what time would I enter, at what time would I leave, whom did I wish to see, why, for how long, with whose permission? Now, let's be clear about this: I was used to filling in forms, Father. I doubt if there's an office in NASA without at least one form filled in by me lying around, with the most complete confession of my past and future. NASA knows absolutely everything about me: when NASA gives me a form, I grab it and write, write everything. I am so conditioned by such discipline that wherever I am, whatever I'm doing, if I come across a form stamped with NASA I automatically fill it in and sign it. But one form, not four forms. He wanted me to fill in four forms, God alone knows why. After a long argument we agreed on two, each with a carbon copy, so that still made four. So, apart from the fact that I didn't see why I had to fill in four forms, an argument broke out as to why I shouldn't put carbons with all the forms at the same time, a procedure which to me seemed logical but to him seemed illegal. When this argument had ended—in my defeat, needless to say—he read the forms and discovered that to the question "Whom do you represent?" I had answered "Myself." And he was angry. What? he said. It wasn't possible for me to represent myself, everyone represents someone else, nobody represents himself, anyone who represents himself is an anarchist, a heretic. He grew even more angry and not even the policeman was able to calm him by saying I must be joking. To calm him down, I had to fill in all the forms again, and this time without carbon paper because he'd discovered that the carbon copies didn't come out so well, and declaring that I represented my publisher, who, poor thing, was a completely innocent party. After this he pushed me into an elevator and drove me into the Sanctum Sanctorum of the new astronauts, which is a very long corridor with a lot of doors, each opening into the office of a new astronaut. Each door is generally wide open so that you can see the astronaut sitting at his desk surrounded by papers and pencils—say about twenty pencils to each astronaut. Why the astronauts should have so many pencils no one has been able to explain to me: at all events they do, and I've discovered something fantastic, they even keep pencils in their track suits, those hard-writing intellectuals. There are six pencils in the track suit and they are slotted two by two in a divided pocket sewn on the left forearm so that they are handy. But why do they have to be handy? For scratching their backs? You certainly don't need pencils to do somersaults, do you, Father? I once said as much to Paul Haney and I added: Why don't you change the pocket from the forearm to the back so that the pencils will be handy for back-scratching and so come in useful at last? But he replied that pencils are for writing with and not for back-scratching, and did not even laugh too much.

In the corridor where the new astronauts have their offices there is also the office of the Master of Ceremonies, who gives you permission to speak with them. This Master of Ceremonies has a Christian name and a surname: I am calling him just Master of Ceremonies out of respect for his family and his ancestors. At first sight he looks harmless enough, indeed nice. He has a soft buttery voice and he himself looks like a huge ball of butter, he's so fat, oily and mellifluous. He waves his buttery hands and pays you buttery compliments and your first instinct is to wish you were an egg so as to fry inside him and then slide down into his great stomach and nourish him and make him fatter. Your second instinct is to come to blows with him, a justice you forgo because you want to see the astronauts and you know that your blows would sink ineffectually into the butter and only make your hands greasy. As a matter of fact, the Master of Ceremonies was wicked. Not consciously wicked, though: he was unaware that he was wicked and thought he was generous, well-mannered and a good servant in the Cause of the Journey to the Moon. In some respects he resembled children who tear the legs off ants because they think ants don't feel pain. The Master of Ceremonies was even quite touching in his obtuseness. This might seem a contradiction, Father, to you, but wicked people who aren't aware that they're wicked are in my view touching. For the bare two hours that had been conceded to me for interviewing the astronauts the Master of Ceremonies had selected no less than eight astronauts: ten minutes each.

"Eight?"

"Yes."

"But it's extremely difficult to interview a person, it's a reciprocal examination, it's a great strain on one's attention and one's nerves. It isn't possible to interview eight people one after the other!"

"Why?"

"What do you mean, why? I just told you why. And then—forgive me, but what can you ask a person in ten minutes? How are you and what time is it and that's all."

"You can tell a life story in ten minutes."

"You may be able to tell yours; if so, you can't have much to say. A normal person can't tell his life story in ten minutes, he can fill in a questionnaire, sir."

"We'll make it eleven minutes."

"What do you mean, eleven minutes! I don't know these astronauts, and I have to try and understand them more than question them. Listen to me, please!"

"Twelve minutes, no more."

"Look, sir, I've come from the other side of the world to understand these astronauts. Europe's a long way away, sir. Sir, I'm here to write a book, not a Gallup poll. Sir—"

"Twelve minutes is the most I can give you. Twelve times eight makes ninety-six, a hundred and twenty less ninety-six leaves twenty-four, twenty-four divided by eight leaves three: so that leaves only three minutes for introductions."

"What are you talking about! What are these calculations? Sir, I haven't asked to see eight astronauts. Let's meet each other halfway: instead of eight you give me only four, and with each of the four, leaving out the introductions, I'll talk for half an hour. That suit you?"

"Half an hour! And only four? Miss, four aren't enough."

"They might not be enough for you, they're enough for me."

"Four can't give you an exact picture of the situation!"

"To hell with the exact picture of the situation."

"Eight."

"Four."

"Eight."

"Five."

"Eight."

"Six."

"Eight."

"All right, all right! Eight."

"It's pleasant to meet such a reasonable woman: women are so seldom reasonable, you know that? Listen, as a token of my admiration I'll get you the one who rides a bicycle. Didn't you ask to talk to an astronaut who rides a bicycle?"

"Yes, sir. I wanted to meet an astronaut who rides a bicycle."

"There. Freeman rides a bicycle. He rides a bicycle, doesn't he?" he asked the Bureaucrat.

"Yes, he rides a bicycle," the Bureaucrat sniggered.

"There. For the one who rides a bicycle I'll give you a full fifteen minutes. Pleased?"

"Delighted."

"But I must remind you that in everything and for everything you must abide by your escort."

"Yes, sir."

"When he says enough, it's enough."

"Yes, sir."

"Here's the material that will furnish you with an exact picture of the situation."

"Yes, sir."

And he handed me twenty-two sheets, from which it appeared that: (1) The new astronauts were all officers in the Navy or the Air Force except for one civilian in the second group and the two M.I.T. graduates in the third group. (2) The new astronauts were all married except for one, Clifton Williams, who was, however, to be married shortly. (3) The new astronauts were all fathers with an average of two or three children each, which made a total of fifty-two new astronauts' children, a truly impressive figure. (4) The vast majority of the new astronauts had blue eyes and fair hair. To be exact: fourteen had fair hair and blue eyes, four had brown hair and blue eyes, three had black hair and black eyes, one had red hair and green eyes. (5) None of them was a Negro. But this is an old argument that it's useless to put to space men. I've tried it several times, and with the most disconcerting candor they reply that no Negro has ever passed the examination, just as no woman has ever passed the examination, however NASA makes no discriminations of race or sex, etcetera, etcetera, amen. Besides, the Russians don't have any yellow-skinned or black-skinned astronauts either. The Union of Soviet Socialist Republics contains men of every color, just as the United States of America does, but Soviet astronauts are strictly white. Being white seems to be an almost indispensable requisite for going to the Moon, which is black. And, thinking these thoughts, I was ready to meet my eight. Better, I wasn't ready in the least. I was very angry and would have given a lot to send them all to hell. But I met Theodore, and everything changed.

Because Theodore, you see, was a poet. How a poet had managed to wind up as an astronaut I don't understand. Far less can I understand how he came to be accepted by NASA, or born in America. What use has technology for a poet? What place is there for him? The most it can allow is a potential Saint-Exupéry like Schirra, dammed by the dikes of his rationalism, his discipline. A poet today is in every sense a danger. You send him to the Moon to take rock samples, for example, and he stands lost in wonder in front of a ruby, using up his oxygen supplies. You send him to Mars to make a technical report and he comes back with a sonnet that goes: "Soft silver hills, how I recall the sight / The woods were blue, and quivering in the night / A sky of green did put its emeralds pale / Upon the hilltops, and the air was light / The bright air lighter than a bridal veil . . ." For Christ's sake, what the hell does that mean, air that was lighter than a bridal veil! Can't you just tell us what's the percentage of hydrogen? Goddam it, did you find water on Mars or didn't you? And Theodore: "Thin diamonds of ice / living tears of joy / shone in the crimson sun . . ." I don't know, I don't know. There are two possibilities: either NASA wanted to have some fun or they didn't realize what a jewel they had. And so it is clear, I think, Father, that I nurtured unbounded admiration, wild gratitude toward Theodore, that nobody to me was worth more than Theodore, not even the ones I liked best, the funny being I'll call my brother for instance, my brother is like myself, but Theodore was what I'd have liked to be and am not: purity, simplicity, faith. You know it, Father, when I see a thing it either makes me laugh or it makes me cry, I get out of it either something funny or something ugly: he always got something beautiful. That's why I shall never forget Theodore, astronaut by mistake, that's why I shall never sufficiently lament having found him and then immediately lost him, like a mirage. Theodore Freeman, born in Haverford, Pennsylvania, on February 18, 1930, son of John Freeman, farmer; graduate in aeronautical engineering from the University of Michigan; captain in the United States Air Force; husband of a girl called Faith and father of a little girl also called Faith . . .

He came in through that door, Theodore, and at first sight you wouldn't have given two cents for him; you'd have said he was one of those awkward country boys who make the mistake of coming to the city and finish up as porters or window cleaners or in other heavy jobs. His body was long, slender. He was almost bald, so he looked much older than his thirty-four years. As for his face, he had a little face with two surprised little eyes and a little smile in the middle, very shy. His hands were shy too and he never knew what to do with them and would occupy them scratching his nose, touching an ear, putting them in his pockets, grasping the chair as if it were about to fall down. His voice was faint, unharmonious, and he would blush when he tore it out of his throat. He spoke without full periods or commas, I'm putting a few periods and commas in what he said, but there weren't any. Degrees, university, Naval Academy, many trips to Europe, the rank of captain, it had all passed over him without grazing his peasant nature that stood out intact, healthy, paradoxical, incredible, like a poppy on an asphalt road. I often wonder how he managed in the bourgeois atmosphere that engulfed him, whether they teased him, and I didn't find an answer. What a strange country America is! At all events, such things were of no importance in Theodore. What was important about Theodore was what he said, felt, thought. Do you mind, Father, if I leave out the rest and reduce it all to the sound track?

"I'm very happy to meet you, Mr. Freeman, because—"

"Oh, not Mr. Freeman! Theodore. My name's Theodore!"

"I'm very happy to meet you, Theodore, because they've told me that you ride a bicycle and an astronaut who rides a bicycle is uncommon. Do you really ride one?"

"Oh, yes! I love riding a bicycle, on a bicycle you're right in the open and you can feel the wind on your face, not a savage screaming wind, a gentle caressing wind and then you smell real scents not the stench of gas but real scents and then you have time to look at the trees the clouds the squirrels everything. These are the things I like, the wind whistling, trees passing slowly, birds squirrels, you see I'm not the kind to stay shut up watching TV I only watch TV on Fridays when Danny Kaye's on the other evenings I take my bicycle and go for a ride. I go out on my bicycle every evening, I take Faith and little Faith with me too and maybe they grumble I don't want to Daddy I don't want to Theodore but I say come on, it does you good to go out on the bicycle! And then I go out on my bicycle in the morning at half past six or seven o'clock when it's cool and the sky is still clean, later it gets dirty, I go for five miles to Nassau Bay where there are geese I love geese so much, the only trouble is I have to ride along the freeway which is the only road and from time to time a car passes me and one day what'll happen is that the cars will sweep me aside and so I'll die goodbye Moon I even come to the office on my bicycle yes I'm the only one who comes by bicycle. What did you say? No, they don't tease me, on the contrary they keep saying they should do it too but they don't I can't understand why people in America don't ride bicycles any more, I went to Norway and the people there ride bicycles and the people in Denmark ride bicycles, here they don't, but I don't see the need for all this speed and hurry, up in the air I can understand it but on the ground!"

"Listen, Theodore: how do you explain this business of bicycles on the one hand and spacecraft on the other? How is it that you can like the world up there if you like it so much on Earth?"

"Ah, I've thought about that and I've decided it must be because I grew up in Delaware, when I was a baby my family moved from Pennsylvania to Delaware which is so ugly. But ugly, flat, so as a child I looked at all that ugliness and said who knows if it mightn't look a bit less ugly if you saw it from above then one day when I was six I said Father will you take me in an airplane? So then my father saved some money and took me up in an airplane and I realized that Delaware wasn't ugly but beautiful when you looked down on it from high above. So what I say is things seen from the ground are often very ugly, seen from high above they're very much less ugly and sometimes they aren't ugly at all and sometimes they're beautiful. What I say is the world is more or less like Delaware, an ugly great world, but when you see it from above it isn't ugly and when you see it from far away it's very beautiful, let me give you an example. I once went to Holland and as soon as I got to Amsterdam I ran to see La Ronde because I like

Rembrandt so much and all my life I had wanted to see La Ronde. I went in there like a shot I so much wanted to see that painting and I tore across the room right up to it if there hadn't been a carpet I'd have skidded and pushed my nose right through the painting and . . . I felt terrible because when I was right on top of it it wasn't as beautiful as I'd thought, neither the light nor the colors were as beautiful as I'd thought, it was a disappointment and in my disappointment I started walking backwards and farther backwards and then something happened. What happened was that as I walked backwards the picture became more and more beautiful it was distance that made it beautiful, until I reached the far end of the room my back to the wall at the furthest point from the painting, and the painting then was very beautiful it acquired all its light and its colors again. The world seen from far away is more beautiful and that's why I fly, and also because there are beautiful things in the world things like La Ronde and I fly to get there quickly to see them. So I think—"

"Nine minutes," said the Bureaucrat.

"What?" said Theodore.

"Nothing," I said. "Please go on."

"I think a lot of folks started flying for the same reason, maybe they don't realize it because they haven't stopped to think about it but that's the reason, as for the Moon, you see while it's true that I love the Earth so I love the leaves and the birds and the wind that doesn't mean that beauty is always green, always full of movement and sound, the desert is yellow but it's beautiful just the same, mountains are silent but they're beautiful just the same, and when they say we will find that the Moon is ugly I say why ugly? Because it's just desert they say because it's just rock and I answer so what? I've been in the Mojave Desert and everyone says the Mojave is ugly, but I thought it was very beautiful. I often go to White Sands for launchings and everyone says White Sands is ugly but I think it's very beautiful. But it's dead they say, there's not a living thing, well I say so long as there's a living person looking at it then it isn't dead any more. And then there are the rockets that leave from White Sands and the rockets are alive and you can't say there isn't a living thing in White Sands. But the Moon's a sad place because only solitude dwells there and nothing else they say, and I reply that solitude is beautiful, silence is beautiful, sadness often goes with company and noise. My father is always alone but he's happy, he's always silent but he's happy."

"Tell me about your father, Theodore."

"My father is a carpenter in winter and a farmer in summer, he never talks and he never takes any notice of other folks' affairs, he lives with my brother who's also a carpenter in winter and a farmer in summer. My family owns a farm and if I go home in the summer I have to work on the farm too which is an old friend anyway because I've known it for so long, I plowed it and sowed it until I was fifteen. Until I was fifteen I was just a farm boy. Like my father I had spent very little time at school, but when I was fifteen I realized that you didn't learn much about things being a farmhand and I said so to my father and my father said you learn about things by reading. So I began to read a great deal and my father took me out of the fields and sent me to school where I did very well. The Senator from Delaware heard that I was good at school, that I used to read a lot and that my father had taken me out of the fields, so he sent for my father and said that if he wanted I could go and study at the Naval Academy with no fees to pay as long as I went on getting such good marks. My father replied it's if my son wants to."

"Fourteen minutes," said the Bureaucrat.

"What?" said Theodore.

"Nothing," said I. "Please go on. Tell me how you became an astronaut."

"Before I became an astronaut I became a pilot: this is what I was going to say when he interrupted me. I wanted to fly airplanes nothing else but the Senator from Delaware explained that the Naval Academy would also get me this, flying airplanes, because the Navy has aircraft carriers. So I went to the Naval Academy then to the university and I became an aeronautical engineer, straight after that I was a test pilot. I was test pilot at Edwards Base in California where everyone wanted to be astronauts incredible how many people want to be astronauts they all put in their applications to become astronauts. I did too for the simple reason the others were doing so but I didn't expect anything, it was like taking a ticket in a lottery, my wife who's a nice cheerful girl who laughs even if she's sad joked Theodore do you want to go the Moon Theodore? I used to joke about it with her but to my great surprise they sent for me to do the examinations at San Antonio and to my great surprise I did well in them, perhaps I did well because I was having fun. I always have fun learning about things and the less I know the more I have the urge to find out a little about them, painting for example, medicine for example and the medical examinations at San Antonio were truly fantastic. I did nothing but ask questions trying to learn, and I had a whale of a time and the doctors kept saying that if I'd studied medicine I'd be a good doctor and that was the only time I've ever regretted anything: doesn't healing people really mean chasing away what's ugly in order to find what's beautiful?"

"Eighteen minutes!" cried the Bureaucrat.

"What?" said Theodore.

"Nothing," I said. "Please go on."

"I didn't have as much fun with the psychological tests. Just think, they asked me what shape an apple is and I kept wanting to laugh because if they asked my father what shape an apple is he'd come to blows with whoever asked him, indeed for a moment I was tempted to do that very thing, this fellow's teasing me I said because I come from Delaware, however I calmed down and told him look in my village in Delaware an apple is round: at which he got annoyed and grumbled that apples are round in any place. Then he asked me what I saw on the sheet of paper he was holding, the paper was blank, I shut my eyes and said I could see a field of grain covered with snow but the snow would melt in the sun and the sun would warm the tender green grain and as it warmed the grain would grow become tougher and stronger, but he interrupted me and said it was a blank sheet of paper and nothing else. He seemed to me more irritated on account of the paper than about the apple, now he'll fail me I thought, but they didn't fail me and here I am."

"Stop!" said the Bureaucrat.

"What's he saying?" Theodore exclaimed.

"He's saying stop," I whispered. "Pity."

"A real pity I liked talking to you we don't have many opportunities to talk in here, I like the way you listen you have a way of listening that makes one feel better and—"

"Stop! Stop! Stop!"

"—and if it's not troubling you I'd like to ask you a favor—"

"Stop! Stop! Stop!"

"—to give my greetings to a friend, an Italian pilot Italo Tonati he's called, I was his instructor at Edwards Base—"

"Stop! Stop! Stop!"

"—tell him I remember him and wish him all the best—"

"Stop! Stop! Stop!"

"Here this is his address."

"All right, Theodore."

"You really will?"

"I really will. So long then, Theodore."

"So long. And thanks, eh? Thanks a lot."

It never even crossed his mind that I was the one to thank him and that it grieved me to see him go. Because this is the ugly thing about the world, Father. Suddenly, in the darkness, you find a Theodore and then immediately you lose him. Five months later Theodore died. His plane blew up, he was flying, and he died. Then a year after, you understand, Father, a year after, Tonati died too. In the same way, in Paris. His plane blew up, he was flying, and he died.

24.

It was after Theodore left that I realized the way in which the business was run. Like this. The meetings took place in a little room next to the office of the Master of Ceremonies. Inside the little room there were three chairs, a table, a poster of the Saturn rocket and the slogan GOING TO THE SKY. Or something like that. I was underneath the GOING TO THE SKY and the Bureaucrat was a little further over. Suddenly the door would open and the Master of Ceremonies would enter with an astronaut, introduce him to me, listing his flight hours, the number of his children, his infinite virtues. I would listen with an idiotic expression and say: "Oh! Oh! Oh!" Then the Master of Ceremonies would introduce me to the astronaut, listing the divine masterpieces I'd written, the glorious exploits I had performed, the fantastic excess of merit I concealed. The astronaut would listen with an equally idiotic expression and say: "Oh! Oh! Oh!" Then the Master of Ceremonies would raise his fat finger, as if he were joining us in matrimony, and threateningly and mellifluously squawk: "Eleven minutes! No longer!" and take himself off with his enormous behind, leaving us in embarrassment: in spite of the presence of the Bureaucrat there was something obscene, unhealthy, about the ritual. Then I would sit down and the astronaut would sit down. I would look at him, he would look at me. I would be silent, he would be silent. And then we would offer each other a cigarette, while the cigarettes collided and broke. Or we would go through the ceremony of lighting them, finally burning our fingers. This would help. Are you hurt? No, it doesn't matter—just to say something, even shyly, until the ice was broken. But when the ice was broken, the Bureaucrat would leap to his feet and cry: "Eleven minutes! Eleven minutes!" At the same moment, as if by magic, the door would open, the Master of Ceremonies would come in again with another astronaut, and everything would begin again. It happened this way six times, Father. Not seven because the performance changed at the end, thanks to my brother. Nevertheless six are quite a few, don't you think? And this must be why I can't tell you much about them, apart from the fact that most of them were bald and you'd have thought they were older than they were. If they weren't bald, they spoke as if they were. If they didn't speak as if they were, there always came the moment when they reacted like bald men. In any case, they were old. So when I ask myself what the new astronauts are like, I answer they're old. In a land where youth is a pagan and cruel cult, the representatives of youth are old.

Why I don't know. To start with, I thought it was because from the age of twenty they were all married with offspring: a family is wearing, it kills any laughter. Then I thought it must be because they are all ex-Army and the Army atmosphere is an atmosphere that could turn a newborn baby gray. One day, though, I saw the two civilians who had graduated from M.I.T., aged thirty and thirty-one, and they both looked nearer forty. Finally I thought it must be because the discipline, the responsibility, the exhausting nature of their work bled them of all the bloom of youth. But this won't do either. My adopted brother is also an astronaut, is also ex-Army, and has no less than four children, and yet he looks like a boy. Why? I don't know. Do you know, Chaffee? Do you know, Gordon? Do you know, Bean? Do you know, Armstrong? Do you know, White? Do you know, Cernan? No, you don't know. I mean you don't understand what kind of oldness I am speaking of, what kind of aging, of withering. Isn't that why you're shaking your heads? Dammit, I see. You're shaking your heads because you say I'm wrong. All right, I'm wrong: eleven minutes aren't much in which to get at the truth, and when I knew you better I even saw some hair on your bald heads, some laughs among your wrinkles, your damned solemnity. It doesn't change a thing for me. What do you say? That I'm wrong just the same? All right, let's both read what you said to me and then we'll decide whether I'm wrong. Or rather, we decide nothing. Let's leave things as they stand, remembering that this is what I think. And let's go back to my journal, Father.

The first old man was the youngest of the astronauts. He was twenty-nine and physically looked eighteen. Small, cute, he looked like a resurrected James Dean: the same face, the same smile, it broke your heart to think they would shut him inside that cone and send him up like an innocent puppy. I looked at him and I thought: What do you know about interstellar tempests and radioactive belts? What are you doing among the grown-ups? Do you play the tambourine? Are you the flag-bearer? Run, child, run! His skin was smooth, his voice was childlike.

His name was Roger Chaffee: they had picked him with the third group. He was born at Grand Rapids, Michigan, and he was a lieutenant in the Navy. We sat down, coughed, lit cigarettes for each other. Sound track:

"I imagine you must be very excited at the idea of going to the Moon, Lieutenant."

"Not in the slightest. I'll go, there's no doubt about it. But I'm not bothered by impatience or curiosity. For me the Moon is just a way of serving my country and the first journey to the Moon simply means demonstrating the technological resources NASA and my country have at their disposal for reaching the Moon. Anything else is just fantasy. Adults don't live by fantasy."

"What! Doesn't it mean anything to you to land on the Moon?"

"To set foot on it, you mean?"

"Yes."

"From the technical point of view the actual landing is very interesting inasmuch as it poses a number of problems that aren't easily solvable. But I wouldn't feel put out if I had the job of staying in orbit in the Apollo capsule instead of making the landing in the LEM. Ours is a collective effort and I just play my part in it."

"Lieutenant, why did you become an astronaut?"

"For the same reason that a good driver wants to race in a Ferrari. A pilot automatically wants to become an astronaut, providing he has the requisites. I had them, starting with age. For the third group you had to be born not before July 1, 1929, and not later than July 1, 1935. I was born in February 1935. I think I hardly need to add that my intention in joining the program was to make myself useful to my country."

"The Moon isn't something that concerns only the United States of America, Lieutenant."

"I'm a patriot."

"So I see."

"Yes."

"Well, you must have been very enthusiastic when you heard there was a space program."

"Not in the slightest. Anyone who had anything to do with aeronautical engineering knew that it was just a matter of time, and I'd been studying aeronautical engineering since I was sixteen. Why did I study it? Certainly not for romantic reasons, I've never had any dreams about seeing the Moon and all that stuff, like I said before."

"Lieutenant, what do you think of imagination?"

"Imagination is necessary in order to be successful and in order to do any job. Without imagination you can't even invent a machine. But imagination must be held in check by a consideration of what is logical and useful, otherwise it becomes a childish instrument. And none of us are children."

"Lieutenant, how did you get on in the San Antonio exams?"

"Very well. The physical tests were no problem: I have an excellent organism. I can stand the centrifuge up to eighteen G, for example. I've seen people, even some of my companions, really upset by the centrifuge—people who vomit and so on. All I get is a feeling of pressure on my stomach. As for the psychological tests, they went equally well because I wasn't worried. It takes a lot to worry me."

"Did they show you the all-white photograph too?"

"Yes, why?"

"What did you answer?"

"Nothing. There was nothing to say. They showed me this white sheet of paper and told me to make up a story about it. I told them I couldn't make up a story because it was just a blank sheet of paper and nothing else. They were very pleased. Others said it was a snowstorm, a wall covered with whitewash, and nonsense like that. For me it was just a blank sheet of paper and nothing else. After that they showed me a pornographic photograph, really pornographic, and asked me to make up a story about it. I suppose they wanted to see if I had a morbid imagination, stuff like that. I told them I couldn't make up a story because it was just a pornographic photograph and that was all."

"Lieutenant, do you like reading?"

But I'd like to ask him: do you enjoy Mickey Mouse? More than that actor, I realized, more than a tambourine player, a flag-bearer, he made me think of Mickey Mouse when he fights for survival and dignity. You like Mickey Mouse, don't you, Father? You say that he who doesn't appreciate Mickey Mouse doesn't appreciate the struggle for life.

"Yes. But I don't have time. At my age there's no time for reading, there's too much to do. When I read, I read whatever comes to hand: anything from comics to history books. Never novels, of course."

"Why never novels, of course?"

"They don't interest me because they have nothing to do with reality. History books are about reality. One book I'm trying to get through is *The History of America:* full of information. I like it. Full of facts."

"Lieutenant, how do you spend your Sundays?"

"On Sunday I go to church. I'm a practicing Presbyterian. Then I go home to play with my children and my dogs. I have two children, a boy of six and a girl of three. Sometimes I go to the lake and do some waterskiing to keep myself in trim. I have a rowboat too, to keep myself in trim. Sunday is a day I use for keeping myself in trim. When I'm not taking exercise I study. Basically I use Sunday for studying. Geology especially. Geology is my specialty."

"Stop!" said the Bureaucrat.

"But we've barely had eleven minutes," I protested.

"The eleven minutes start from the moment they arrive," said the Bureaucrat. "What else do you want to know? Hasn't he told you everything? Or are we going to start wasting time again like we did with Freeman?"

Lieutenant Roger Chaffee stood up to indicate that he was in full agreement with the Bureaucrat. He held out his hand, a fragile delicate hand, and gave me his James Dean smile. His little teeth looked like milk teeth. He said so long, went out, small, slender, obedient, it broke your heart to think they would shut him inside that cone and send him up, like an innocent puppy. Innocent? As he went through the door I heard him grumbling: "Gee, what a bore. I hate wasting time." And I felt it would not be necessary to ask him if he was a Turtle. Probably he didn't even know about James Dean and Mickey Mouse.

———

The second old man was thirty-five years old and had six children. He was short and thick-set, with black eyes and black hair, his brow wrinkled by a thousand repressed curses. I liked him and I felt I'd seen him before because he belonged to a type that had been so familiar to me in my youth: the partisan handyman, taciturn, determined, discontented: remember Berto, Father? You always used to say that Berto could do anything except make a kite. He could destroy a bridge single-handed, cut six telephone lines on the same day, disarm a German patrol and then get them to fight on our side to win our war, and it seemed impossible to me that Berto could do such difficult things and yet not be able to make a kite, so one day, remember, I asked him: "Berto, will you make me a kite?" And Berto answered, "Baby, while others were learning to make kites I was learning to make war, be quiet." It was the only time Berto ever refused to do anything for me, remember? Because Berto was very obedient and agreeable; you'd tell him to do something and he'd do it without thinking twice, and with a big smile. Well: the second old man was like him. His name was Richard Gordon, they'd picked him with the third group like the other one, and he was a lieutenant commander in the Navy. He talked jerkily, slowly, sparingly, and kept his voice down. I liked him a lot, apart from that gravity, untouched by that big smile. I sat down.

"Tell me whatever you like, sir. Whatever you think is important or whatever you like best."

"My father was a woodcutter. Americans aren't all rich like Europeans think they are. My father was poor. We were all poor. In the summer I used to work on my uncle's farm. My uncle wasn't poor, he had a farm. For three years I also worked as errand boy in a drugstore. Delivering parcels. Cleaning the floor. Then I went to the university to study chemistry. But I went on working because I needed the money. To spend on girls and that kind of thing. My father couldn't spare me any money for girls. I studied chemistry at the state university, then I joined the Navy."

"Why did you choose to become an astronaut?"

"I didn't choose anything. They did the choosing. I really hadn't thought of being an astronaut. I let myself be influenced. I liked flying, so I joined the Navy. Aircraft carriers. In the Navy they made me a jet test pilot. A lot of test pilots were applying to be astronauts. I let myself be influenced. And I applied too. I'm easily influenced. They tell me to do something and I do it. That's all. They accepted me."

"It's a fine career, an exceptional career."

"You might think so."

"What don't you like about it?"

"One thing. Not being able to read any more, not being able to listen to operas any more. I used to read a lot. Mainly the classics. Now I've stopped. I can't manage it. I don't have the time, I don't have the urge. And this depresses me. I say to myself: If only I had read more before. I'll always have a gap. A gap inside. Like operas. I always used to go and listen to operas, Verdi, Puccini. When my ship was cruising in the Mediterranean, for example. When I got to Naples or Genoa. By the time the ship was in port I was already in the theater. And every evening I went back to the theater. Every evening till the ship sailed again. It was beautiful. It was long ago. I've given it up."

"Why have you given it up?"

"Because we're technicians. Either you're a technician or you're not."

"What do you mean *we?*"

"We. All of us. The team."

"Oh, forget the team!"

"I can't. I must not. We're a team. What do you have against teams?"

"Look, everything. Never mind."

"O.K. Let's go on."

"And why did you become a technician?"

"I was good at mathematics and chemistry. They started saying I should study mathematics and chemistry. In America this kind of thing's a cult. Everyone'll tell you to study mathematics and chemistry, hardly ever music and literature. Maybe that's right. We're advancing so quickly and we need mathematics and chemistry. We need technology, not poetry. I have two brothers and two sisters. One of my two brothers works for Boeing Aircraft in Seattle, the other's in another aeronautical firm. One of my sisters is married to a technician, the other teaches chemistry. My elder daughter is twelve. She wants to study engineering. Father, she asked me, is it a good idea for me to study engineering? I said yes."

"And operas? And the classics?"

"Too bad."

"What do you mean, too bad? You said you were sorry."

"Yes, but I made my choice."

"You said you were influenced."

"Yes. But now I'm in it, and nobody's forcing me to stay in it. I could leave tomorrow morning, but I'm not. I want to stay here. This is no longer a time for laughing, for amusing oneself. It's time to work. Great responsibilities lie ahead for us. And, good Lord . . ."

"You religious?"

"Sure I am, I'm a Catholic. I go to Mass on Sundays, and I confess, I take Holy Communion, as a good Catholic should. I grew up like that and it fits me all right, thank God. Don't you thank God?"

"No. For what?"

"For everything. For the life that He gave you, the food that He gives you, that He'll give you until He calls you to Him."

Gee! Father!

"Are you always so serious?"

"I guess so."

"Don't you ever laugh?"

"Oh, yes! Sometimes."

He laughed a laugh that was like the shooting of Berto's machine gun: loud and dry. His eyes shone a direct glance, a rifle barrel. The right guy to have had with us at that time, Father, yet . . . Can one live without making a kite?

"And don't you get bored?"

"No, I don't get bored. I don't have time to get bored. Who has time to get bored in here? We have to learn to renounce things. We have to learn to resign ourselves."

"At your age?"

"I'm old."

"Thirty-five, old?!"

"Ten minutes!" said the Bureacrat. "Hurry up!"

"Goodbye, then, Mr. Gordon."

"Goodbye. It's been interesting. Nothing else you want to ask?"

"Yes, one thing. Are you a—"

"Eleven minutes!" cried the Bureaucrat. "Eleven minutes."

So he jumped to attention, automatically, from discipline, despite that big smile, turned on his heel and left. Without leaving me time to finish my question, to ask him for a kite.

The third old man was thirty-four and looked like John Glenn's young brother: the same freckles, the same fair coloring, the same ease, he had even been born in Ohio. Nevertheless certain things distinguished him from John Glenn—his lack of vivacity, his diplomacy and his shoulders that were extraordinarily rounded for such a strong physique. His mouth was ironical, but an irony full of caution. His voice was quiet, his movements economical. His name was Neil Armstrong and they'd picked him with the second group. The most interesting piece of information about him, for me, was that he didn't have a service background. The only astronaut civilian I was to meet. And perhaps because of this he entered like someone visiting the dentist. And I felt indeed like a dentist, I was tempted to ask: Is it a molar that hurts or a canine? I would not have been at all surprised if he had answered: "No, Doctor, it's an incisor." Sound track:

"What a fine thing, Mr. Armstrong! You're not from the service!"

"I came from NASA, where I was an electronics engineer and a jet test pilot. It isn't so different. I mean, I've got just as much discipline as the others and discipline is the main thing you need if you're going into space. Besides, the reason they pick servicemen isn't because they're more suitable than civilians; they pick them because they've got them all neatly packaged and pre-selected so it's easier to dig up the right man. You know everything about a serviceman, including how far you can trust him. But they knew everything about me too: I've been with NASA for several years."

"However, becoming an astronaut must have given you great joy."

"I wouldn't know. Let me think. . . ."

"Haven't you thought about it before?"

"To me it was simply being transferred from one office to another. I was in one office and they moved me into this one. Well, yes, I suppose I was pleased. It's always nice to gain in status. But I don't have any personal ambition. My one ambition is to contribute to the success of this program. I'm no romantic."

"Do you mean you don't have a taste for adventure?"

"For heaven's sake, I loathe danger, especially if it's useless; danger is the most irritating aspect of our job. How can a perfectly normal technological fact be turned into adventure? And why should steering a spacecraft be risking your life? It would be as illogical as risking your life when you use an electric mixer to make yourself a milkshake. There should be nothing dangerous about making a milkshake and there should be nothing dangerous about steering a spacecraft. Once you've granted this concept, you no longer think in terms of adventure, the urge to go up just for the sake of going up . . ."

I observed his mouth. Perhaps not the molar, nor the canine, nor the incisor. It was probably the wisdom tooth.

"Mr. Armstrong, I know somebody who would go up even if he knew he wouldn't come back. Just for the urge to go up."

"Among us astronauts?"

"Among you astronauts."

"I rule him out. If you knew him, he'd be a boy, not an adult."

"He's an adult, Mr. Armstrong."

"But who?"

"It doesn't matter. Let's talk about you. Leaving aside the milkshake, I suppose you'd be sorry not to go up."

"Yes, but I wouldn't get sick about it. I don't understand the ones who are so anxious to be the first. It's all nonsense, kid stuff, just romanticism unworthy of our rational age. I rule out the possibility of agreeing to go up if I thought I might not come back: unless it were technically indispensable. I mean, testing a jet is dangerous but technically indispensable. Dying in space or on the Moon is not technically indispensable and consequently if I had to choose between death while testing a jet and death on the Moon, I'd choose death while testing a jet. Wouldn't you?"

No, it wasn't the wisdom tooth that hurt. That one was healthy, so healthy as to be too healthy. It was something else, Father, a lack of pain, I would say, a good cry such as children have when they want the Moon, no matter if they have to die to get the Moon, that exquisite infancy which stays in us, as a gift, even when we are adults with all our teeth, our prudence.

"No. Confronted with such a dilemma, I'd unhesitatingly choose to die on the Moon: at least I'd get a look at the Moon."

"Kid stuff. Nonsense. Die on the Moon! To get a look at the Moon! If it were a matter of staying there for a year or two . . . maybe . . . I don't know. No, no, it would still be too high a price to pay: because it's senseless."

"Did you spend all your young years at NASA, Mr. Armstrong?"

"I spent them traveling: Europe, Asia, South America. So I saw what there was to see, I understood what there was to understand, and here I am."

"Were you in the war, Mr. Armstrong?"

"Sure I was. In Korea. Seventy-eight combat missions. I'd be lying if I said they'd done me any good."

"Do you have any children, Mr. Armstrong?"

"Sure. One seven and one two. How could I not have children at my age?"

"Ten minutes," said the Bureaucrat. "Hurry!"

He stood up. "I'd better say goodbye. I have to go in the centrifuge."

"I don't envy you, Mr. Armstrong."

"Yes, it's very disagreeable: perhaps the thing I hate most. But indispensable."

"Time's up! Stop!"

"Goodbye."

"Goodbye."

The fourth old man was thirty-two and completely bald. Indeed, I remember feeling quite put out as I stared at him: it stuck in my throat that a man of only thirty-two should have a skull as smooth as a ball of ivory. But his ears saved him: they were very comical, enormous, more like the ailerons of a plane than ears. You'd no sooner see that skull of his than you saw the ears and it made you feel better, made you think: If God gave a man ears like that, he can't be deaf and anyone who isn't deaf won't talk like Neil Armstrong. Apart from the ears, his face also saved him: jovial, likable, with a big mouth full of good humor. Alan Bean. He didn't seem used to the name himself yet, and every time I said Mr. Bean he laughed like crazy. Considering my own name isn't much better than his, I finally stopped calling him Bean and started calling him Sir. He too was a naval Lieutenant Commander and they'd picked him with the third group. Any tooth to extract, Mr. Bean, Sir? If only I could do something: to extract just a little tooth, for instance. It wouldn't do any harm and I would have some amusement. Just doing something. And what about if we get up and take a walk? Or play some football, even better. Otherwise I too would get bald. Help, Father! Help!

"Mr. Bean! Oh, what on earth made you so bald?"

"Worries. You'd go bald yourself if you stayed in here. What do you think? That I have fun like you do? That I go everywhere like you? That I know lots of people like you? Here we live like white-collar workers. Always the same things, the same faces, the same timetable, it's not the sky we go to, it's the office! It's a boring petit-bourgeois life here. The only surprises are training trips, or extra time when you've got to the office late. So when you get home the soup's ice cold and your wife won't even heat it for you maybe. Home and office, home and office. And ice-cold soup. If it weren't for an occasional movie!"

"You go to the movies?"

"Sure I do. If you don't go to the movies here, where else can you go? What do you think? Here we're in the provinces. It's lucky we can even go to the movies. The first Seven never can. Everybody asking for their autographs and so on. But us, who knows us, who recognizes us? We're unknown astronauts, thank the Lord."

"So you aren't happy, Mr. Bean?"

"I'm happy enough. Being an astronaut, gee! But as for having fun, I had more fun when I was an officer in the Navy and I used to travel. Naples, Pisa, Rome. Everywhere, I used to go. But I've never been to Venice."

"You've never been to Venice?! You're going to the Moon and you've never been to Venice?!"

"Gee! What can I do about it? The ship never went as far as Venice. I used to tell myself: have patience, sooner or later you'll get to Venice. And now they've made me an astronaut, and the very same year they made me an astronaut the ship went to Venice. I know it: I'll see the Moon and I won't see Venice."

"Listen, Mr. Bean . . ."

"Eh, eh!"

"Listen, sir, couldn't you slip away to Venice before you go to the Moon?"

"No, it's too late now. There's lots of reasons why it's too late now, can't you see that I'm bald? I'm shut in here now and I'll never get out except to go up there."

"I shouldn't be so sorry."

"Gee! You're not jealous, by any chance?"

"Of course I'm jealous, sir. I'm jealous and how. The Moon and Mars and . . ."

"Mars, yes. The idea of going to Mars appeals to me too. I'd go even if the journey took me two years, four years. But in twenty or thirty years, when the moment to go has come, I'll be too old. I'm old already. What can you do about it?"

Tell him, Father. Tell him what we can do about it. We can get up and take a walk, and we can play some football, and we can slip away to Venice with a NASA airplane, just to make NASA angry, just for a taste of disobedience, and then we can scream with enthusiasm for going to the Moon, well, Mars is better, agreed, but the Moon isn't so bad either, it's rather exciting, for Christ's sake!

"So that leaves the Moon. That's not to be undervalued, is it? Just the very thought that you mightn't come back. Do you think it's to be laughed at, the thought of going to some place and maybe not being able to come back?"

"What do you mean, not come back?"

"I mean not come back. Don't you think about it?"

"I most certainly don't. Beg pardon: but if you don't come back, it's no longer a mission. It's a sacrifice, a martyrdom. A mission means going and coming back; the journey to the Moon will be a mission, not martyrdom or a sacrifice on the altar of service."

"But does it matter to you whether you land on the Moon?"

"Not to me, no. Look, we're pilots and what concerns us is the journey, not the landing. Take the pilot who does Rome-Tokyo in three hours. He doesn't care about arriving in Tokyo, what he cares about is making the flight in three hours. It's the same with the Moon. It's going there that matters: going and coming back, not the landing."

"What are you saying?"

"I'm saying exactly that."

"But how about your curiosity!"

"Gee! Curiosity about what? I'm not a child any more. I'm an adult now. And also I'm a guy who travels when he's told to and goes wherever they send him."

"Then Venice, the things you told me about your travels, your ship that never got as far as Venice . . ."

"Venice, Venice! What do you think I'd do in Venice at my age? Venice is a young person's dream, the little streets, the gondolas, the girl to photograph with the pigeons . . . But now . . ."

"Now?"

"Gee! You know how old I am? Thirty-two, nearly thirty-three!"

"And you think that's a lot?"

"It is a lot. It's not the age for illusions, adventures."

"Not the age for illusions, adventures?!"

"Surely not."

I'd have killed him, or at least pulled out a tooth, all his teeth, incisor, canine, molar and so on.

"You're all the same, by God!"

"Eh, yes. Yes, we're all the same."

"For heaven's sake! You aren't feeling sad, all of a sudden? Up with your ears! Smile! You smiled so well, by God! Come on, let's change the subject. Have you any children?"

"Two. The older one is seven."

"I can imagine how proud he must be to have a father who's an astronaut!"

"He's always asking me why I'm not a sheriff: his friend's father is a sheriff. He says when he grows up he wants to be a sheriff, he says being a sheriff's fun but being an astronaut isn't. And, between you and me, he's not wrong—"

"Twelve minutes!" cried the Bureaucrat.

My fourth old man stood up quickly.

"Here we go. Back to the office. Thank you."

"Thank you for what?"

"Stop!" yelled the Bureaucrat. "Stop!"

"For the conversation, for the fun. Are you—"

"Stop! Stop!"

"May I ask you one more thing, Mr. Bean?"

"Stoooop!"

And so he went. And I never found out.

The fifth old man was thirty-four, a marvelous old man, his beauty so celestial that it didn't even provoke profane thoughts, desires. The angels of Paradise must have faces just like his—long, slightly suffering, with straight noble nose, gentle firm mouth and those gentle patient eyes. Like the angels, he was all pink and gold, pink skin, golden hair and eyeslashes; he was tall, slender and a little sad. You know him too now, yes, the first one who went outside the Gemini capsule to go floating in space, flying weightless and saying it's great, I like it, and the other saying come back, and he replying no, just a little longer, it's great, I like it. He was called Edward White, this angel, father of two more angels called Ed and Bonnie Lynn, husband of an additional angel called Patricia, all of them pink and gold, he had come here to Hell with the second group. So now what? Can one ask questions of the angels? And if one can, what does one ask them? How are St. John, St. Mark, St. Luke and St. Matthew up there in Heaven? What's the Gregorian chant that St. John, St. Mark, St. Luke, St. Matthew prefer up there? Do they play it on the organ, the harp? Or on the rays of the Sun? Respectfully I ignored his teeth. Angels' teeth are sacred, untouchable by us sinners of Earth. Besides, he said everything himself.

"I thought of becoming an astronaut when the first Sputnik went up and it was clear that being an astronaut would soon be a career. We talked about it, in the family. I come from a family of fliers. Father is a general in the Air Force and I'm a captain in the Air Force, my brother has just qualified in the Air Force School and if he can he'll become an astronaut too. When the first Sputnik went up, I was working with Deke Slayton on Project Gravity Zero, a study of weightlessness. Deke and I were the only ones who were exclusively concerned with this: we both used to make experiments with Ham, the chimpanzee who later preceded Alan Shepard in sub-orbital flight. Deke and I used to pilot the plane and Ham would be a guinea pig for the few minutes' duration of weightlessness when we nose-dived. Then Deke took Ham's place and used to make the experiments on himself, I would pilot the plane. Deke liked Ham very much, and he didn't like tossing Ham around like that, he used to say that no one had ever asked Ham's permission and Ham had never volunteered. Deke was also very cheesed when they put Ham in the Mercury capsule: for the same reasons. Poor Ham, do you know he's dead? In Washington, of bronchial pneumonia. They put him in the zoo and that winter it was very cold, he wasn't used to the cold."

I looked closely at the angel to see if he was laughing. I can't ever help laughing, you know, when I think of Ham, especially because of the cartoon that you showed with satisfaction that day, the one where Ham was portrayed near a bunch of bananas, in his hands a newspaper announcing the flight of Al Shepard. Out of indifference or, better, scorn, Ham was grumbling: "So what?" But the angel wasn't laughing in the least. And mourning Ham increased his sadness: or should I say solemnity? Doesn't solemnity feed on sadness?

"Deke and I had been together ever since Germany, there are only six years between us. So when we heard the first murmurs of Project Mercury in 1957 Deke said: Don't you budge, better go on studying. I'll go and if they take me, I'll see what kind of a thing it is. If it's a good thing or not. Naturally they took him, without even thinking twice about it. Oh, Deke's extraordinary. After he'd taken the exams he told me all about it and said the tests were awful, terrible, they'd throw you into ice and then into boiling heat, they'd spin you around at a fantastic speed in the centrifuge and you suffered a lot: but it was worth it, I should volunteer. I hesitated a little: I wasn't as good as Deke and I didn't want to look bad, especially in front of him. But he said: You're as good as I am, better, all you need to pass is to be a first-rate pilot and you're a damn first-rate pilot and they'll take you. I finally volunteered. Deke was right: as far as being hard goes, the tests were hard, all right. And think: the ones for the second group weren't as hard as the ones for the first group. The ones for the third group were even less hard: eventually they realized that certain tortures were useless. As far as being hard goes, they were hard, all right, as I was saying. But when your heart's set on something, everything is less hard, don't you think? My heart was set on going to the Moon: I was very happy when they took me. And I'm very happy now too because now it's certain that I'll go to the Moon. Although I don't really agree with the others over certain automatic systems . . ."

And here he plunged into such a complicated speech that I don't even remember it, and then I was distracted by something: a lot of little wrinkles around his eyes, exactly like you have, Father. It was so startling to find so many wrinkles in all that pink and gold, to think that they were the same as yours, Father, because you're sixty-two and he was thirty-four. It was like, I don't know, finding that you get wrinkles in heaven, that even the angels grow old, and it was disagreeable, perplexing.

". . . there's really only one thing about the age I live in that annoys me: television. There was a time when my wife and children used to watch television all the time and we never talked. I hated that instrument, I who don't hate anything or anybody, so—"

"Stop," shouted the Bureaucrat. "Eleven minutes, stop!"

I was just going to say to the angel: pardon me, don't be offended, but are you a Turtle, yes or no? But I didn't have time. The startled angel stood up, bowed, and disappeared in a cloud of incense, Gregorian chants, Alleluia.

The sixth old man was thirty and I defy the Heavens and the Earth, the living and the dead, to say that that creature was thirty—eaten away by God knows what melancholy, he had such a faded drained expression on his little face that it seemed he could never have been young. Maybe many years ago he too had been twenty, he too had been a boy, a child. But that day even the memory of that distant time had died in him. Sad furrows sucked in his cheeks that were marked by very fine scars, deep lines made his mouth droop at the corners, and his sunken eyes bespoke infinite resignation, leaden tiredness. I was tired too, made edgy by irritation, by the prolonged unrelieved concentration, by my seething resentment of the Master of Ceremonies and the Bureaucrat. I only wanted the whole grotesque farce to be over, for an end to be put to all the coming and going, and I made no effort to discover something that would arouse my interest in Eugene Cernan, lieutenant of the Navy, graduate in electrical, aeronautical and astronautical engineering, born in Chicago, married, father of one daughter, victim of a system that was all wrong, and of my own cowardly obedience. Why didn't I get up and go? I couldn't care less about what he had to tell me, I couldn't care less about finding out whether he was a Turtle or an Ass, I was tired, fed up, the angel had exhausted the last remnants of my curiosity. Mechanically I questioned him and mechanically listened to his answers: Why did you become an astronaut, Lieutenant? Why . . . why . . . why . . .

"Because I like flying, you see I'd wanted to fly ever since I was a child, and you get satisfaction from participating in something that paves the way to the future, I come from a family that isn't rich, you see, my father is a mechanic and we never had much money, I've always had to work hard to get anywhere, I was born in Chicago and Chicago is hard, my father sacrificed a lot for me, taking a degree was painful . . ."

No, Father, you couldn't say he wasn't likable. On the contrary, he was nice, very good, he openly professed a life that was decent and deserved respect, a past that had been clean and courageous, he made a great effort to see that I could understand what he was saying: but his words were lost on my ears like the sound of the sea when you get used to it so you don't hear it any more. The splashing of one wave after another, then the splashing of another wave and another, for hours, for years and centuries, forever, and every wave sounding like the one before it, foam, seaweed. Weren't their stories all exactly alike? It was only to be expected, I know. But there are ways and ways of telling the same story: what my eyes have seen will never be the same as what your eyes have seen, our words will be different, our conclusions will be different; so why, why did they all use the same words, the same adjectives, as if they'd learned by heart some carbon-copy speech? Why did you feel you'd heard it all before, even when there was something different about what they said?

". . . we in the third group are naturally less prepared than all the others: and not only because we started later. Because at the beginning NASA had higher standards, they've slackened a little since. The second group are much better than we are, and the first group are the best of the lot. But this isn't the only difference: there's the matter of fame. They have it and we don't; even if we did have it we wouldn't have it to the same degree, and a man who's famous is less inhibited than an ordinary man. And lastly there's the war: they fought in it and we didn't. But the truth is that there are other experiences that are worth as much as fighting in a war. Work, for example. I've worked hard, so hard I often feel I've been working for a hundred years, and hard work makes you adult, as capable of deciding what's right or wrong as anyone who lived the tragedy of killing or being killed . . ."

And he was intelligent, Father, sure he was. Very intelligent, perhaps even more intelligent than the others. Nevertheless when the Bureaucrat yelled his Stop I felt liberated from a weight, from a nightmare, and I said goodbye to you without regrets, Lieutenant Cernan. Don't take offense, please: I don't want to sound mean or ungrateful, I promise you that I admired and respected you, and what I reproach you with, Cernan, also goes for Chaffee, for Gordon, for Armstrong, for Bean, for White, for the others whom I don't know, so please don't be hurt: but as I watched you go I felt like your daughter. Yes, Cernan: your daughter. Yes, White: your daughter. Yes, Bean: your daughter. Yes, Armstrong: your daughter. Yes, Gordon: your daughter. Yes, Chaffee: your daughter. I've seen more than you have and I felt as if I were your daughter. I'm more tired than you are and I felt like your daughter. I'm the same age as you and I felt like your daughter. Because I'm having fun in my thirties, I'm savoring my thirties like a liqueur: I'm not dulling them with a precocious carbon-copy old age. Listen to me, Cernan, White, Bean, Armstrong, Gordon, Chaffee, all of you: being thirty is wonderful, so is being thirty-one, thirty-two, thirty-three, thirty-four, thirty-five! They're wonderful years, those thirties, because they're free, rebellious, untrammeled, because the anguish of waiting is over, the melancholy of decline hasn't begun, because we're lucid, finally, in our thirties! If we're religious, we're convinced of our religion. If we're atheists, we're convinced atheists. If we have doubts, we have doubts without shame. And we don't fear the mockery of the young because we're young too, we don't fear the reproof of adults because we're adults too, we aren't afraid of sin because we've learned that sin is a point of view, we aren't afraid of disobeying because we've learned that disobedience is noble, we aren't afraid of punishment because we've concluded that there's nothing wrong with loving each other if we meet, of leaving each other if we lose each other: we no longer have to settle accounts with a schoolteacher and we don't yet have to settle them with the priest and his last sacrament. We settle up with ourselves and no one else, with our own adult grief. We are a field of ripened grain in our thirties, no longer green and not yet dried: lymph flows through us at the right pressure, full of life, and our joy is alive, and our grief is alive, we laugh and cry as we shall never be able to again, we think and understand as we shall never be able to again. We've reached the peak of the mountain and everything is clear up there on the peak: the way we came up, the way we'll go down. A little breathless but still fresh, we'll never again be able to sit down halfway and look behind and ahead and reflect on our good fortune: so then why isn't it like this with you? How is it that you seem like my fathers, crushed by fears, by boredom, by baldness? What have they done to you, what have you done to yourselves? What price are you paying for the Moon? The Moon is costly, I know. It's costly for all of us, but no cost is worth that field of grain, no cost is worth that mountain peak: if it was worth it, it would be pointless going to the Moon, we might just as well stay here. So wake up, stop being so rational, obedient, wrinkled! Stop losing hair, growing sad in your sameness! Tear up the carbon copy. Laugh, cry, make mistakes, disobey! Break the nose of that Bureaucrat, break his stop-watch. I say this to you in all humility, with affection, because I admire you, because I see you as better than myself and wish you would be much better than myself, much: not so little. Or is it too late now? Or has the System already broken you, swallowed you up? Yes, that's what it must be.

It was breaking me too, little by little. Instead of getting up and going, I went on sitting there under GOING TO THE SKY like an idiot, like a robot.

25.

So there I stayed, sitting at that table, motionless as a robot, thinking that the System is a cancer devouring even the most healthy, rebelling is no use, at first you rebel at the top of your voice, then quietly, then not at all, and at this point you are accepting the System too. You know this, Father, every dictatorship works this way: you raise barricades, you take your gun and you place yourself there to fire, to fight, you soon waste the ammunition and space out the shots to gain time; in the wait you realize they are too many, your enemies, they'll win this battle, you'd better withdraw to resist them with words, with peaceful behavior, and you yawn while they advance, you get sleepy, and when they catch you you're sleeping. Almost sleeping, I was waiting for the last one. But the last one didn't appear. Through the half-open door came the agitated whispering of a dialogue between the Master of Ceremonies and somebody else.

"He says he won't budge, sir."

"He won't budge!"

"No, sir. He says they all go in and out of that room as if it was a dentist's office and he's all through with the dentist."

"All through?"

"Yes, sir. He says his teeth are all right now."

"Try and get him to change his mind."

"You can't budge him, sir."

"Is he crazy, then?"

"No, sir. He's quite calm. He's humming and making a paper airplane."

"A paper airplane!"

"Yes, sir."

"Tell him there's a lady waiting for him in this room! Tell him one can't be so rude to ladies!"

You could hear the sound of footsteps going away. And for the first time since I'd been in there I addressed the Bureaucrat.

"Who are they talking about?"

"Charles Conrad. Known as Pete."

"And who is this Charles Conrad known as Pete?"

"He's an astronaut in the second group."

"I like the sound of this Charles Conrad known as Pete."

"You do?"

The footsteps returned. The dialogue went on.

"He still doesn't want to, sir. He says he begs pardon, he didn't know it was a lady, they just told him it was some writer. But he says he doesn't give one cent for writers, whether ladies or gentlemen. And then he says . . ."

"And then?" gasped the Master of Ceremonies, full of hope.

"And then he says that the lady shouldn't write about him. He doesn't give a damn about it. However . . ."

"However?"

"He wants to make it clear he has nothing against the lady, who, as he realizes now, is the lady of Project Cheese, a Project he likes very much indeed, and then he's a well brought-up boy, but only has it in for the dentist's office because last time he went the dentist hurt him a lot."

"And then?"

"That's all. He's humming and whistling. He's finished the airplane. He's got it in his pocket to take home to his kids."

By God. The thing was becoming interesting. How did he know about the dentist? Cautiously I came forward, addressed the Master of Ceremonies.

"Sir. I have two suggestions to make."

"Let's hear them."

"The first is to let me leave. I warmly urge this suggestion, sir, I advise it with all my soul. Without meaning any offense to NASA or the Moon, eight astronauts in one day are too many. I'm tired. And now I have a really exact picture of the situation in my mind, sir. To please me, sir. As for the second suggestion, it is that we leave this room and go to this astronaut, who, between ourselves, is quite right."

"I refuse," announced the Bureaucrat. "The regulations say that interviews take place here, in this room."

"The regulations only apply up till five in the afternoon, after which time it's no longer office hours," murmured the Master of Ceremonies in perplexity.

"In that case I'm going home," said the Bureaucrat.

"Fine!" I said.

"Right," said the Master of Ceremonies.

"Goodbye," said the Bureaucrat.

"Send for Jack," said the Master of Ceremonies.

The Bureaucrat departed and I bade him farewell, silently cursing him. Jack arrived. Jack was Jack Riley, the man who four months before had been present at my interviews with Glenn, Shepard and Slayton. I like Jack a lot because he has a face like a sleepy cat and an adorable way of following interviews: he goes into a corner and falls asleep. I greeted Jack with enthusiasm, but don't misunderstand: I was genuinely depressed at the thought of facing another astronaut, I'd have given anything to get out of it. But since I was obliged to go on with it, I'd gladly spare a little glance for that crazy fellow. I couldn't help being struck by his refusing to see me, like royalty.

"Jack, do you mind taking the lady to see Conrad?" asked the Master of Ceremonies.

"No, no," said Jack.

"It's no longer office hours," said the Master of Ceremonies.

"So what?" said Jack.

"Thanks," said the Master of Ceremonies and for a moment I felt sorry for him, I was about to forgive that bunch of fat: can you believe that? Poor Master of Ceremonies. After all, how could he be blamed for the System? He hadn't invented it. They paid him to apply it blindly, that's all, and he was a victim of it as much as I, as Eugene Cernam, as the others. Look how sweating and unhappy he was. He couldn't stand any more—he was even going to give up the introduction ritual, he was so exhausted. Thank God! But no. He wasn't giving it up in the least, that damn man. He was reading the introduction this time. He was using a written biography. He grabbed the sheet of paper out of Jack's hands and, moving his fat finger as if conducting an orchestra, he declaimed:

"Charles Conrad, Junior. Astronaut. Lieutenant Commander in the Navy of the United States of America. Born in Philadelphia on June 2, 1930. Graduate of Princeton University. Pilot on aircraft carriers since 1954. Test pilot since 1959. Married, with four sons. All boys! Member of the Institute of Aeronautics and Astronautics! hobbies: golf, water skiing, swimming, paper airplanes . . ."

Here he stopped, dumfounded, redder than a tomato.

"Jack! Who gave you this sheet?"

"He did, sir," said Jack, biting his lip to hold back the laughter.

"Who wrote 'paper airplanes'?"

"He did, sir," said Jack, biting his tongue too.

And that's how I found another brother at last, Father.

———————

My brother was sitting at his desk in his office, which is small. But my brother is small too and so the office fitted him nicely. Above his trousers, which I guessed had no crease, he wore a lizard-green sweater, short-sleeved so it allowed one to admire the anchor tattooed on my brother's left forearm which he flashed around as if it were a sapphire bracelet. The anchor was drawn for him in Copenhagen by the specialist who tattoos the King of Denmark, and he wants everyone to know it, so he never stops scratching it, or waving his left forearm about, or smoothing his hair with his left hand. His hair, well, in recent years my brother had also lost his hair, or at least a good deal of it. His forehead now spread extensively, taking up a third of his skull, which left little room for what's left. But where he still had hair it was fair, such as we all have in our family, and in any case, listen, his baldness didn't detract in the slightest from his youth, which heroically defied every System in the world. At the age of thirty-four my brother looked no more than twenty-two and, if it wasn't for his hair, even twenty or eighteen.

My brother was sturdy, well-built as small men are when they're well-built, and his little face was tanned gold by the sun and had a big nose in the middle and two fine blue eyes and, lastly, a very wide mouth that he used for laughing. He also used it for chattering, God knows he chatters, but chiefly he used it for laughing, which is a great good fortune because when my brother laughs you laugh with him and you even laugh if you want to cry. I suppose this must be because of his teeth, which are the funniest in the world: very, very short, each one separated from the next as if they had all offended one another, and the biggest gap is between the top front two, which are a quarter of an inch apart. He can stick a cigarette between them if he wants to, and he does, although everyone complains that such things are unheard of, but he does a lot of things that aren't heard of. He makes paper airplanes and says they're for his little boys, but everyone knows they're for himself. He drinks an undrinkable drink called root beer that some people give to growing children, hoping in vain it may make him grow a little too. He collects ridiculous hats and wears them instead of his helmet when he goes up in a plane. He flings himself into experiments on survival in the jungle, living on boa constrictors and announcing that boa constrictors are excellent boiled and roasted. And he announces it quite happily, because he's always happy and he really believes that boa constrictors are excellent boiled and roasted. Lastly, he is training to go to the Moon and I don't know what I wouldn't have given if he could have gone with Theodore, can you imagine? Not that my brother could look at the Moon as one looks at a Rembrandt, far less make speeches about ugly things becoming beautiful, only Theodore could do that; my brother is a mathematician and nothing else, he doesn't know the first thing about art and poetry, he understands nothing about it, he hates intellectuals, highly sophisticated people, he claims that they are psychopathic, a threat to the health of his mind, that's the mind of a simple guy who doesn't need the analyst; but if those two went together, anything could happen, anything, and we'd have a new Divine Comedy, Father.

Going to the Moon is, in fact, an old passion of my brother's, he's wanted to do it ever since he was a boy and he won't give it up even if it costs him his life. Naturally it sometimes happens that his dream weighs heavily on him and he realizes the mess he's got himself into: Who put the idea into my head, who made me do it, I'm not staying here, etcetera etcetera amen. But the mood soon passes, he remembers he was in the Navy, where for the least little thing they used to lock him up or make him stand at attention and sing "Oh! I love the Navy! Oh! I love the Navy!" and he becomes obedient again, disciplined to the point of martyrdom—how shall I put it?—ready for any sacrifice, for any prison. He likes smoking, for example, but he doesn't smoke. He likes drinking, but doesn't. He likes women, but doesn't look at them, walks around with his eyes shut, and one day, you'll see, he'll fall down a manhole if he carries on like that. He hates lectures, but he gives them —in high schools, in universities, in old ladies' clubs, wherever NASA sends him to defend the Moon, and it goes without saying that they shouldn't send him to speak; he's not the type for it, you see what I mean? He always starts, they tell me, by telling a joke that has nothing to do with the Moon, then he suddenly squares his shoulders and goes to the blackboard, where he writes theorems that nobody can understand. His disappointed public yawns and falls asleep. But when this happens he smiles and shows those teeth of his, and people who are sleeping—would you believe it?—promptly wake up, see those teeth, start smiling themselves, and so the lecture proceeds.

When he's giving lectures and also when he's not, my brother travels around: he's one of those who travel the most, if someone has to go to some place in America or elsewhere you can be sure it's my brother who'll go. Someone has to check the LEM controls, for example? It's my brother who goes. Someone has to look over a modification of the Saturn rocket? Someone has to be shut inside the Apollo spacecraft for seven days? Someone has to train the third-group astronauts in some Arizona desert? It's my brother who goes. Why, I don't know. He says it's because he's the best, no one can beat him when it comes to training, no one can compare with him as an engineer, no one can touch him when it comes to astrophysics, don't forget he studied at Princeton, etcetera etcetera amen. But what I suspect is that Slayton keeps him traveling all the time so as not to have him under foot, to keep him away from Houston, where he always causes confusion, great noise, distractions. In fact, my brother is only in Houston on weekends, which he spends at home helping his wife, who has to look after those four kids, poor woman, she's a great girl, he explains. Of what his help consists nobody knows, nor is it easy to see in what way he could be of any help to a wife with four children. But he says he helps and I believe him. I always believe whatever my brother says, I do, even his fibs. However, on Monday morning his help comes to an end and he leaves once more while his wife shouts: "Thank God, one less around me, go-quickly-or-I'll-lose-my-mind!" So it was truly a great stroke of luck that I met him that day. Wouldn't it have been frightful to have a brother like that and not know it? I'd have been poorer and this book would have been poorer too—and we'd all have been poorer.

It's also true, Father, that sooner or later, somehow, I'd still have met him. First, because sooner or later, somehow, brothers always meet —as you say yourself when you meet a brother. Second, because wherever I went after Houston, there was my brother. When you reach a place, I promise you, all you have to do is look around and there he is. Especially if a rocket-launching is about to take place, at Las Cruces, for example, or Cape Kennedy. You don't even need to wonder whether he's there, ninety-nine percent of the time he's there, sprawled by the swimming pool, waiting for von Braun to fix the rocket which breaks down on the eve of a launching, God knows why, with his eyes shut, happy, surrounded by lots of women devouring him with their smiles. The reason they devour him with their smiles is banal enough: in shirt and trousers my brother's rather unprepossessing, but in swimming trunks he looks like an advertisement for sun-tan oil, the type that's considered attractive in America. However, don't worry about it, and don't worry about the fact that he's an astronaut either: he's never given himself airs on account of his job. My brother's a friendly type, he makes friends with everybody, young and old, good and bad, stupid and intelligent, and he has an extraordinary way of making friends: first he looks at you as if you were a ghost or a dentist, then he opens his mouth and starts pointing out his teeth to you. That's what he did with me, at least.

"Here, look, tell me if I'm right or wrong. They aren't diseased. They're all separate, so what? You can't say they're diseased."

"No."

"And that can be cured too, you know. He fixes a gadget in, then he tightens it and they draw closer together, as if they were cold. Then he takes out the gadget and ho! There they are, shivering with cold. I must have it done. They're ugly like this, aren't they?"

"Well, no. They're white and clean. They're rather an odd shape, if anything. A bit on the short side."

"That's nothing. It was worse before—you couldn't even see them. You could only see the gums. Little grains of rice stuck out of the gums and those were my teeth. So I had them cut."

"Cut?"

"Cut. Not to make myself beautiful, you understand. Out of kindness, because I could never laugh; it shocked people. And when they weren't shocked they used to say: poor-boy-look-at-him-so-young-and-lost-his-teeth-already. So I had to look solemn, everyone thought I was solemn. In the end I got tired of people thinking that, and I went to the doctor. And zig! zag! he cut back the gums. One by one. Thirty-two times."

"God!"

"My name isn't God. My name's Conrad. Pete Conrad. Get it?"

"I know. Well, then: shall we draw this tooth, Pete Conrad?"

"Roger!" He opened wide his mouth with resignation.

"No, no. I meant let's talk."

"O.K., let's talk. What'll we say, what'll we say?"

"Look, say anything you like. Except for one thing: that you've dreamed of flying ever since you were a child. I've already heard that from six or seven of them. If you say it too, I'll open that window and jump out."

He bounded like a cat, flung open the window.

"Jump."

"Oh, no! You too!"

"Come on, jump. Jump!"

Jack, who had gone into a corner to sleep as soon as he'd come in, opened one eye.

"Pete, if you throw her out of the window, a lot of people will thank you, but you'll have the entire press against you and her Embassy will make a lot of fuss." With which he shut his eye again and went back to sleep, or pretended to sleep; I doubt whether even Jack could sleep when my brother's talking. He is so funny, Father. He restores our faith, you understand? He proves that one can survive space contamination, that there's still hope, that they aren't all automatons in this kind of society. Do you follow me? When you meet someone who's spent years and years in the Navy singing "Oh! I love the Navy! Oh! I love the Navy!" and then spent years more living between electronic computers and the LEM, you don't expect much. You mention Einstein to him, for example, and you're immediately filled with dread that he'll start expounding the damn theory of relativity, the one I don't understand and when I do grasp it I forget it again within the hour so we're back at the beginning again every time, and God knows why they take no notice of me when I protest that they're wasting their time, I don't understand it, I forget it. Well, with my brother none of that happened. I mentioned Einstein and instead of the theory of relativity he told me the story of Einstein and his ice cream—as you will hear. This strikes me as very important and you must take it into account, Father. Now I'll get back to my brother, who's standing in front of Jack.

"Who's throwing her? She's throwing herself. Can you tell me why?"

"Because you're all so boring. I feel as if I'm interviewing dress designers, not astronauts. Dress designers saying: oh, I started dressing dolls when I was a child."

He bounded like a cat again.

"Dress designers? I know one of them. He's called Pierre Balmain, he's in Paris. I'll tell you about it. First you must know I studied at Princeton . . ."

He looked at me from beneath his eyelashes to see if the information impressed me. I feigned the deepest amazement.

"Princeton! For heaven's sake!"

"A lot of people haven't even heard of Princeton," he added suspiciously.

"Are you kidding? It's one of the most glorious American universities. Einstein used to teach there and then Oppenheimer."

My brother happily scratched his anchor.

"I didn't attend Einstein's classes because he only taught seniors. But I knew him, though. Boy, what a character! First there was his hair, so long he could have braided it. Then his eyes, good, wicked, beautiful, ugly, sad, gay, everything. Then his sweatshirt."

"His sweatshirt?"

"Yes. White, with short sleeves, and a picture of Popeye printed across the front. Popeye, you know? The one who eats spinach to grow strong. Einstein used to wear it for eating ice cream."

"For eating ice cream?"

"Yes, otherwise he used to mess up his good shirt. He liked strawberry best. You know, the kind with whole strawberries in it. The trouble was he didn't want his ice cream in a dish, he wanted it in a cone. And then he never stood still while he ate it, he used to walk while he ate it. And then he didn't walk normally, he used to hop while he ate it. Like this."

He went behind the desk and started hopping on one foot.

"That was because he had one foot on the pavement and the other foot in the street. Boy, what a man! I loved that man. Not for his theory of relativity, for the way he used to eat ice cream. Then, one time, he dropped his ice cream."

Again he looked at me from beneath his lashes to see if the information had impressed me.

"For heaven's sake!" I repeated.

He happily scratched his anchor again.

"Yes, he dropped his ice cream. Boy, what a sight! He swore like a madman and he looked at his ice cream on the ground: there was a strawberry in it as big as this. You know, one of those real big ones. Then he calmed down and went to get another ice cream. But he didn't find any more strawberries like that one."

"Who told you all this?"

"My own eyes told me. I used to follow him. I followed him around for months, Einstein. At lunchtime I always used to rush out to see if he was buying an ice-cream cone or not. Man! It was Einstein!"

He was silent for a moment, looking for an end to his story. And in his own way he found it.

"And then, well, then he died and I wept."

"Now I'd really like to see how you're going to get around to that dress designer," Jack remarked and even opened an eye the better to savor his mischief.

"I'm coming to it. So I was at Princeton. Well, I don't know why this Balmain came to Princeton. But anyway he came and some of the boys and I met him and he said to call him up if we were ever in Paris. Two years later I went to Paris because I was an officer in the Navy. And I called him up."

"What's all this got to do with the Moon?" Jack grumbled. "She's here on account of the Moon."

But my brother took no notice.

"Boy, what a stroke of luck! First thing he showed us the dresses and they didn't interest me at all: but inside the dresses there were the models and they interested me a lot. Next thing he gave us each a model to drive around with us to the various spots. Man!"

He was pensive for a moment.

"Mine was a bit tall. I tried to exchange her, but she was too tall for everyone, so I was stuck with her. Boy, was she tall! Say, why are they so tall, those girls? I'm five-six. How tall are you?"

"Even less. Much less."

He looked at me kindly.

"Never mind. The main thing in life is to carry one's height with dignity."

"Pete! The Moon!" Jack grumbled.

"O.K. The Moon. First she says: Say whatever you want. Then you pester me with the Moon. All right, then. My father used to fly in balloons."

"Balloons?"

"Balloons, balloons. He still says there's nothing like balloons and he's absolutely certain we could go to the Moon in a balloon. I used to think so too when I was a child. Then they explained to me that you needed an airplane and so I fell in love with planes. Whether you throw yourself out of the window or not."

"All right. I'm not going to throw myself out of the window."

"How can I help it if I like flying? All my life I've dreamed of nothing else. At Princeton I was still thinking about flying. In the Navy I was still thinking about it. So when the first selection came for men to fly in the Mercury capsule I went out for it with Jim and Wally Schirra. We were in the Navy together. We were all three going through the Aircraft Testing School. Man, were they foul exams that time! Jim—"

"Jim who?"

"Jim Lovell. Friend of mine."

"Lovell is another astronaut of the second group," Jack explained magnanimously.

"Wally was accepted, but Jim and I weren't. Man, did we feel bad! They apparently wanted nine, not seven. And we were in the first nine. Then they decided to take only seven and so they left us two out. Evidently we weren't as good as the others."

"Maybe they'd only wanted seven in the first place," I said hearteningly.

"Yes, that's true, isn't it? Anyway when they were wanting others for the second group they called us immediately." He scratched his anchor to remind me it was there. "Of course they didn't tell us anything about the Moon and all that. They only talked about the Moon a lot later, when I'd gone back to my aircraft carrier with my tail between my legs. Not that I didn't like my aircraft carrier—we got around and we saw a lot of places that we thought were very far off. But now there's only the Moon and it seems just a step away. Man! But, you know, it's really odd the way we talk about the Moon. This rock, that rock. You take a rock here, I take a rock there. Then you take a handful of dust here, I take a handful of dust there. Bah! You'd think we were going to market to buy grapes or apples. And in the end it seems as near as New York. But the Moon's a long way off, man! Going there won't be a picnic!"

"Von Braun says it'll be a picnic."

"My foot! Let him go if he thinks it's a picnic! My foot! Hey, do you really want to steal the Moon with that Project Cheese?"

"Yes, I do. You help me?"

"Sure. If Jim comes too. Or Dick Gordon. I like cheese."

"Good. We'll discuss that. Now let's be serious."

"Serious?"

"Yes. Let's work. Are you afraid once in a while?"

"Sure, I'm afraid! What a question! Sure, I'm afraid. I'm sometimes afraid in planes too. When I have to land on an aircraft carrier, for example. I'm telling you, it's no joke landing on an aircraft carrier. They look big enough, but when you have to land on them they're as small as a pea. A pea in the middle of the sea. And you've got to land on that pea. Bah! Picnic, my foot! Let *them* go if it's a picnic, instead of sending us!"

"There you go again with that *us.*"

"The others told me when I asked them: What's she like, this type that's writing about the astronauts? She ought to be locked up, Dick Gordon tells me, she gets mad when you talk in the plural. Boy! You know something? You really should be locked up. Beg pardon, but how can I say I? I'm only a mouse in that thing and that thing is in actuality directed by the thousands and thousands of people behind me. My responsibility is exactly the same as their responsibility: how can I say I instead of we? It's the same on the Moon. Three of us go, not one. You aren't by any chance one of the ones who think we're heroes?"

You know what I think about it, Father. In my opinion they are heroes. But the previous evening, in my room at the King's Inn, I'd happened to see a television lecture given by Professor John Dodds of Stanford University and this pale old man, with his typical intellectual face, had said something to make you think. Today, he had said, there is great confusion about the concepts of greatness and heroism: celebrity is often confused with greatness and bravery is often confused with heroism. The fact is that greatness is becoming more and more difficult because it is becoming more and more difficult to be oneself, face things by oneself. Gandhi was himself and faced things by himself. Lincoln and Churchill too. Kennedy, already, wasn't able to be himself and face things by himself; behind him was the apparatus of the party, of Congress, of billions of dollars. Death was the only thing he faced by himself, and this restored his greatness. The same argument could be applied to heroism. A lot of people, Professor Dodds had said, picked on astronauts as a symbol of modern heroism. Supposing they are right; what conclusion does that lead us to? That today the hero is no longer a man on his own. The hero today is a group of heroes. But the word hero includes an idea of solitude: the hero is a hero inasmuch as he's on his own. A group can be heroic, but not heroes. And who's on his own today? Nobody except a rebel. Conclusion: there's only one kind of hero in the world today, and that's the rebel.

"Did you see Professor Dodds on television last evening?" I asked. "Channel Seven, eleven-thirty?"

"At night I sleep," he replied. "I go to bed at nine. You're crazy if you think I'd watch Professor Dodds. Why?"

"Nothing. I just wondered. He gave a lecture on the concept of heroism. In your opinion, who's a hero today?"

My brother scratched his anchor. Sometimes it helps him to think. Then he shrugged his shoulders in perplexity.

"Uh!" he said. "Let's see . . . Uh! A hero, for example, is

someone who lets himself be killed sooner than kill another. Get me?"

"Got you."

"Well, then, if you really want to know, in my opinion a hero isn't even the man who lets himself be killed sooner than kill another; maybe he lets himself be killed because he loves that other person, and because he hopes he'll go to Heaven, so then it doesn't count. So he's no longer a hero. Well, if you really want to know, in my opinion a hero is a man who goes down the street in his underpants because he wants to demonstrate his belief in something."

What do you say, Father? There wasn't even any need to ask him whether he was a Turtle. It was really unnecessary. I already knew the answer when I whispered into his ear.

"Are you a Turtle?"

"You bet your sweet . . ." he yelled, wildly happy.

The prescribed oath, the password of Turtles.

26.

Cactus plants and clumps of mesquite, white expanses of sand and desert, desert, desert. Not a house, not a hut, not a single pond in sight. Only silence and desolation. New Mexico, laboratory of the space age, cradle of the new civilization. Was this truly the scene of battles between the pioneers and the Indians, the covered-wagon rushes, the angry Apache raids? Had this truly been the scene of the war between Federal men and bandits, was it really here that Billy the Kid had shot at Sheriff Pat Garrett? Yes, it was. But all that was pre-history. History began down there among the dunes of Alamogordo, where they made the Great Hole of July 16, 1945: the Day of the Bomb, remember? They suspended it on the top of a hundred-foot tower, took shelter inside the little fortress of steel and concrete, raised a small lever, and the Devil exploded in a mushroom from which arose another mushroom and then yet another mushroom: and on the ground a round scar, seething with radioactivity. Some idiot wanted to erect a monument among the dunes of Alamogordo. Somebody, a saint maybe, prevented him. The Great Hole carpeted with weeds was by now a circle of barbed wire enclosing nothing in the midst of nothing. I didn't see it and I wasn't sorry, there were better things to see, Father. There was the city of Juarez, the true Mexico. Sombreros, boots and spurs, tequila, that dirt that appeals to us who are forever washing ourselves, that sloth that appeals to us who are forever hurrying. The border between El Paso and Juarez is an open gate: American citizens pass through it saying U.S.A. I showed my passport and they said there was no need.

"Haga como le gusta a usted, no se incomode, guapa!"

"Muchas gracias, señor!"

"De nada, de nada!"

"Se va por aqui a la Plaza Grande?"

"Todo derecho, guapa."

How heart-warming to speak Spanish. What sweet pleasure to walk along pavements made like pavements, among snotty children and women dressed in red and garish green, with a voice singing *"Hay luna y mi corazon te llama":* the Moon is out and my heart is calling to you. What a comfort to sniff the smell of sweat and garlic: the hell with hygiene, deodorants, chewing gum. Besides these things, nobody asks you who you are, where you're going, what you're doing, whether you're dieting or not, whether you believe in God or not, nobody stops you because you're using your legs instead of wheels, nobody leers at you: "Car broken down? Need any help?" You tell them: I've come to see Little Joe and they think you've come to see your young nephew who's called Joe, Joselito. You tell them that Little Joe's not a nephew but a rocket and they burst out laughing. "Le doy a usted el pesame," I offer you my sympathy. A gate, a friendly tongue, and within the space of a few yards your nightmare is over: you're free again, Father.

I don't know how long I sat there in the Plaza Grande, drinking tequila, listening to that monotonous sing-song *Hay luna y mi corazon te llama*, watching a pigeon doing his droppings on an old man's shoulder and the old man not chasing it away. An hour, maybe, two hours: time here passed differently, it was shorter. Short like happy afternoons spent with a loved one when all is well, you think it ought to last forever but instead, dammit, darkness is falling already, because of a word, a look. Before going to Las Cruces I wanted to see Fort Bliss, the huts where von Braun and Stuhlinger had lived. I stood up reluctantly and maybe this was why, when I saw them, they meant nothing to me: huts of wood now rotten, a barracks in the wide plain. I grumbled to the driver thank you, drive on, and immediately left El Paso: a city neither new nor old, neither clean nor dirty, destined to vanish like its river. For years the Rio Grande has been a bed of nettles, partly because men altered its course, partly because it ran dry. Life is now flowing toward Las Cruces: forty-four miles from El Paso, forty-four thousand inhabitants pressed together between the junction of State Highway 70 with State Highways 80 and 85. It's from Las Cruces that you reach White Sands, the sandy desert reserved for missiles. And it's at Las Cruces that everyone gathers whenever NASA picks White Sands for a rocket-launching. There was a time when Las Cruces was a tourist center, a village built around the crosses of a massacre that took place in 1848. People used to come to attend the fiestas of July and mid-September, to visit the Carlsbad Caverns that preserve traces of the troglodyte era, to enjoy the sun that shines here in perpetual summer and is a good dry sunshine, beneficial to sick people. They used to come to see the Pueblo Indians, who dressed in deerskins, spoke a strange dialect in which *no* means *yes* and the real *no* doesn't exist, evoked the dead and the spirits to ask for rain, considered money as something unclean. They used to come to see the mountains, pink and pointed, never trodden by man: they used to come to pick the flowers that grow in the middle of the desert and bloom only for a single night; they used to come to roll about in sand which is white as snow, light as face powder and clings to you like dust. But the Devil exploded, leaving that round scar, and everything changed. The Pueblos forgot about the dead and the spirits, started wearing shirts and blue jeans, selling little plastic bags of trinitite; the Carlsbad Caverns were enriched with elevators and snack bars where you can get hot dogs and fizzy drinks; the Army took over White Sands completely, Las Cruces became what I saw now from my taxi as I arrived from El Paso—an ugly copy of Florida or Texas, signposts saying *Off Limits,* asphalt ribbons, motels. My motel was called The Palms. There wasn't a single palm to be seen. It was identical to the Cape Colony Inn or the King's Inn: a quadrangle of rooms around a courtyard with a swimming pool in the middle, a lot of automatic cells to drive one mad.

Jack, the publicity man, was already there, together with other characters from Houston, Los Angeles, Washington, who had been given the task of explaining to the press the importance of the Little Joe launching. He came to meet me with his tired gait, his sleepy face, and immediately loaded me with papers which said that Little Joe weighed fifty tons, that it was called Little Joe because it was small compared with the others, that the area in the White Sands zone leased to NASA by the army was ninety square miles, that NASA was at my service if there was anything at all I wanted to see.

"What is there to see besides space laboratories and missiles, Jack?"

"Bah!" said Jack.

"She could see a ranch," remarked a very tall fat character who turned out to be one of Jack's colleagues, Ben James. "New Mexico is ranch country."

"And where are the ranches now?" said Jack.

"Six months ago there was one a few miles from here," Ben James suggested.

"Are you kidding? Six months ago!" said Jack.

"It's not so long," Ben James murmured.

"I'd say it was a very long time ago," Jack concluded. "Anyway, would you like to take her to see the ranch? Come on, take her to see the ranch. Get going, both of you."

So we went, Father.

It was a fine ranch at first sight. With a fine house, a fine garden, a fine swimming pool in the garden and, all around, the enclosure meant for cattle. Odd that there was only one cow: very skinny, all skin and bones. Odd too that the swimming pool contained no water and was covered with withered leaves.

"There's no water in the swimming pool. Have you noticed, Ben?"

"No, there isn't."

"And there aren't any animals there in the enclosure."

"No, there aren't."

"But where are they, Ben?"

"How should I know where they are?"

"And the ranch hands, Ben, where are they?"

"They're nowhere about, obviously."

"Maybe they're in the house. Shall we try?"

"I dunno," said Ben. And he followed me with a mortified air, sorry, as if he were saying: Oh, Lord, what made me put it into her head to see a ranch?

The house was intact. The kitchen door was ajar, as if the owners had just gone out to ride the range. There was a checked tablecloth on the table and on the tablecloth were a dirty saucepan, a few plates and two or three glasses. There were other plates and glasses on the dresser. In the adjoining room there was an unmade bed. A woman's dress hung on a coat hanger.

"Anybody there?" I yelled.

I was answered by the sound of tinkling glasses. The door had slammed in a gust of wind and made the glasses tinkle.

"Anybody there?" I repeated.

"Who do you suppose is here?" Ben grumbled in exasperation. "The house has been abandoned. They've gone. Left."

"Gone?"

"Obviously. They've sold the land to the government and they've gone to live in the city."

"Leaving everything like this?"

"What else should they do? It costs more to move furniture than to buy it now. So, three or four suitcases and they're off."

"But Ben! One gets fond of things!"

"Romantics like you get fond of things. Practical people don't."

I looked at the woman's dress, then at a pair of shoes: there was also a pair of shoes in the bedroom. I listened to that impossible silence. Doesn't silence seem impossible when there's an unmade bed with bedclothes, and a woman's dress and shoes? I tried to convince myself that Ben was mistaken.

"Ben, we used to leave everything like this when the air-raid warning sounded and we had to run—during the war. But we were hoping to come back. Maybe they're hoping to come back too."

"Says you! The whole zone is in the hands of the Army now and sooner or later they'll flatten everything. Two or three bulldozers, and down!"

"Maybe they come here weekends. Maybe we'll see them arriving before long."

"Are you kidding! The place is in the firing area now, you can only come here by day, the missiles are launched at dawn. Christ, Jack was right. Six months is a long time. A long time."

Outside, the cow was licking at a puddle of mud.

"Scram! Scram!" Ben shouted. And he aimed a kick at it, flapped his hand nervously.

The cow looked at us with eyes swimming with melancholy and reproof. Then she lumbered toward the boundary, her parched skin flapping as she went. We returned to The Palms.

Anyway that was a day for spending at The Palms: everything that takes place on the eve of a launching is concentrated in two places, the launch base and the motel. To all intents and purposes taken over by the rocket community, the motel becomes a space stronghold and it is amusing to wander around and spy on its temporary inhabitants. The NASA characters, for example, who, having escaped from the prison of Houston, become more free and easy, like schoolboys on vacation: they've left their helmets behind. Then the representatives of suppliers, North American, Garrett, Douglas, the firms who have collaborated in the construction of the rocket, are even funnier because they look at you as much as to say: I made it, what do you expect? And they seem like husbands whose wives are about to give birth: will it be a boy, my God, will it be a girl, will she need a Caesarian, won't she? Then the journalists. You can picture them, all right, Father. After all, I'm one of them. Listen, journalists are always a disaster when they get together. Nothing ever suits them, they spit on everything, make a nuisance of themselves over every stupid little thing, carry on as if the world were holding its breath waiting for their verdict. But space journalists! Seeing them, or rather hearing them, the first thing you'd think is that they were the ones who invented rockets, so the scientists are wrong in not asking their advice. Ah, if von Braun had telephoned them, if he'd said: excuse me, I'm sorry to bother you, but would you put this small screw here or not? And when the journalists are women, listen, they're really worth meeting. For some mysterious reason they found themselves involved in the business, learned that liquid hydrogen can be used as fuel, and it was like removing the veil from Moslem women—it unleashed them. They're never quiet, they keep on reminding you that they know about certain things, at press conferences they get wrathfully to their feet and ask such terrifying questions as: "Why did you use a propellant that through capacity 95 develops a thrust of 750,000 tons instead of 751,000?" Or: "Why do you give the delta V and delta T for your OAMS burn instead of giving the GMTRC or a RET of 05g? You would go into a 15-degree roll rate when you reach 100,000." And now, Father, the astronauts.

I don't have to tell you that they are the gods of the whole business, the reason why men, women, children staying in other motels all pour into the NASA motel on the eve of a launching, overwhelmed by a sudden need to swim in that swimming pool, eat in that restaurant, drink in that bar. The astronauts know it, and even if the rocket doesn't really require their attendance, they rarely fail to be there. But there are a lot of astronauts, as you know, at that time there were twenty-nine of them; if they all had to attend every launching, they wouldn't be able to train, to study, and you and I would have to go to the Moon. So five or six of them come, or seven or eight; and this is the whole point, because no one ever knows which of them it'll be, and the people have the same expression as children about to open an Easter egg with a novelty inside: Mommy, what d'you suppose is inside the egg? Mommy, will the egg break? The egg breaks a few hours before the rocket is fired, when they arrive in their jets and enter the motel together—a spectacular entrance. All of them, every single one, wear their blue flying suits. It creates a certain effect, that blue blot approaching. If it isn't pale blue, it's orange and that's equally effective, that orange blot approaching. Among the group of five or six, seven or eight, there's nearly always my brother, and my brother is dramatic. Lastly because the setting for their entrance is often a cocktail party: the eve of a launching is inevitably embellished by a cocktail party held at the motel. Outdoors, if it doesn't rain.

This time it was staged outdoors, right by the swimming pool. And the public already seemed very excited about the Easter egg when someone pointed out that it was getting dark: odd that the astronauts hadn't arrived yet. From Houston to the military airport at Las Cruces takes barely three hours and from there to The Palms less than twenty minutes. Each of them was flying his own plane and so . . .

"But what does Control Tower say?"

"Control Tower says he saw them land all right."

"Then why haven't they got here?"

"That's what everyone's saying."

"You don't think they've gone to Juarez, to Irma's?"

"Who's Irma?"

"It's . . . a spot. You know, a spot."

"Oh! Oooh! Please!"

"You don't suppose they've been kidnapped?"

"They might have been kidnapped."

"Get me? With Mexico only a stone's throw away."

"I've never believed in the Russian desire for peace."

"But what use will ours be to the Russians if they don't speak Russian?"

"They can teach them, can't they?"

"They're patriotic, they'll never learn."

"Powers was patriotic too, but he learned."

"Don't talk nonsense."

"Let's be sensible, how were they coming to The Palms?"

"By car, how do you think?"

"And who was going to drive?"

"One of them, of course. Who did you think would drive?"

Everyone had his say and there were many pale faces: the suspicion that the Russians had captured them to take them to Mexico City and from there to Havana and then to Moscow was for most of them as heartbreaking as the suspicion that they might be having a night out at Irma's, a dive where a good family man shouldn't even stop for coffee. Vainly I tried to console them, saying: come on, suppose they have gone to Irma's, what harm is there in that, better Irma than Cuba, yes or no? By the way of reply they glared at me in such a way that I felt like Irma myself: there are those who would rather see them interrogated by Castro than in a brothel. Believe me, Father! Then someone came running in.

"They've found them! They've found them!"

"Where? Oh, God, where?"

"Not at Irma's, I hope!"

"Keep cool. It wasn't Irma's."

"Thank God! Where, then?"

"In a ditch! They turned over in a ditch!"

"Is it bad? Is it bad?"

"The car's a wreck."

"Are they dead?"

"No one knows, no one knows!"

"The police! Get the police!"

"The doctor! Get the doctor!"

"Quick! Let's go! Quick!"

A good many of them went. I'd have followed them if I'd had the courage, but I didn't, Father. Although I hadn't known them long, it was as if I'd always known them, as if they were part of my family, Father. Slowly, irresistibly, they'd been working their way into my life, my affections, and for some minutes I felt the same anguish I feel when something happens to you—an accident, an illness. My first thoughts flew to Theodore, I remember. And also to Pete, of course, and Slayton and Schirra and Shepard, but first of all to Theodore. Theodore was already the one I loved best and what did it matter that our meeting had been so brief? Clock time doesn't count: you can live with someone for twenty years and he's still a stranger to you; you can spend twenty minutes with someone else and he's part of you for the rest of your life. God, that remark of Wernher von Braun's! "There's a fifty-percent chance that they'll die on the Moon. The other fifty percent is that they'll die here on Earth, the way they drive." What had happened? Then a voice burst on my ears. A voice very familiar to me.

"That pimp! That idiot! I saw him, he saw me! I flashed my lights, he flashed his lights! I moved over to my right, he moved over to his left. He'll hit us, I said. He'll hit us, that son of a bitch . . ."

It was Pete. Filthy. I'll never again see anyone as filthy as he was. Earth, soil, dirt of every kind covered his face, his hands, his blue flying suit, what little hair he had was no longer fair but black. And behind him came the others: Shepard, looking more put-out than I can tell you, Gordon Cooper, Jim Lovell—Pete's best friend—and lastly Slayton. That was all.

"Eh, Pete!"

"That son of a bitch! That idiot! I saw him, he saw me. I flashed my lights, he flashed his lights. I moved over to my right, he moved over to his left—"

"Eh, Pete!"

"He'll hit us, I said. He'll hit us, that queer . . ."

"Pete!"

"Oh! Hi!"

"Pete! Where's Theodore?"

"What's Theodore got to do with it?"

"He isn't hurt?"

"What do you mean, hurt? No one's hurt. I swung into the ditch, it's either the car or us, I said to myself. I've got quick reflexes. What do you want Theodore for?"

"Nothing. I was just asking if he was with you."

"Theodore, Theodore! They all want Theodore! You've got me, isn't that enough? And there's Jim, isn't that enough?"

"Yes, sure. I was only asking because—"

"Jim! Hey, Jim! This is Oriano of Project Cheese!"

"Oriana, not Oriano."

"Oriano—aren't you my brother?"

Jim bowed. He was tall and fair, with a long smiling face full of teeth and lips, a horsy face; his eyes were blue and patient and naïve. You've heard about Jim Lovell, haven't you? The one who stayed up in the cosmos fourteen days—you liked him, remember? You said he was well-bred, aristocratic. I thought the same that night. He was well-bred and there was something aristocratic about him and you couldn't understand how he got along so well with Pete. Maybe Pete dominated him a little. Extraordinary how tall men often let themselves be dominated by small men. What's more, I'd have let myself be dominated too, as you'll be able to tell by the following tale. I'm telling it to you not so much to illustrate the kind of atmosphere that surrounds these very famous launchings as to show you the change that was taking place in me. Corruption, you'll call it. O.K., call it corruption, if you want to, and let's say that it's a very slow process. Like catching a cold. You never know how or why a cold starts. Suddenly you sneeze and realize you've got it. So then you start thinking where did I catch it, why, maybe it was that piercing draft, that sudden wind, and you can't track it down, you can only conclude that you must have been in the state for catching cold, the germs found you an easy prey and you couldn't dodge them.

Slayton had gone to the restaurant with Shepard and Cooper. Pete, Jim and I went to a drive-in. My brother has a passion for drive-ins, those shacks by the roadside where you can get a Coca-Cola, a hamburger, a complete meal without getting out of your car and without forks or knives. He maintains that such food is good, infinitely better than French food or Chinese food, he knows nothing about certain things such as eating in a proper civilized way, with a proper civilized wine of a good year and so on. And there we sat in the car, eating and talking about Project Cheese. By now everyone in NASA had heard about it, and Pete was very enthusiastic: the more I think about it, he was laughing, the more I'm drawn to the conclusion that our geologists are a lot of lying bastards and the Moon isn't made of rock, it contains inexhaustible supplies of cheese with holes. Nevertheless, he suddenly exclaimed, the plan was faulty in one respect.

"Have you realized?"

"Not I," said Jim politely.

"Because you're slow on the uptake. And you too. But, begging your pardon, it's so obvious. We can't steal the last quarter of the Moon."

"And why not?" said Jim politely.

"Because if we steal it we'll have nowhere to put our feet or the LEM, amateurs! To steal and then take off again, we need to have a leverage point."

"O.K., then. We'll leave the last quarter of the Moon," said Jim politely.

"It's also better aesthetically," I remarked. "I've always liked the last quarter of the Moon better than the whole Moon."

"Fine fools you are! And what about arousing suspicion? A quarter-Moon that remains a quarter-Moon permanently will arouse more suspicion than a lunar eclipse, won't it? If the Moon disappears altogether, we can always say it got tired of playing satellite to our planet and went to play satellite to another. But if a quarter of the Moon goes on staying there, everyone'll realize that we stole the other three quarters."

"Yes," said Jim politely.

"And who will they blame? Me, of course. Anything that happens, they blame me."

"We'll have to think of something else," Jim and I chorused.

And we started trying to think of something else. It was a beautiful May evening, the kind of evening you like, with a light breeze ruffling your hair. I had almost got over my disappointment at the absence of Theodore. Pete and Jim were taking his place with friendliness, cheerfulness. The only thing I didn't like was the drink imposed by Pete: that root beer I mentioned in another chapter, the one in which I first met him. Root beer is a kind of black liquid that from a distance looks like coffee and you drink it cold, but when you drink it it doesn't taste like coffee, it tastes like medicine, cough syrup, I don't know. Well, listen: I can drink anything, even whiskey, which stinks if you ask me. In Persia I drank pomegranate wine once, and I got it down. In Brazil I drank maté once, and I got that down. In Japan rice brandy, in Dakar I did it with cabbage tea. But root beer, no, that I cannot get down. And yet it was this that triggered off the game. Should I say game?

"Got it," Pete announced, licking his lips that were wet with root beer. "We'll found the "Oriano-Pietro-Giacomo Root Beer Corporation Incorporated and we'll sell root beer on other planets. It'll make us richer than stealing the Moon."

"How'll we do it?" asked Jim politely.

"We'll have a chain of drive-ins, of course!"

"A chain of drive-ins!"

"Sure. Drive-ins always catch on in desert areas and you can't deny the Moon is desert. The other planets are probably desert too and so—"

"It's true there's nothing that bothers you like being thirsty when you're traveling, especially in desert areas," said Jim politely.

"This chain of drive-ins will be salvation from thirst. From thirst, hunger, everything. Obviously as well as root beer we'll sell hot dogs, French fries, hot doughnuts. Nothing fancy, of course: no knives, no forks. Nothing fancy."

"Pioneers don't need knives and forks," said Jim politely.

"Some people will turn their noses up, you have to expect that. But the moment'll come when even the aesthetes will be grateful to us. One thing's certain—on the other planets people will have to travel around by car or something like a car, so from time to time they're sure to need refreshments."

"Ah, yes," said Jim politely.

"And then you know what I say? If we don't do it, someone else will. So we might as well be the ones to do it."

"That's true!" I exclaimed.

Or should I say the words came out of my mouth, Father? That they came out like a sneeze? Sure, a sneeze. Because down with senti-mentality: what would you build to survive where there's nothing at all? The Pitti Palace? Rheims Cathedral? You'd build little fortresses, Father, inns where you can get refreshment: and the inns of our day are drive-ins. Ugly, yes, an outrage to the landscape, agreed. But when you're thirsty, when you're hungry, you don't look for beauty: you look for something useful and nothing else. No Pitti Palace, no Rheims Cathedral can quench your thirst, assuage your hunger; only drive-ins can and nothing else. No? Listen, Father: in his *Martian Chronicles* Ray Bradbury has drawn a great character, the one called Parkhill, the astronaut who lands with the fourth expedition to Mars. Sam Parkhill is ignorant—quite the opposite of Jeff Spender, the archeologist who falls in love with the towers of silver and crystal, the remains of an ancient magnificent civilization. Sam Parkhill couldn't care less about towers of silver and crystal. He's a beast, he shoots at them, destroys like HR in Los Angeles, remember? that Bill in Houston. But when Spender yelled in torment: "We Earth men have a genius for spoiling everything beautiful, we'll call that canal Rockefeller Canal, that sea the Dupont Sea, we'll set up hot-dog stands next to the golden sarcophagi," Park-hill gave voice to words both terrible and true: "Go to hell! We've got to settle down somewhere!" And it's Spender who dies, Father, and Parkhill who survives. With evil? With evil. With ugliness? Yes. Yet I don't feel I can blame him too much when he sets up his stand for hot dogs, French fries and doughnuts, and says to his wife, who has joined him with the barrels of beer: "We'll have to work hard, Elma. We'll be flooded with people who want to eat, Elma, people who want to drink."

"That's true, Pete," I repeated.

"Not a stupid idea, what do you say?"

"No, not stupid at all."

"They won't be works of art, but they'll serve the purpose, won't they?"

"Yes, Pete. They'll serve the purpose."

"We can always hang up a few pictures," said Jim politely.

"A few reproductions of some good paintings."

"Mona Lisa or the Three Graces."

"Mona Lisa with a glass of root beer in her hand."

"The Three Graces dancing around a barrel of root beer."

"Those who come after us can make beautiful things."

"After they've had something to eat and drink."

"None of us is Sam Parkhill."

"Sam who?" Pete shouted.

"Just a man. It's not important."

"Well? Is it a deal?"

"It's a deal."

And we went back to The Palms, laughing like children. But we knew that the game wasn't entirely a joke and that the joke contained a great truth. Over the great truth we were in agreement and because of that I felt at ease with them: as we entered the bar I was even able to face Slayton's look, that tired look that seemed to reprove the world, an accusation stretched on taut steel wires. I faced those steel wires and saw that they knew all: that we would take drive-ins to the Moon, that we would contaminate space with hot dogs and pies. Full of resignation, they were just waiting. And just asking to go up there before we got there. I went up to him like Sam Parkhill going up to Jeff Spender.

"Hi, dolly."

"Hi, Deke. What are you doing?"

"Drinking whiskey."

"Will you come and sit with us?"

He reluctantly climbed off the bar stool and silently followed us to a table, bringing his glass of whiskey. As he passed, the women eyed him greedily, the men seemed to cower slightly. Only Pete seemed able to stand up to him, Pete who looked so small next to him and yet was so strong—because basically they were made of the same stuff, distinguished only by different kinds of wisdom, different ways of facing the sacrifice.

"Know what, Chief? We've formed the Oriano-Pietro-Giacomo Root Beer Corporation to install a chain of drive-ins on the Moon, on Mars and on the other planets."

"Ah, yes?"

From an infinite distance the Chief turned that accusation stretched on taut steel wires and set his sights on Pete with eyes like two rifles. Pete faced up to the attack, nose in the air.

"Yes. And to make them pretty we'll hang up some pictures: Mona Lisa with a glass of root beer in her hand and the Three Graces dancing around a barrel of root beer."

"Ah, yes?"

"I don't think he approves," Pete remarked to Jim.

Jim remained prudently silent. I didn't know what to say: I had suddenly lost Parkhill's boldness.

"He's got no business sense because he's got gray hair," Pete insisted, still with his nose in the air.

"That's not true," I said. "He's got chestnut hair."

"Gray."

"Chestnut."

"It's gray," grumbled the Chief. And he bent his head to show me. His head was a carpet of velvet, his hair was cut very short. And it was gray.

"Convinced? Satisfied?" Pete gloated.

The Chief, without a word, went on drinking his whiskey. At the end of the bar a jukebox was playing something sad, two or three couples were dancing. But it was as if all these things didn't concern him at all, as if he didn't see them or hear them. Suddenly he pricked up his ears at some sound that only he could hear and his lips framed some words as if he were talking to himself:

"The wind'll rise tonight."

Pete was rummaging through my handbag, fishing out little combs, lipsticks, identity cards, hairpins, and arranging them all around Jim's glass. He went on, undisturbed.

"I hadn't noticed."

"Nor had I," said Jim politely.

"It'll rise. It's rising already," the reluctant voice repeated.

"How anyone in here, with all this smoke and all this noise, can say the wind is rising, don't ask me," Pete grumbled, sniffing at a bottle of perfume he'd taken from my handbag.

"The wind'll rise and there'll be a sandstorm."

"Here's hoping! God willing! We'll stay here another thirty-six hours!" Pete cried, putting everything back in my handbag.

"Why? Won't the rocket go?" I asked.

"It'll go, it'll go," Pete chanted.

"It won't go. But we'll have to be up at three, all the same. We'd better all go and get some sleep. It's midnight already."

He spoke in the decided way of one who is used to being obeyed, and I would have obeyed him if it hadn't been for Pete.

"The twist! They're playing the twist!" Pete yelled.

I let myself be dragged off for the twist and when we returned to our table the Chief had gone. Outside the wind was rising. I fell asleep listening to the wind and I had a dream, Father.

The dream took place on Mars, and on Mars I was Elma Parkhill, owner of a drive-in on the Dupont Sea. The drive-in was identical to the one I'd been to with Pete and Jim, a few planks fixed up like a shack, and it spoiled the whole landscape: blue fields beneath a great green sky, crystal city with golden sarcophagi. But I was frying, frying hot dogs, French fries, doughnuts, with Pete and Jim, and I was happy. "Elma, we'll make a wad of money this year," Sam Parkhill was saying and then he peed in a golden sarcophagus. "Loads of money, Sam, loads of it. But don't pee in the sarcophagus," I was repeating as I picked up a barrel of root beer. Suddenly Jeff Spender arrived, the archeologist of the expedition. His hair was gray, cut very short, a velvet carpet: he set his sights on us with eyes like two rifles and his look was a reproof to the world. "A glass of root beer, Mr. Spender? Some French fries, Chief?" I asked. But he refused everything with a curt gesture and, speaking in a voice that was suddenly your voice, Father, he answered: "We Earth men have a genius for ruining everything. I told you, Elma, men will always be the same: on Earth or on the Moon or on Mars. I'm disappointed in you, Elma. You're no longer my daughter." Then Jeff Spender pricked up his ears at some sound that only he could hear and, as if talking to himself, said: "The wind'll rise tonight and sweep away your damn drive-in."

27.

At three in the morning the sandstorm was blowing up. And it was my brother who yelled the news at me on the telephone.

"Wake up! Out of bed! It's three o'clock and that guy was right. Christ. He's always right."

"Who, Pete?"

"The Chief. Who else? Wind, sand, the works. If you go out in it, it'll blind you."

"Then I'm going back to sleep."

"The office says the wind'll drop. If it drops, it goes. Out of bed! Out!"

It's ghastly waking up in the middle of the night: I don't know how these space people can do it. They wake up at half past two, at three, sometimes they don't go to sleep at all. They truly have iron health.

"My God, what a sacrifice! Where are you, Pete?"

"In the damn hall, that's where. Ready to go. With Jim. We'll have to spend all night in the cold, dammit."

"And what'll you be doing all night in the cold, dammit?"

"Recovering the capsule, that's what we'll be doing. I hang around there with Jim, waiting for her to come down. When she comes down, I pick her up. Providing she doesn't land on my head."

"Who?"

"The spacecraft. It might come down in the right place, and if I'm in the right place too, it would squash me like a fly."

"Couldn't you get out of her way?"

"Right. I hadn't thought of that. You're on the ball, brother. So long, eh? So long. Oh, it's cold! It's so cold! I'm small, I feel the cold!"

It was really cold: the cold of the desert, a biting cold. Shivering, I went over to the restaurant to get some coffee. The restaurant was full and the tables were set as in the daytime. On the counter there were hard-boiled eggs, roast beef, French fries, everything as it was by day, and people were lining up with their plates to serve themselves. I was sleepy, but I was awakened by a reluctant voice behind me.

"Have you slept?"

"Less than two hours."

"The night before a launching you go to bed, you don't stay up dancing the twist. Eat something."

"I'm not hungry."

"You'll get hungry enough out in the cold. Eat."

He filled up my plate as if I were a disobedient recruit.

"Will it go, Deke?"

"No. It won't go."

"The meteorological office says the wind should drop."

"Your little brother's meteorological office. The meteorological office is wrong. Eat. So long."

He left shortly after with two Senators who had come to Las Cruces for the launching, as representatives of Congress. Shepard and Cooper left in another car. Jack told me that only Pete and Jim were assigned to capsule recovery, the other astronauts would stay in the blockhouse with the scientists and technicians. Around the motel there was a coming and going of cars, of buses, and everywhere such excitement, the kind that precedes important baseball games, you know? Low voices talking in broken phrases far off in the darkness, hurrying shadows that disappeared and appeared again . . . When everyone had gone, I took a seat with Jack in the last bus, which was empty except for us and the driver, a young Negro. Unwillingly the driver started up the engine, drove off. Jack was in the back, having a quiet sleep. I sat in the front and you were so distant, Father. So far away.

Maybe because it was the first time I was going to see a rocket-launching. Maybe because I felt so alone inside that bus and undistracted by faces, sounds. Maybe because Theodore's words came back into my mind: "Beauty doesn't have to be green or full of sound, the desert is yellow but it's beautiful just the same, mountains are silent but they're beautiful, I often go to White Sands and it isn't true that it's ugly, beauty is something you have to look for, and if you look well you'll find it yes because there is beauty everywhere, even where there's only silence, the silence is beautiful and the solitude too . . ." Maybe all these things together, I do not know: the fact remains that dawn would never look so divine to my eyes. Never again, Father. The dawns I remembered were dawns in the city: shuffling of footsteps on the pavement, a screech of brakes from a passing car, a voice calling. Or they were dawns in the woods: the singing of birds, the rustle of branches, the whisper of a thousand invisible awakenings. Or they were dawns by the sea, a wash of waves, a caress of moist wind, a flying gull, you know? Dawn over the desert is different, Father. It is a silent dawn, motionless, petrified, without the pulse of life, soundless. Dawn and nothing else. Here no birds sang. No branches rustled. No water flowed. No footsteps shuffled. Only the silence that not even the bus could break as it slid along the asphalt, only that darkness that spread even to the sand, to its chalky whiteness, its cacti. A darkness that loomed over you, blocking your way like a hedge, but suddenly we were through it and it was dawn, light, colors never seen before, gold pink violet, slashes of gold in the pink and the mauve, tremendous and glorious, terrifying and sublime, without tenderness, a dawn out of Genesis.

What did it matter if at a certain point the spell was broken and like a blow in the eyes you saw towering missiles, soldiers with revolvers, signs reading MISSILE RANGER CENTER, and heard suspicious voices? Beyond the mountains that enclose the prohibited area like a great basin, the miracle was beginning again, and there he stood. The rocket. Silvery, slender, with that white vapor issuing from his bowels, that soft whistling issuing from his mouth. A rocket hasn't got bowels, you'll say, or a mouth. A rocket's just a rocket, you'll say, a machine, not a living thing. But I tell you that a rocket is no longer a machine, he's a living thing, he breathes, and that vapor is his breath, that whistling is his cry. You know why he's crying? Because it hurts to be burning and he understands that he's going to die. Like a man. Because like a man he has lungs and nerves and brain: do you find it grotesque, Father? I bet you do, Father. You understand only plants and animals and you don't admit that anything can live without green, without blood. You smile if I call it *him*. You answer me that when people speak of a rocket they say *it*. Well, I say he. He, him. Not it. And you have to see him to understand him, Father. And when you've seen him you feel moved, you feel sorry that he's going to die. You feel sorry he's standing there all by himself in the middle of the desert, a condemned creature waiting for his last hour, his execution . . . Isn't dawn always the hour for executions?

I was very happy to hear that the meteorological office had been wrong as the Chief had foretold, that the wind wasn't going to drop, that the sandstorm wouldn't calm down before late evening. I looked at the rocket, I looked in his eyes, and with closed lips I said to him, "Courage, Little Joe, courage. Be strong. Your execution has been deferred by a day."

28.

It often happens: a breath of wind and the rocket doesn't go. If it isn't a breath of wind, it's a grain of sand. If it isn't a grain of sand, it's a drop of rain: as if God were having fun humiliating us, making fun of the creatures we invent only so we may kill them. And the astronauts are pleased because this way they get a longer holiday: no geology classes, no tortures in the centrifuge, sweet idleness by the swimming pool, where they gather like schoolboys playing hookey. Look at them there. Shepard with his aloofness, Jim with his English-aristocrat grace, Cooper with his stubborn taciturnity, Slayton with his usual inaccessibility, and lastly Pete: in the most absurd bathing trunks a man could wear, red and brown striped, down to his knees. What a temptation, all of them, for the women staying at The Palms. Like an excited swarm of flies descending on a slice of buttered bread, the women gather on every side, desperately trying to attract attention. Uttering shrill little cries, diving from the high springboard, losing shoulder straps, while Pete shuts his eyes in fright and squeaks: "What's happening? What are they doing?"

"Come on, don't be a hypocrite. They're flirting with you because you're astronauts."

"You don't. You've only got eyes for Theodore."

"Theodore is Theodore."

"And who am I?"

"You're my brother."

"Listen, gal, how many of these brothers have you got?"

"Very few. Theodore is one. You are another . . ."

"And the Chief? Come on, you like the Chief."

"Yes, but he's not my brother."

"Why?"

"Because it is difficult, almost impossible, to be my brother in such a world."

"I don't understand."

"You cannot understand, brother."

"Boy! What does it mean, being your brother?"

"It means being like me."

"Am I like you?"

"Somehow, sometimes."

"When?"

"When you say that a hero is a man who goes down the street in his underpants because he wants to demonstrate his belief in something. And when you collect funny useless hats. I do too."

"Theodore isn't like you. He doesn't collect funny hats."

"Not really. But when I was good, when I was a child, I was like Theodore. And when I am good, when I am a child, sometimes it happens, I am like Theodore."

"Boy! And don't you like Jim?"

"Yes, but he never talks."

"Well, he smiles a lot."

"So I've noticed. Is he shy?"

"We're all shy. Aren't you?"

"No."

"Shy people are usually lonely people. Then you're not lonely?"

"Yes, I am. Lonely and alone."

"Why?"

"Because I want to be."

"Don't you get bored being alone?"

"No. In fact, I'm always alone, even when I'm with people."

"What people?"

"A man. People."

"Not me. I can't live alone. The only thing that gets me down about this damn Moon is that when you're walking on it you're alone: there isn't so much as a dog you can say 'Look' to, or give a shove to, get me? I enjoy walking with people, I talk to them, when I get home and those four boys jump all over me and my wife grumbles: 'The other day you know what they did, they broke my grandfather's portait, they tore the living-room curtains,'—well, when this happens I am happy. Because people say: 'But what do they do, these astronauts, what do they do?' They don't do anything special, get me? They don't do anything different from anyone else. They have boys who jump all over them, a wife who complains 'did you see, they broke Grandfather's portrait, they tore the dining-room curtains, and then there are the bills to be paid, the rent, how are we going to manage this month, etcetera etcetera amen.' And then sometimes they get fed up, these astronauts, and they curse Mars, the Moon: they'd like to be—I don't know— dictators of Portugal."

"Dictators of Portugal?"

"I would. If it weren't that my kids might throw it in my face one day—'Daddy, why were you dictator of Portugal?'—I'd have a shot at it. I've got a friend there, a minister or something: he'd give me a hand to get out of debt for the Coca-Cola."

"What Coca-Cola?!"

"Well . . . I must tell you that I like wine and this minister gave me a bottle of wine. I was so pleased with the wine that I stole I don't know how many gallons of Coca-Cola from the Navy—you know, the concentrated stuff. Then I took it to the minister, diluted the concentrated Coca-Cola with a lot of water, multiplying it like Our Lord at the Marriage in Cana. He was so grateful that he said: 'Listen, if you want, I'll make you dictator of Portugal.' Man! If anyone's going to be dictator, why not me? I wouldn't bother anybody, I'd spend all day by the sea eating peanuts, I wouldn't have any more problems paying rent, etcetera etcetera. And I'd tell it to go f--- itself, that damn Moon where I'll have to walk by myself."

Pete was in great form that day. And that was the day I promised him the wine: remember all that business about the wine, Father? Traveling will spoil it, you said. Come on, let's put it in bottles, I said. I haven't got any bottles, why should I buy bottles for those Moon people I can't stand? I'll buy them then, what's that got to do with it? All right, buy them then, buy them, Romeo the farmer won't put any wine in them anyway. Why won't he? He won't because I'll tell him not to. But what have they ever done to you? Mother protested, why have you got it in so for those poor boys? Go on, give them a little wine, it'll do them good! I'll give them exactly nothing. And Mother: you're wrong, besides you could write on the bottles *This is the wine that is drunk in the heavens*—think of the success. What are you saying, woman, some things I don't stoop to, what do you take me for, I'm an honest man, how dare you? So in the end I had to buy the wine myself, forty-eight bottles of Chianti picked by the wine expert Stefano Zaccone of Aqui and bottled by the Marchese Alberto Pizzorni of Alessandria, twenty-four bottles for Pete and twenty-four bottles for Jim, who otherwise would be hurt, and do you know what happened? Well, I've never told you, every time the subject cropped up you turned your back on me. But I'll tell you now. What happened was that when everything was ready to be shipped we discovered that exporting wine to America was forbidden, except with a special permit from the President or someone. I wrote to Pete and Jim to get this special permit from the President or someone, but Pete and Jim refused, saying Johnson would probably take us for alcoholics and we'd lose our jobs. I reported to Marchese Pizzorni that Pete and Jim were afraid of losing their jobs and he suggested we ask the Red Cross for help. I wrote to Pete and Jim to ask the Red Cross for help and they replied Oriano, we can hardly say we're sick. I had to bother the Ministry of Foreign Affairs, the State Department, the Immigration Bureau, the Wine Traders Union, and it was only after three months that the bottles left on a ship that stopped at the Azores, at Newfoundland, then went down the St. Lawrence to Toronto. At Toronto the bottles were loaded on a train that crossed Indiana, Illinois, Missouri, Oklahoma and finally reached Houston, Texas, and when they reached Houston, Texas, well, the forty-eight bottles were almost all broken, Father. Satisfied?

"Pete, if I send you the wine, what'll you do?"

"I'll bring Theodore to Cape Kennedy for you."

"To Cape Kennedy?"

"Sure. In fifteen days they're launching the Saturn rocket."

"And you're coming?"

"Sure I'm coming: who'll fire the rocket if I don't? I'm coming and I'll bring Theodore."

"It's a deal."

"So long then, I'm going to bed. I've got to get up at two, remember? I'll ring you, huh? I'll wake you before I go."

A little group of teenage girls were hanging around the swimming pool, pretty little things. One was wearing a sweater and pants of very pale pink jersey and in this outfit she jumped into the water, then came up the steps and jumped in again. All wet, that jersey became more transparent than Cellophane and, well, do I make myself clear? The eyes of Cooper and Shepard seemed to fall into the water with her, Jim was shaken by a tremendous fit of coughing, only the Chief remained calm, but at the third plunge he loosened his tie. I was struck by this, I remember, because it was as if the gesture made a noise and everything around us stopped: the wind, the sand, our very breath. That gesture gave one a glimpse of a repressed temptation, of a need to get over his wall and shout: hey, guys, I'm here! I clenched my fists, I remember, and silently said to him: come over the wall, come over, you're young, you're strong, you're alive, forget your dignity, by God, stop thinking about the Moon and the stars. But he only straightened his tie, got to his feet, buttoned his jacket to the last button and went off with heavy tread.

"So long, people."

"So long, Deke."

"Get to bed early, eh?"

"Yes, sir."

He didn't come to the cocktail party that evening, and Pete didn't either. Jim, Shepard and Cooper came and they were surrounded by the local girls, who had rosettes pinned to their bosoms and the word Miss Something on the rosette. The party was organized by the local Chamber of Commerce and it gave me a chance for a last attempt to show you obedience, Father. A letter from you had reached me at Houston, the one where you talked about Indians, remember? "It appears that you're about to go to New Mexico and perhaps you don't know that there are some Indian reservations there, especially Apache-Mescaleros. It would be much more intelligent to visit them than to waste your time with rockets and it would disintoxicate you a little. Why don't you visit them?" I asked the local Chamber of Commerce representative if I could see the Indians and he answered very happily that they had somebody just for that, a lady called Jeanette: when would I be leaving Las Cruces? Immediately after the launching of Little Joe. O.K., Jeanette would take me there right after the launching of Little Joe. O.K. And I went to bed and was awakened at three by Pete's call.

"Out of bed! It's three o'clock!"

"Oh, God, Pete. Has the wind dropped?"

"Dropped nothing! The meteorological office says it won't drop."

"Then I'm not coming. It won't go anyway."

"It won't go! But we still have to go. Maybe he'll decide it'll go and it'll go. Christ! He's always right."

"Who?"

"What d'you mean, who? The Chief. Who else? He looks like Moses standing there with his finger in the air. So long."

"So long. See you at the pool this afternoon."

"At the pool, at the pool!"

The restaurant was as full as the night before. Tables were set, roast meat and potatoes on the counter, people lined up, plates in hand, that reluctant voice behind me.

"Hi, dolly."

"Hi, Deke."

"Have you slept?"

"Five or six hours."

"More than enough. Come on, eat."

"Will it go, Deke?"

"Yes. It'll go."

"The meteorological office says no."

"Your little brother's meteorological office says no. The meteorological office is wrong."

"But the wind's still blowing and so's the sandstorm."

"The wind'll stop inside of two hours. And so will the sandstorm."

Two hours later it had all stopped. Jack and I reached the launch area at five o'clock and countdown was already at "sixty minutes." Erect on his place of execution, now alone in the middle of the desert, Little Joe was waiting, doomed to die, no longer hoping for pardon. His breath was panting, the vapor issued thick from his bowels, his whistling was as heart-rending as a call for help. "As you know, it will explode at a height of twenty-five thousand feet," Jack was saying. "The explosion will fire the rocket of the Escape Tower and the Tower will separate, taking with it the Apollo spacecraft. See the spacecraft up there on top?" Yes, I could see it. It looked like the hood that they used to put on prisoners to take them to the gallows, and the two portholes in the Apollo were the eyeholes in the hood. "See the Escape Tower? On top of the Apollo?" Yes, I could see it. It looked like a top hat placed on his head for a game, a cruel joke.

"Why are you shivering?"

"Who's shivering?"

"You're shivering. Are you cold? Do you want my jacket?"

"No, Jack. It doesn't matter."

"I told you to bring your coat. Sergeant, have you got a jacket for the lady?"

"Please, take mine, I'm not cold."

"Thank you, Sergeant."

The enclosure was full of troops. Generals, sergeants, privates. There were more troops than journalists, NASA officials, representatives from supply firms. And they weren't cold, but I was trembling even in the jacket, as if instead of Little Joe it was I who was going to my death. Who knows, maybe the Chief and Cooper and Shepard were also shivering a little in the blockhouse down there. Who knows, maybe Pete and Jim were a little moved as they waited among the mesquite and the cactus down there.

"Attention! Forty minutes . . ."

Foolishnesses, Father. They were not moved at all.

"Attention! Thirty minutes . . ."

It wasn't an agony for them.

"Attention! Twenty minutes . . ."

How long that agony was, how cruel. And how cold the voice over the loudspeaker. Like the voice of one commanding a firing squad.

"Attention! Nine minutes . . ."

How still the hollow was. The sky was a metallic blue. It's over, Little Joe. A few more seconds and they'll kill you.

"Squad! Atten-tion!"

Be strong, Little Joe.

"Five . . . four . . . three . . ."

Farewell, Little Joe.

"Two . . . one . . ."

Now, Little Joe.

"Lift-off!"

A burst of flame out of the Apocalypse. A bellow out of Genesis. And Little Joe sways uncertainly, shudders, rises, slow, less slow, now fast, faster, very fast, a soaring arrow leaving behind a flame-colored comet, beautiful, elegant, full of grace, of dignity. Die well, Little Joe, die a little higher up, much higher up . . . He broke up without warning. He disintegrated suddenly with a roar that seemed a shriek of pain and the sky in that spot became thousands of sparks, shattered steel falling down in long silver rain, tears that sparkled like jewels. I was looking at the silver, the jewels, and I didn't see the tower that was shooting away, carrying to safety the three men who weren't there yet. I saw it when it was already climbing, arrow again and comet again, and then I saw the spacecraft separate and drop like lead, devouring the miles, a white stone coming back to Earth, and suddenly it burst in a great red flower that became two red flowers that opened and there were three red flowers, three parachutes coming down with no hurry now, floating in the air, and then they plunged down behind a mountain to give the spacecraft to Pete, whom I could imagine swearing and pouncing like a cat.

"Did you like it?" Jack asked.

"Yes, I liked it."

"A lot?"

"A lot, Jack."

"Hey, you're not going to cry?"

"I am, though."

"For Little Joe?"

"No, not for Little Joe."

"Then what for?"

"Because . . ."

I wasn't able to say it, Father. I wasn't able to say that for one stupendous minute I had made my peace with men, I had realized that men are truly great, Father. They're still great when they substitute plastic grass for grass, and change urine into drinking water, and use wheels instead of legs, and forget the green and the blue, they're still great when they turn Paradise into Hell, when they kill the creatures they've given life to. And I was proud to have been born among men instead of among trees or fishes: I was proud because . . .

". . . because, Jack, you see, for one minute it seemed as if I saw men gambling with God."

29.

So it wasn't exactly the best day for my visit to the Apache-Mescaleros, Father. But the trip was all arranged and that nice little woman named Jeanette couldn't have been more eager to take me, to leave as soon as possible. It would take nearly two hours to reach the reservation. We left at eleven. Slayton, Shepard and Cooper were still in the blockhouse examining the results of the launch, Jim and Pete were still in the middle of the desert studying their capsule. Goodbye, swimming pool. The morning was hot and Jeanette very likable—a little face full of wrinkles, a head of white curls, and necklaces, bracelets, earrings of turquoise or silver, gifts from her ex-pupils when she used to teach music and English to the Apaches. She had taught them for fifteen years and she loved them most tenderly.

"I so much like taking people there. But nobody ever asks to see them. Are you going for a feature?"

"No, no."

"What then? It seems so odd that you want to go out there. I mean, I don't know, you seem so interested in other things. The Moon . . ."

"Well, I'm curious to know what the Apache-Mescaleros think about the journey to the Moon."

"The very worst; I can tell you that. I've never asked them, but I'm sure of it. I was on the reservation when Teller, Fermi and Oppenheimer exploded the bomb. At five in the morning. Nobody had told those poor Indians anything about anything, of course. Nobody knew anything about anything, and when the bomb exploded . . ." Jeanette drew a long breath. "They came out of their huts yelling, the sight of that mushroom just drove them crazy. They gathered in front of the church on the high ground and they weren't even able to pray. They just kept yelling, like coyotes. Stop yelling, I kept telling them. Listen to your schoolteacher. Pray instead. But they just kept yelling like coyotes. What do you expect them to think of the journey to the Moon? With loathing, they think of it. With all possible loathing."

"Jeanette, did you see the Little Joe launching?"

"Yes, I saw it."

"Did you like it?"

"It left me cold. Or rather, it irritated me. Those cursed space people. They take away your land for their stupid missiles and they don't even ask permission. All they ask you is: do you want to cooperate with us? If you say yes, they have you out in a flash and pay you a fifth of what your land's worth. A friend of mine had a house and a ranch right there where we were this morning. They flattened her house, dismantled her ranch, and all she has to show for it is a little bundle of dollars. Today the government owns three-quarters of New Mexico; nobody does any farming or stock-raising any more. The rockets have put an end to that too, the agriculture here is ended by money. The Moon, the Moon, what are *we* getting out of the Moon? The bases at White Sands and Holloman belong to the Air Force; the space men and their families buy everything at military stores. What are *we* getting out of the Moon?"

"Indeed."

She glanced at me suspiciously.

"What does that mean: indeed?"

"Well, that I understand."

"Uhm. The stock-raisers had managed to irrigate the desert and hundreds and hundreds of ranches were springing up here in New Mexico. Thousands of horses and cows were grazing. Now the irrigation pipes are all rusty and the wooden fences are all rotten. There's nothing left. Only rockets, missiles, rockets! They do nothing but fire rockets, missiles. We're enraged."

"Indeed."

She glanced at me suspiciously again. "On every road there's a sign: *Danger—Peligro.* But where does the danger end? At the edge of the road? The railroad runs alongside White Sands for miles and miles. A deflection of a fraction of an inch and the missile lands on the train. Or a car. We're sick of their space effort. We're sick of the Moon. Aren't you?"

"You see, Jeanette—"

She didn't give me time to finish.

"You've had the Revelation, haven't you? You've been touched by Grace."

"Who says so, Jeanette?"

"Your eyes say so. I learned from the Indians how to understand people by looking at their eyes. There's something in your eyes that tells me you're very different from yesterday. I didn't see you yesterday, but I'm sure you were different. Probably you were different this morning too. Then, at six, when that contraption went up, you changed."

"I don't know, Jeanette."

But I did know, Father. And I hesitated to admit it because I wanted to be very sure. Because it was too important. It was the same as finding yourself on the brink of doubt when you're about to leave one religion and embrace another. A trace of doubt still existed, nourished by Jeanette. And it held me back, with the fear of not having defended myself hard enough. But soon it would be over because I had seen men gambling with God and the new religion was bewitching me, finally to leave me serene and maybe happy.

"I don't know, Jeanette."

"Liar. Your eyes . . ."

"What's in my eyes?"

"Stars, my dear."

I closed them abruptly, with a rather false laugh, saying it was just sleepiness and I was going to have a nap. And I really did fall asleep.

I awoke in the forgotten fragrance of leaves. We had left the desert, were climbing a mountain and the whole world here was in leaf: forests of fir and pine, meadows of clover, coolness. There were even cypresses: I hadn't seen them for so long. The cypresses of home. It was so long since I'd seen birds, butterflies, rabbits. He had stopped at the side of the road, the rabbit, and he was looking at us unafraid, only annoyed. A lovely spot, wonderful. It was a bit spoiled by the small houses, the television aerials, the cars, but it was almost perfect. Besides, we'd soon be reaching the reservation of the Apache-Mescaleros and then it would be perfect.

"Lovely spot, Jeanette."

"You'll see."

"When will we get there?"

"We're there already!"

"Already? We've only been traveling for just over an hour, Jeanette."

"I drove fast. You were sleeping, anyway."

"I see. What are these small houses?"

"The Indians' houses."

A terracotta-colored youth with a checked shirt and blue jeans was leaning against a hedge and listening to a transistor radio.

"Who's that?"

"An Indian. What did you think?"

A girl with tight-fitting pants and bleached hair was crossing the road, tottering on high heels.

"Who's that?"

"An Indian girl! What did you think?"

And the elegant lady who was receiving me in her office, arrogantly holding out pounds of papers I would never read, information about the Apache-Mescaleros, who could she be? And this old woman whom I asked for a drink of water, who answered not water because it isn't sterilized, better a Seven-Up, who could she be? And this damned beatnik who was spitting chewing gum at my feet, who could he be? And this Catholic priest who was telling me about the progress of the Mescaleros in their catechism lessons? Did you really expect, Father, that I would find Indians dressed in doeskin and living in tents? Did you really expect that their wisdom would be immune to the witchcraft that had cast its spell on me, that the flash of a bomb would be enough to frighten them, to leave them uncorrupted? You know them well, Father, the Apache-Mescaleros. They are the peasants you speak with every day in Chianti who can no longer do without television and emigrate to the city, who are no longer satisfied with a Lambretta and buy themselves a 600 to drive a few miles. They are Gianni, Romeo, Romeo's daughter, the road-sweeper, the shepherd who brings us cottage cheese in his Volkswagen. Gianni who refuses to spray the vines with copper sulphate because it's troublesome and he'd rather use fungicides —he was told about them by his son who doesn't want to work on the farm and works in a factory in Florence. Romeo who won't beat down the chestnuts because it's such an effort and it isn't worth it, who's going to climb up to the top of those trees, give me a helicopter and I'll go up, this is 2000, isn't it? His daughter who doesn't want to work in the fields and prefers to be a slave in the city and even refuses to strip the irises because it spoils the polished fingernails she's so proud of, and she keeps up with fashion, on Sundays instead of wearing her best dress she wears blue jeans as they do in America. The road-sweeper who sweeps the road with a transistor radio in his belt and knows more about the Giants and the Yankees than he does about the football of Rome and Milan. The shepherd who without his Volkswagen feels lost, a motorcycle isn't enough for him, a bicycle makes him sneer. You know them, Father, the Apache-Mescaleros.

"Twenty-five years ago, when I came to be a schoolteacher here, it was very different," said Jeanette, "but the old folks have died and the young are the same as they are in Las Cruces and El Paso. They don't even speak the Mescalero language any more: now they can only speak English."

"Is that so?"

"Why not? Aren't they American citizens? And we were the ones who changed their language, their dress, their customs, so should we condemn or despise them?"

"No, no."

"You seem disappointed."

"Not in the least, Jeanette. But . . ."

"But what?"

"I'd still like to find one of the old ones—an old Indian, I mean. Not for myself. For my father. He likes the old Indians. If I could find just one . . ."

"There is one!" Jeanette said happily. "There's the son of Geronimo."

"Geronimo?"

"The dreaded Apache who used to scalp every white man he met. The one who scalped thirty-six of them on the hill where the church stands now."

"Perfect. How old is he?"

"Eighty-five, eighty-six."

"A real Indian?"

"A real Indian."

"With a flat nose and terracotta-colored skin?"

"With a flat nose and terracotta-colored skin."

"With a feathered headdress?"

"Yes, a feathered headdress."

"And he goes *ugh?*"

"He goes *ugh.*"

Dear Jeanette started the motor, drove off toward Apache Summit, the highest point of the Sierra Blanca, home of the son of Geronimo. The asphalt road was very wide, we got there in half an hour. A place of enchantment. God, those fir trees tall as cathedrals, those ceilings of branches, that fragrance of violets.

In the midst of the cathedrals of green there rose, complete with neon signs, a modern snack bar.

"That! Geronimo's son shouldn't allow it, Jeanette."

"Are you kidding? It's *his!* He got rich with this snack bar."

"Jeanette—"

"No, keep calm. This is the very Indian you're looking for. If you aren't careful, he'll scalp you."

He scalped me, all right, that rogue. For a picture showing him at the age of six in his father's arms, he asked no less than two dollars and a half. For a little book that related the story of Geronimo he wanted no less than eight dollars. For a lucky charm with a hen's feather he asked me for no less than twenty dollars. He sat at a table laden with these delights, with his feathered headdress, his terracotta-colored skin, his flat nose, and with every *ugh* my wallet grew thinner.

"Listen, son of Geronimo, don't you think this picture's a bit expensive?"

"That's the price and I'm not coming down. *Ugh!*" he replied in perfect English.

"But the price of this little book isn't the price you said. Look: it's printed on it. The price is one dollar and ten cents."

"The dollar ten doesn't include the signature, and this little book is signed by me, son of the Terrible Geronimo. The signature of the son of the Terrible Geronimo is worth six dollars and ninety cents."

"Son of Geronimo, you know you're a really modern character?"

"I'm modern, yes."

"If I buy your lucky charm with the hen's feather too, will you make me a present of your photograph?"

"No."

Jeanette intervened. Poor Jeanette, there were tears in her eyes. How odd, she was whispering, how odd. Two years ago he wasn't like this at all. You'd say the rockets have changed him too.

"Son of Geronimo, this is a friend. You know what she does? She writes about the men who want to go to the Moon."

"The Moon?"

The son of Geronimo stiffened all over with pride.

"Son of Geronimo, I know that you don't want to go to the Moon. But if you'll give me your photograph just the same, I'll give you two dollars."

He didn't even listen to my offer.

"Who said I don't want to go to the Moon? I want to go to the Moon and how. *Ugh!* We must go to the Moon and to Mars too.

And I'd like you to know, my son works on the rockets. And my grandson works on the rockets. And so does my son-in-law!"

"Ugh!"

Outside the sunset was coming alight in flames of gold and red. Soon evening would fall and if I didn't reach El Paso before night I'd miss my plane. I touched the mortified Jeanette on the shoulder and asked her to take me away, please. In the plane I compared the photograph of the son of Geronimo with the photograph of Little Joe. There was no doubt about it, Father. Even from an aesthetic point of view, Little Joe was better.

30.

I am wondering to what extent you've already guessed what I'm going to tell you and to what extent it will grieve you. To others, indeed, our argument might seem a game for intellectuals, but we know that it isn't. Sophistries have never amused us. So you'll recall, Father, that on that second journey I wrote to you very seldom, I telephoned you even less, that the week at Las Cruces and the two weeks afterward I maintained such an obstinate silence that Mother grew alarmed and was afraid somebody had kidnapped me. Well, I made excuses, I said I'd been busy, also I'd forgotten to post a letter. Lies. The truth is that I didn't feel like talking about it either on paper or by phone. It would have meant arguing and I didn't want to argue. I was preparing myself to leave you. No, don't misunderstand me, not to leave you on the level of feelings. In my feelings I will, I would never leave you, even if I went to Alpha Centauri. You're the best I have, you're the only ones who have never betrayed, hurt, sold me.

I mean to leave you on the level of reason, Father, on the level of ethics. To put it more simply, or more cruelly, the world you had taught me to love no longer suited me. Because of a rocket-launching? you smile. Because of Little Joe? Father, of course not. Great loves, real metamorphoses, are never heralded by sudden bolts from the blue. The process that had led me to weep for Little Joe had begun very much earlier; and don't ask me when. Can you tell me when you began not believing in Heaven and Hell? Can you recall the year, the incident, the hour? I can recall only that one day when I was a child I realized that God didn't have a beard, that He didn't sit on a cloud, that His angels weren't protecting me in the least, and from this there gradually blossomed the thought that would tear me away from churches, from lighted candles, from the easy code of ethics the priests give us: those who are good go to Heaven and the wicked end up in Hell. No, Little Joe had merely served to make me realize that I liked it down here, in the future.

Not that I forgot its atrocious defects, its abominable faults, Father. Discovering that there's no Paradise and no Hell, that everything is born and dies with us, doesn't at all mean forgetting about Good and Evil. I hadn't become blind, Father. I could still see HR who wanted to knock down the Pyramids to build supermarkets, the bulldozers destroying forests to replace them with cement, my son growing up with no knowledge of the green and the blue, the bald heads of astronauts old at thirty, the face of the Bureaucrat, of those who in their obedience to the System demand the right to be all alike and happy. I didn't demand that right for myself. On the contrary I was shouting my right to be different—poorer, yes, but different; more stupid, yes, but different; unhappier, yes, but different—because I didn't know, I'll never know what to do with happiness distributed by ration card, like something to eat. Neither was I shutting my eyes to what was wrong. I was simply accepting the wrong as the price I had to pay for the dreams. Everything has a price, Father: you taught me that when they tortured you and threw you back into prison streaming with blood. Liberty has a price, justice has a price, dreams have a price. And just as you had paid your price, I would pay mine: with pain. It had been painful, Father, to realize that. More painful than when, as a young girl, I had resolved the problem of Heaven and Hell, because that had been a crisis of adolescence; this had been a crisis of maturity. Crises are illnesses: when you're young they leave you stronger than before, when you're grown-up they leave you full of pain. Thinking about this, I was on my way back to Cape Kennedy: happy to see my friends, to see the launching of the Saturn rocket, to be going home. Now I liked Florida that I'd described so cruelly in my letter before Mother's illness. Suddenly it was my home.

I returned to it on a Sunday evening, Father. The Saturn launching was scheduled for dawn on Tuesday. Instead of Cape Colony, I got off at the Holiday Inn. NASA headquarters was there, and waiting for me was Gatha Cottee with a Texas hat as big as his ignorance about Verne. I flung my arms around the neck of that mountain of flesh and remained dangling there like a fly on an elephant's eyelash.

"Gatha, are you a Turtle?"

"You bet your sweet . . ."

"Can you answer for another, Gatha?"

"If I'm allowed. Ask me."

"Dr. Bill Douglas."

"I'm allowed. He's an Imperial Turtle."

"Oh, thank you, Gatha! Thank you."

"And Project Cheese?"

"Fallen through, Gatha. We realized it wasn't practical. Now we're in the drive-in business. We're going to install a big chain of drive-ins on the Moon, on Mars and the other planets. And we'll sell root beer."

"Who's we?"

"Pietro and Giacomo and I. In English, Pete, Jim and I."

"Now, that *is* an idea. Can I come in on it?"

"You're hired. Chief storekeeper."

"Can Dr. Douglas be in on it too?"

"We'll need a doctor."

Dee O'Hara appeared soon after. Without the nurse's uniform she seemed even more like Mother.

"Dee, are you a Turtle?"

"You bet your sweet . . ."

"Long time no see, Dee."

"Yes. You still owe me that old idea of yours."

"What old idea of mine?"

"Yes. Remember? When you didn't laugh about me being an OB nurse. Also you seemed to find it obvious."

"I still do."

"So?"

"I'll tell you some other time, Dee."

"You fake!"

"How are the boys, Dee?"

"You won't be short of company anyway, this time. They're all here."

And they were. The Holiday Inn was swarming with known faces, voices by now familiar. Stan Miller, HR, Bob Button, Jack Riley, Paul Haney, Joe Jones, Bart Slattery, Ben Gallespie, Ben James, Dee O'Hara, her joyous cries, claps on the back, warmest hugs, cocktails at every pretext: "You know, this is an important launching; it isn't Little Joe." "They spent years constructing that monster: at last it's going up." "A great opening night, guys. Let's drink to it." "Hey, has von Braun come?" "Of course. Three Senators from Washington too." "And the astronauts?" "Quite a few of them. They're arriving in twos and threes." How many? "A dozen or so." Electrified, excited, everyone had something to say, to ask, even more than at Las Cruces—as if a school had broken up. And in this school I was splashing about like a fish in water. When I met Pete, on the eve of the launching, it seemed as normal to me as meeting a colleague in the office. His naturally dramatic entrance didn't even surprise me.

"Dammit! Where could I find you if not in a lounge drinking and smoking? I say: where's the brother? They say: drinking and smoking. Dammit! I even put on my dark blue."

As a matter of fact, the way he was dressed he looked as if he were going to ask his wife's hand in marriage: with a shirt, tie, cufflinks in his cuffs. A disaster. To complete the disaster, he had even parted his hair: what little hair he has.

"God, Pete! What have you done to yourself?"

"I made myself look elegant."

"Jesus! Why?"

"To bring you the present."

"You've brought me a present?"

"Yes! Your Theodore!"

There he was, awkward, tall, spare, with those two surprised little eyes, that little smile in the middle, those timid hands that he never knew where to put and now he was using them to scratch his nose, now putting them in his pocket, now clutching a chair with them as if he were about to fall over . . .

"Theodore!"

"Good evening, hi, how are you, how are you? I'm glad to see you again because Pete told me you wanted to see me I wanted to see you too I told Faith too, you know who I'm seeing this evening, I'm seeing that Italian girl who's going to look for Tonati you know she always sends me her greetings she says nice things about me, how are you, how are you?"

That weak voice, unharmonious, without commas, crouching at the bottom of his throat, with a timid laugh in the middle, and when he tore it out of his throat he blushed.

"I'm fine, Theodore."

"Faith says did you tell her about when Tonati gave us that beautiful plant? I didn't tell her I answer but as soon as I see her I'll tell her, so here goes he wanted to give us a plant he knew I liked plants and he went into a shop where they only had plastic plants. No, Tonati would say, I want a plant. Isn't this a plant? the assistant would say. But no a real plant Tonati would say. What do you mean a real plant? the assistant would say. A real plant with real leaves Tonati would say with roots. Oh I see said the assistant you want the kind that die that's what the assistant called them, plants that die, so he had a plant sent over from another shop and then he said to Tonati but this one'll die. But it hasn't died and it's produced a fine flower I'd like Tonati to know that."

"Oh, Theodore!"

Pete was chuckling, happy.

"I brought him, huh? I brought him. They didn't want me to, you know that? They kept griping: You're too many as it is. I had to swap for him."

"Swap?"

"Yes. Either Jim or him, they kept saying—or do you think you're going to the Rio carnival, or taking them all out dancing? I picked him. Jim stayed behind. Man, how he swore! Now you'll have to send the wine to Jim too."

"You can count on it."

"As much for him as for me."

"Half for you, half for him."

Dee showed up, with her beautiful smile.

"Well, shall we go and eat?"

"O.K. Let's go and eat."

And then we went to eat. It was beautiful being all four of us together, I and Dee and my two adopted brothers. We had nothing sensational to say to each other and yet it was beautiful: every sentence acquired flavor, every gesture acquired meaning, every look drew us closer. I suppose you feel the same when you're with friends you feel close to. And don't tell me no, it's not true because you're a woman and I'm a man. It made no difference that Dee and I were women, it never did, it caused no embarrassments or barriers. It does not, when the faith is the same, and the dreams. Do I make myself clear, Father?

". . . I was saying, inside the blockhouse there's a painter paid by NASA to draw the rocket as it leaves—"

"What are you making up now, Theodore. There's no time even to photograph a rocket on the way up."

"I'm not making it up I know how fast the rocket leaves but that painter he has time to paint it I saw him with my own eyes, get me? He stands there at his little window with his pencil and paper then when the flames get going he starts making scrawls, I've seen him!"

"What are his drawings like?" asked Dee.

"Well, there's the rocket that looks like the pistil of a flower then there are the clouds that look like petals like a lily I'd say a bit abstract I don't know whether they're beautiful but it's beautiful that he's making drawings that's what I mean that someone sends him to do them I mean there we are squashed together like in a bus in the blockhouse, space is precious, there are only a few little windows and not everyone can stand by a window, get me? They don't give one to everybody, they've never given me one. But they give one to him and to me that seems a good thing even if his drawings are ugly."

"Yes, of course, Theodore."

"I can't explain it but I know it's good isn't it Pete?"

"Well, yes. It means we aren't so ignorant, that we have respect for art, etcetera etcetera amen. It makes me sore to see him standing at the window and I'm not: but I realize he's got his uses too."

"Why, Pete?" Dee asked again.

Pete thought at length, then took a pencil and drew a half-circle on his hand.

"There. The cockpit of my plane is like that. Well, more or less like that—I can't draw. There. This evening when I was flying from Houston, all alone with my jet, the Moon came inside here, see? And it stayed there, framed like a picture. White, round, clean. Boy, it was beautiful! Really beautiful. If I were an artist, I could have drawn it. But I'm no artist, I can only fly a jet, and that artist in the blockhouse . . . etcetera etcetera amen. Man, it was beautiful! Theodore, you'd have written a poem about it."

"I don't write poems."

"She says you do. She says you're a poet. A real one. That story about Rembrandt and about why you like flying, etcetera etcetera etcetera amen."

"How about you, Pete: why do you like it?"

"Why, why, why. Always asking why. You're like my oldest kid, always asking why. How should I know why?"

"Why, Pete?" asked Theodore.

"Boy! Because I like the sky."

"Why do you like it, Pete?"

"Boy! Now you're starting too. How should I know? Because it's big. Bigger than the sea. It's big, and I'm so small."

This kind of talk, Father. And then I don't know: we walked, the four of us, along the beach, our shoes in our hands, close to the water. The water washed over our feet and we laughed. But wait, something happened that evening, something I'll never forget as long as I live. It happened when Theodore suddenly stopped and raised his surprised little eyes to the Moon and stood there looking at it.

"There she is!"

So then Pete stopped too, and I stopped too. And it had a strange effect on me, looking at it with the two of them who would be going there. An old question came into my mind.

"You know, Theodore, you know, Pete: I often wonder what you'll be thinking at the moment when you go up."

And Pete, immediately flinging himself into one of his incredible performances: "There I'll be, stretched out inside that thing, sweating, and I'll think oh, why did I ask for trouble like this, why? Who made me do it? Commander, are you ready, Commander? they'll ask from the ground. And I'll say: no!"

"No!"

"What do you mean, no? Commander! I said nooo! Commander! How do you feel, Commander? Very bad! Commander, is there anything we can do for you? Yes! What do you want, Commander? I want to get dooown!"

"Down!"

"Naturally they'll think I'm joking. They'll say he's always joking, that guy, because he's got courage. What courage, fellers! And with this misunderstanding they'll light the damn fires, the thing'll start vibrating, I'll hold on to my seat, yelling I want to get down, oh God I want to get down, but they'll think I'm joking again, so they'll shoot me up there, like the man in the Luna Park cannon, and I'll cry and cry . . ."

"And cry . . ."

"I'll cry. For three days and three nights I'll cry: and they'll think there's some disturbance on the radio and they won't realize I'm crying. So I'll get to the Moon."

"Stop it, Pete!"

I was doubled up with laughter. But Theodore was listening with a strange smile.

"You'll get to the Moon and then you won't be the same any more, Pete," he whispered. "You won't be the same because you'll get snooty because you're on the Moon and when you come back you won't say hello to your old friends."

"It's not true!"

"You won't take them out for a drink any more and you won't go for walks along the beach with them any more."

"It's not true!"

"You'll say you weren't afraid at all and you'll become a loathsome hero."

"It's not true!"

"You'll cover yourself with medals and you won't be our brother any more."

"It's not true!"

"It's true."

"Then I won't tell you what I'll do on the Moon."

"Come on, then, tell us!"

"I'm telling you. I'll arrive on the Moon and I'll get out. I'll point my finger at the TV camera and I'll shout: Orianooo! Theodooore! I haven't changed, I'm not going to change! Orianooo, Theodooore! I'm no different today than I was yesterday, and tomorrow I'll be the same as today!"

"Listen to him!"

"And then there'll be a turmoil down on Earth: What did he say? What does he want? Fellers, Pete's gone mad! He's gone mad on the Moon! And then they'll telephone the White House to tell them Pete's gone mad on the Moon, at the White House they'll go nuts—the traitor, he's gone mad on the Moon—and they'll telephone Congress and there'll be a great commotion, they'll say the traitor, he's gone mad on the Moon, and . . ."

"Listen to him!"

"And there'll be a real scandal. At the Kremlin they'll say: fine people you've got, fine people, going mad on the Moon. And our Ambassador will tell Congress. Congress will tell the White House. The White House will tell NASA. NASA will tell the Chief, and he'll yell through the radio: rat, coward, etcetera etcetera amen. Because I'm always getting hell, whatever I say, whatever I do, and they'll slit my throat . . ."

"Stop it, Pete!" Dee roared with laughter.

"But I'll point my finger at the television and I'll say: Well, you know what? You're boring me. Then I'll switch off and I'll go for a walk on the Moon like Snow White in the forest. Whistling, singing. A little sad because I'm by myself and I don't like that one bit, but whistling, singing. I'll gather a little handful of dust here, a hunk of lava there, you know, like Snow White gathering flowers and mushrooms, then I'll get back into the LEM with my basket of flowers and mushrooms, I'll return to Earth and they'll shut me up in a lunatic asylum like that Hiroshima pilot. Etcetera etcetera amen."

"Pete, you're great!" I groaned. God, I'd never laughed so much. And I turned to Theodore. But Theodore wasn't laughing at all. He wasn't even smiling any more.

"Theodore, what will you be thinking when you leave for the Moon?"

"I don't know," said Theodore.

"What do you mean you don't know?" Pete yelled.

"I don't know," Theodore repeated. "I thought about it just now too but my mind's a blank. I can't picture myself at the moment of taking off for the Moon. I can't see myself."

"You can't see yourself!" Pete grew indignant. "You're an astronaut and you can't see yourself taking off for the Moon? What kind of a stupid astronaut are you?"

"I can't see myself, can I help it? I'm always telling Faith too, you know it's funny but I can't see myself going to the Moon, whenever I think about it I see black. Maybe because the sky is black up there but I can't picture the sky being black it isn't black it's blue. With birds flying in it."

"Shut up!" Pete grumbled.

"How can I help it? That's the way it is maybe I'll never go to the Moon."

The sea was roaring and spilling little blue medusas onto the beach: different from the ones we find on our beach. Ours are big, white, round, but these were small, blue, they had a kind of comb on their backs, a cock's comb, and they made me shudder. But was it the medusas? I stopped looking at the medusas and looked at Theodore and I shuddered again. Theodore was looking at the Moon. Yet he didn't look at it as Pete did: he was looking at it with sadness and his little face was white as the white of our medusas. As if he knew, Father, as if he felt that . . .

"Well, shall we go?" Dee grumbled. "It's getting cold."

"Yes," I said.

"And tomorrow we have to get up at three," Pete said.

"Yes," I said.

"We need sleep."

"Yes," I said.

"And I don't like to hear certain things."

"No," I said.

"What are you saying?" Theodore shook himself. During our bickering he had kept on looking at the Moon without opening his mouth.

"I was asking Pete if the rocket will go up tomorrow," I lied.

"Oh! Do you think it will go, Pete?"

Pete sniffed the air as the Chief would. Then he assumed the solemn expression of one pronouncing a verdict.

"I say it'll go."

"Then it won't." Theodore smiled, blushing.

———————

And it didn't go. The weather was good, countdown had reached "fifteen," in the press enclosure everyone was ready, telephone in hand, eyes fixed on the great skyscraper that towered on its pad by the edge of the sea: but a valve had failed and so the launching was put off. To fix the valve would take two days. Two days of vacation, of idleness at the swimming pool. Stretched out under a big umbrella, I was staying with my new friends who had given up diving into the pool and were lying sunbathing. Hi, Theodore. Hi, Pete. Hi, Gordo. Hi, Al. Only Grissom, Schirra and the Chief were missing, hidden God knows where and to do what. And there were two I'd never seen before: one of them tall, good-natured, so bald that his head was gleaming; the other stiff, wiry, with thick hair in a crew cut. He attracted attention, this one, because of something special in his feverish sharp eyes and because of the scars that disfigured his body. The least glaring of them was spoon-shaped, right over his heart, so that you wondered how he could still be alive with such a scar over his heart. The most glaring one, on the other hand, was in the middle of his chest: very red, rectangular, like a patch of flesh sewn on to cover a tear. What struck you, however, was not its unusual shape, but the offhand dignified way in which he wore it. He carried that patch of flesh as if it were a label printed with his name, and he presented it to the horrified curiosity of his neighbor as much as to say: don't mind, you'll get used to it after a while.

But I didn't get used to it, and I went on staring at that label, and all at once I heard his voice. Dignified and gentle.

"I did it in Korea, carrying my kit bag. There was a march over the mountains, the kit bag was heavy. The straps were rubbing here on the sternum. I got a blister. The blister wouldn't heal and so they cut it and it left this mark."

"Forgive me."

"Why? There's no harm in looking and you can hardly help it. I thought you'd like to know how I got it and so I told you."

"Thank you."

"My name's Frank Borman. I'm in the second group."

"Hi, Frank."

"And my name's Tom Stafford," said the good-natured bald one.

"Hi, Tom."

"Pete's told me about Project Cheese, but he also said you've given it up, you're in the drive-in business now. Can I get in on it?" said Tom.

"It depends. Are you a Turtle?"

"You bet your sweet . . ."

"Yes, then, yes."

"Then me too," said Frank.

"Me too," said Gordon Cooper.

It was the first time I'd heard his voice and for a moment I was immobilized with surprise. He had in fact a sharp small voice, not just a voice, a tiny voice. It made you uncomfortable because it seemed odd that such a handsome virile man should have such a tiny voice.

"Yes, sure. Any Turtle can join the drive-in enterprise."

"What's all this about drive-ins that everybody but me knows about I want to hear about it." Theodore broke in.

Pete and I exchanged a guilty look. Then Pete cleared his throat.

"It's not the kind of thing for you."

"What do you mean it's not the kind of thing for me, if it's the kind of thing for Turtles it's the kind of thing for me I'm a Turtle too, let's not start on that."

Pete leaped up like a cat and flung himself into the water, the coward.

Gordo came to my aid, with his tiny voice.

"It's that she and Jim and Pete have founded a corporation for setting up a chain of drive-ins on the Moon and Mars, to sell root beer there."

"Oh, no!" Theodore groaned.

"Oh, yes!" Gordo replied. And he shut his eyes to indicate that that was the end of it as far as he was concerned, he'd already done too much talking.

"Theodore, try to understand. Don't you go to drive-ins yourself when you're hungry and thirsty?" I ventured.

"What a question I go to them but they're ugly they always spoil the landscape and I ask you, should we spoil the landscape on the Moon and on Mars too?"

Pete's head emerged, warlike, from the water.

"We won't spoil a thing because our drive-ins will be beautiful. They'll have paintings and the Three Graces dancing around a barrel of root beer, etcetera etcetera amen."

"Oh, no!" Theodore groaned.

Pete did a somersault in the water.

"If you don't like the Three Graces, we'll have La Ronde."

"La Ronde, no!"

"You're a bore, Theodore."

"I'm right. Maybe on Mars there really are palaces towers the remains of something beautiful and you go and put up your drive-ins. I don't understand you this kind of thing makes me angry because it seems like a game but it's only a game in a manner of speaking and I know everything starts as a game but then it really happens."

Pete came out of the water, shaking himself.

"Yes. A damn bore. When I think I swapped Jim for you . . . I won't swap for you again, not even if this damn girl begs me on bended knees. We'll set up our damn drive-ins whether you like it or not. We have to eat, don't we? We have to drink, don't we? Shut up."

"But I don't understand you," said Theodore and he looked at me with such disappointment that I couldn't answer him. I could only sit there and gaze at him with remorse. In his swimming trunks he was very white, as if his skin had never been touched by a ray of sunshine, and his shoulders were bowed as if they bore the weight of all his sorrow: among those strong bodies and suntanned backs he looked like a sick man among the healthy, and this made me timid. Have you ever watched a bunch of kids playing in the street? There's always one who's whiter or sadder or smaller and he's the one the big kids just tolerate and order around: you stand there, you keep quiet, don't butt in. So you feel a tenderness, something special for him, you'd like to tell him, but somehow you can't speak to him, at least not as you'd speak to him if he were alone, he makes you feel timid. Well, that's how I felt at Cape Kennedy with Theodore. Odd how little we said to each other during those days, how shy he made me feel. Or perhaps I was distracted by the others and by my desire to understand them. Tom distracted me because he's very talkative, the kind who forms friendships rapidly, and he talked about things that didn't make you feel guilty. For example, the work he was doing with Wally Schirra at St. Louis, where they were both preparing for the first Gemini flight as stand-ins for Gus Grissom and John Young. The picked men were Grissom and Young, but he and Schirra had to be ready to go just the same, and then in six, eight months they would have their flight.

"Unless you become too old."

"How old are you, Tom?"

"Thirty-four."

"And you think you're old?"

"Yes. I'm old."

"You're not old, you're bald. Why are you so bald?"

"You'd grow bald too with waiting."

"Waiting for what?"

"The opportunity. The Moon."

"Are you that eager for it?"

"It's being so eager that makes me old. For some, I know, the trip is just a geological expedition. For me it's a dream I've had since I was a child. I'm stamping my feet with longing to get there."

"What do you think, Tom, when you look at it?"

"That's what I think. I look at it very often. At St. Louis, sometimes, in the evening Wally and I sit out on the terrace and stay there looking at the Moon. It's sort of funny, I know."

"No, it's not funny."

Gordo, on the other hand, distracted me with his silence, the serenity with which he kept falling asleep. How could he sleep like that? Even during the six hours preceding his flight, when he was shut inside his Mercury capsule, he had slept: can you believe it?! No lift-off had been as dramatic, as plagued by delays, as Cooper's. Inside the blockhouse, in the control centers, in the journalists' enclosure, everyone was sweating with anguish; but he was sleeping. He slept and woke up only when they went on with countdown. "Gordo, this is it." "O.K., I'm ready." "Twenty, nineteen, eighteen, stop! There's another delay." "O.K., then I'll get some sleep." One hour, two hours. "Wake up, Gordo, this is really it this time." "O.K., I'm ready." Twenty, nineteen, eighteen, stop! There's another delay." "O.K., then I'll get some sleep." Two hours, three hours. "Wake up, Gordo. We're off." "O.K., I'm ready." "Twenty, nineteen, eighteen, seventeen, sixteen, stop! There's another delay." So it was repeated, four times, for no less than six hours. Six hours walled up inside that steel coffin on top of the rocket, vibrating and swaying about—but how could he sleep?

"But, Gordo, can you sleep whenever you want to?"

"Sure."

"You mean that at any moment you can shut your eyes and say now I'm going to sleep?"

"Sure."

"Even if you aren't sleepy?"

"Even if I'm not sleepy."

"But when you were up there on top of the rocket, how could you sleep?"

"What do you mean, how could I?"

"How could you?"

"There was nothing else to do."

"Nothing else to do?!"

"Well, what would you expect me to do? Read the newspaper?"

"But didn't they make you nervous, all those delays?"

"No."

"You felt all right, then."

"It was hot. But I felt all right."

"So you calmly slept."

"So he calmly slept," Pete said loudly. "Leave him alone!"

Pete distracted me for the simple reason that he was Pete: he'd even distract a priest in the church, that one. And Frank, well, Frank distracted me with his being so special. He had a quality of grace and dignity that didn't go with scars of that kind. These were the marks of a gladiator, to use an expression dear to Dr. Celentano: but he was no gladiator. You knew this from his sharp feverish eyes that followed every and any thing that happened—in a watchful silence very different from the silence of Gordo. Since the story of the kit bag in Korea, Frank hadn't said another thing. Yet I felt that no detail escaped him: neither my unusual shyness with Theodore, nor my curiosity about the others, nor the questions I was asking myself about him. Actually I was scrutinizing him every now and then as if to steal some secret from him, but all I gained was the picture of a high forehead, a thin nose and two thin lips. Then Pete launched into one of his usual performances: this time a scene of despair over some speech he was to give in Philadelphia, his native city. And then that scene happened.

"Man, how do I start it? I've exhausted all my little stories. And my mother'll be there, my sister'll be there, my old school friends'll be there, etcetera etcetera amen. I can't make a poor impression, I can't! I've got to capture the attention of that audience! I've got to find a beginning!"

The others were laughing, amused.

"A beginning for Pete!"

"Who's got a beginning for Pete?"

"Please produce a beginning for Pete!"

Then Frank Borman stood up with a serious, serious smile and, pretending to drape himself in Mark Antony's toga, at the same time laying his fingers over his dreadful rectangular patch, he began to declaim:

"Friends, Romans, countrymen, lend me your ears!/ I come to bury Caesar, not to praise him./ The evil that men do lives after them,/ The good is oft interred with their bones;/ So let it be with Caesar. The noble Brutus/ Hath told you Caesar was ambitious;/ If it were so, it was a grievous fault,/ And grievously hath Caesar answer'd it./ Here, under leave of Brutus and the rest—/ For Brutus is an honorable man;/ So are they all, all honorable men—/ Come I to speak in Caesar's funeral./ He was my friend, faithful and just to me;/ But Brutus says he was ambitious,/ and Brutus is an honorable man./ He hath brought many captives home to Rome,/ whose ransoms did the general coffers fill;/ Did this in Caesar seem ambitious?/ When that the poor have cried, Caesar hath wept;/ Ambition should be made of sterner stuff:/ Yet Brutus says he was ambitious,/ and Brutus is an honorable man."

Here he stopped, Mark Antony in swimming trunks with his crew cut and his scars from Korea. And without removing his fingers from the patch, without losing his serious, serious smile, he looked silently at Theodore, who stood up and cleared his throat.

"Ahem, well now, let's see . . . How does it go Frank how does it go?"

"You all did see . . ."

"Ahem, yes. *You all did see that on the Lupercal/ I thrice presented him a kingly crown,/ Which he did thrice refuse. Was this ambition?"*

"Gordo!"

Gordo remained stretched out lazily on his rubber raft and barely moved his lips.

"Yet Brutus says he was ambitious,/ and, sure, he is an honorable man."

"Tom!"

Tom hunched his shoulders, very worried.

"Eh! This is it! Help me, won't you?"

"I speak not to disprove what Brutus spoke,/ But here I am to

speak what I do know . . . Come on, Tom! *. . . You all did love him once, not without cause;/ What cause withholds you then to mourn for him?/ O judgment! thou are fled to brutish beasts . . .* Come on, Tom!"

"*And men have lost their reason,*" Tom intoned happily.

"*Bear with me;/ My heart is in the coffin there with Caesar . . .*"

"*And I must pause till it come back to me,*" Pete shouted, wildly happy at remembering his line. "And that's how you think I ought to start in Philadelphia?"

"You'd make a good impression," Frank remarked. Then he removed his toga, his fingers from the patch, and sat down again—with his serious, serious smile.

"Thank you, Frank."

"Not at all." And at the same moment he leaped to his feet, they all leaped to their feet, as if they'd been struck by a whip. The swimming pool fell silent.

"Morning . . ." said the reluctant voice.

As clamped shut as an oyster in its shell, alone, already dressed in his pale blue flying suit, the Chief stopped in the middle of the group of men standing stiffly at attention.

"The launching is postponed for two days. It'll be the day after tomorrow morning. I'm leaving. I'll be back tomorrow evening. Three of you will stay, the others leave with me. We're not on vacation. O.K.?"

"O.K., Chief."

The Chief pointed at the first.

"You, Frank, go back to Houston."

"Right," said Frank. And he threw me a glance of defeat.

"You, Tom, go back to St. Louis."

"Right," said Tom. He too threw me a glance of defeat.

"You . . ." He turned to Pete, who was desperately keeping his fingers crossed. "You . . . stay."

"Right!"

"You . . ." He turned to Theodore, who was waiting resignedly. "You stay too."

Theodore's face was happy.

"You stay too, Gordo. All right?"

"All right."

"All right, great! So now Ted and I can go and have a dip, eh?" my brother cried.

"So now you and Ted can drive me to the plane," said the Chief dryly.

"Should I come too?" Gordo's little voice piped up.

"No. You go to sleep, Gordo, go back to sleep." And he left, clamped shut more tightly than any oyster in its shell, alone, in his pale blue flying suit.

"So long, dolly."

"So long, Deke."

The sun was scorching and Gordon began to smooth oil over himself against sunburn. Then he held out the bottle and told me to do the same. Mechanically I obeyed him. And meantime I was watching the Chief as he went away, followed like a king by his two squires. And I was glad that his squires were my brothers. I was glad to stay there reflecting on what I had seen and heard—these gladiators in swimming trunks reciting Shakespeare. There, Father, by a swimming pool at Cape Kennedy on the eve of a launching. What a pity, Father, that you weren't there too to watch them, listen to them. It had been a great sight, believe me, a great sight. I felt full of faith and pride, I felt truly proud of them. And I finally understood Stig's letter that had reached me the previous evening from Stockholm: "Here, in old Europe, the same old things. Princess Désirée has got married, Princess Margarethe is about to get married, Khrushchev is coming on a visit. The rest is silence."

31.

"When are you leaving?" Gordo Cooper asked, waking up after a little nap. Then he stretched out on his stomach, rested his face on his folded hands and stared at me, for the first time inclined to speak at somewhat greater length. There were only the two of us left beside the swimming pool.

"After the Saturn launching."

"Going straight back to Italy?"

"Yes."

"Are you glad to be going back?"

"No, I'm sorry. You know, like when summer vacation is over and you are a child and have to go back to school. The same thing, more or less."

"You call this a vacation!"

"It has been for me."

"You did nothing but grumble. The others say you did nothing but grumble."

"I grumbled because I had a fever, a high fever. Ray Bradbury says that after a fever you either get cured or you die. You can't go on being ill forever. But I did not die, and now I'm well. I got cured."

"Cured for better or for worse?"

"It depends on your point of view. My father would say for worse. I say for better."

"And now that you're cured, what will you do?"

"I'll write the book."

Gordo scratched his chin rather suspiciously. He shut his eyes and opened them again.

"Jesus! God knows what you'll write. What'll you write?"

"Everything. What I've seen, as I've seen it; what I've heard, as I've heard it; what I've thought, what I've suffered. Everything, more or less."

"It must cost you quite an effort?"

"Sometimes. But mostly it hurts. It hurts a lot, you know. Like beating yourself. And then, when you've beaten yourself pretty thoroughly, the others start beating you too. Those who don't understand, or don't believe, and who criticize."

"Then why do you do this job?"

"Why do you do your job, Gordo?"

"Because I believe in it."

"Well, I believe in mine too, Gordo."

"Yes, but sometimes I'd like to stay up there in Carbondale and do nothing."

"What's Carbondale?"

"It's a spot in the Colorado mountains; my mother lives there. We've got a ranch in Carbondale, my mother and I. It's beautiful, you know. Lots of vines, and we make wine, like you. But in wooden vats, the old-fashioned kind like yours. And we make brandy too. And then there's lots of fish in Carbondale. I like fishing. I was born at Shawnee, Oklahoma, and down there everybody goes fishing: those beautiful lakes and rivers. At first I used to go fishing here too, with Grissom; there used to be fish in the pools near the launch pad, there aren't any now. They must have been baked by the gusts of flame. Only the sharks are left. But in Carbondale there are tiny tiny fish that swim upstream like trout. There are times when I'd like to stay up there in Carbondale and do nothing."

"There are times when I'd also like to stay in Chianti and do nothing. There are tiny tiny fish there too that swim upstream like trout. But you can't spend your life fishing."

"No, you can't. You shouldn't. You'd end up staying in Shawnee, Oklahoma, and not even knowing about Carbondale. And maybe there are God knows how many Carbondales in the sky. You have to look for them, you know that, yes or no?"

"Yes, I know that we have to."

"And that's why I like the job I'm doing, and doing it doesn't hurt me like yours does. It doesn't even cost any effort. For me it's like . . . like . . ." He smiled that white smile, full of strong unblemished teeth: ". . . like praying."

"You are religious, Gordo. Aren't you?"

"Yes, I am. I also go to Mass."

"You even wrote a prayer when you were up in the Mercury capsule, didn't you?"

"I didn't write it. I put it on tape."

"How did it go, Gordo?"

"I don't remember."

"Yes, you do. You repeated it in Congress."

"Congress, you can say *that* again! All that business about having a place in history and nonsense like that. They keep saying: but don't you realize you have a place in history? I tell them what's Carbondale got to do with history? Do you think I look like the type to have a place in history?"

"How did the prayer go, Gordo?"

He blushed beneath the red of his sunburn. He cringed and hunched his shoulders.

"It went: Father, I thank you especially because you let me make this flight. And because I'm here in this wondrous spot and because I see these things that fill me with amazement. These marvelous things that you created . . . etcetera. That kind of thing. Nothing to write home about. But it came into my mind and so I recorded it. Then they made me say it in Congress and it was so embarrassing I wanted to run away."

"Who's run away? Who's run away?" Pete shouted behind us. He hadn't even taken an hour to drive the Chief and come back. Gordo smiled. "You ran away."

"I didn't run away. I put him in his damn plane and I hurried back to give you the news. Gordo, we've been taken for a ride. That devil's left us here to work. All three of us. This afternoon and all day tomorrow. Launch pad and then Merritt Island. Man, am I unlucky or aren't I? I can never settle down in peace to write a fine speech. I told him: Gordo and Ted don't have to make a speech. I've got to make a speech. He didn't even answer. I repeat, who's going to give me a beginning for my speech?"

Silence.

"Boy! Are you all struck dumb? I come, and you're all speechless. I go, and you all talk."

"We don't talk. We pray," Gordo said. "And then we sleep."

He shut his eyes, irritated, and fell asleep. Immediately. Pete made sure he wasn't pretending (he wasn't pretending), then he tapped me with a finger on the shoulder.

"Boy! Were you really praying?"

"Pete, where's Theodore?"

"At the launch pad. I made him go. Tell me, were you really praying?"

"I wasn't, he was. He was saying a bit of his prayer for me."

He seemed stunned. He went up to Gordo, who was snoring,

examined him closely with a frown on his forehead, then came back and seemed even more stunned.

"Boy! Who'd have thought it?"

"Why? Don't you pray?"

He scratched his anchor, revealed his wide-spaced teeth.

"Well, not in swimming pools. Nor in churches either. I mean, I don't go to church and all that. But as for believing, I believe just the same, we all believe, more or less, even those who say: I don't believe in a thing, neither Heaven nor Hell nor anything. But I'd like to see them when . . . Boy! At least three times I've nearly crashed and each time I commended myself to God like crazy. Those damn controls wouldn't be working one goddam bit and I'd pray to God, make them work, God! And you want to know something? I believe God helped me, that He made them work, those goddam controls that weren't working: because I was really going to crash. It's the same, you see, with the Moon. You fool around, you joke about it, but when you think about actually going to the Moon the first thing you do is ask God's help. Then the second thing is you thank Him."

"But what if He doesn't help?"

"Dammit! You thank Him anyway. It's good manners. If I ask you for a match and you don't give it to me, I thank you anyway, don't I? It's good manners. So I ask myself, why should I be polite to you and not to God?"

What strange days, those last two days: how can I explain them to you, Father? We were unexpectedly kind of subdued, we talked in a way we wouldn't have dared to at other times, it would have made us feel ridiculous. Or perhaps it was I who induced it with my new relaxed easy mood. You always judge others according to your own state of mind and mine was a state of great calm barely tinged with melancholy for the end of my journey, now close. When we weren't wandering into metaphysical confidences, in fact, I remained silent and let them discuss their own business: nearly always matters of valves, fuel, automatic systems. At dinner, when we were all four together with Ben James, they talked of nothing else. Now that it was settled that I was part of the community, they no longer bothered about amusing me with sparkling contributions.

"I've told them over and over again: You're sitting on top of a bomb, because the rocket is basically a bomb, and sitting in that capsule is like being in a trap. How can you help yourself? What can you do? You can't do a thing, you don't feel like a man with two hands and a brain, you feel like a guinea pig: leave us free to steer the thing ourselves! It's like talking to a brick wall. They don't even listen to you."

"On the other hand, if you get sick or if you make a mistake, automatic controls offer an advantage: they'll correct you and save you."

"Boy! The days of Lindbergh, those were the good days. You went up in some contraption that was basically a kite and you took the responsibility for everything. Flying by hand, the old-fashioned way! Oh, for my old jet with two wings!"

Their laughter, when it came, served only to nourish their regret.

"Boy! Are you all out of your wits, for God's sake? She's sitting there listening to us, maybe she's a filthy spy, she's pretending to be writing a book so she can steal the valve, and she's going straight back to Moscow instead of Italy. And we'll lose our jobs!" Pete shouted.

"But if she's a filthy spy she must find out some little thing or else she'll go back to Moscow empty-handed and Sedov will shoot her because she doesn't know a thing and I don't want her to be shot so let's give her something can't we?" Theodore replied.

Then Theodore tore up the paper tablecloth and on each little bit he wrote a number—one two three four five six seven eight nine ten— and held them out to me, kindly.

"Here, take these to Sedov and if he doesn't like it tell him: it's not my fault if these astronauts who speak English aren't worth a thing they're dumb I swear it."

The regret at having to leave them, Father. Because in those two days, you see, I had grown to feel affection for them as well as respect, a sort of envy. And my affection for them came from having understood one important thing: that they were not, they are not, different from ourselves, Father, they *are* ourselves. They are ourselves who a century ago, two, three centuries ago, left old Europe and went to seek new shores and new hopes. They are us moved to another address. The address of Gordo, of Pete, of Theodore, of Frank, of Tom, of Deke, of Wally, of Al, of Jack, of Ben, of Howard, of HR, of Slattery, of Dee O'Hara, and the choice was not between us and them, it was between us here and us there, us yesterday and us today, us in my time and us in your time, Father. And if we choose *my* time, America is where we have to go, it makes no sense to stay in the past with its beauty and its silence, our long silence, Father. The evening before the launch I said goodbye to them just as I say goodbye to you when I go, knowing that sooner or later I'll come back. Bye, see you soon, Father. Bye, see you soon, fellows.

They had all appeared again. And, with them, all the excitement of the eve of a launch. Pete kept saying it wouldn't go up, and consequently all doubts vanished. Pete and Theodore were the last to whom I said farewell at the swimming pool once more.

"Bye, then, Pete. So long."

"So long. When'll you be back, eh?"

"I don't know. But I'll be back."

"Meantime send me the wine."

"If you promise to drink it when you go to the Moon."

"I promise—if you come and watch me go to the Moon."

"I'll come, Pete. But I think I'll cry when I watch you go to the Moon."

"You damn well won't cry! You'll be pleased and how because nothing in the world matters to me as much as going up there. Understood?"

"Understood."

"And tomorrow morning, when that thing goes up, you've got to think this, that one day I'll be going up with it too. Roger?"

"Roger."

"And you must say: he'll be there inside it, my brother. And you must be proud. O.K.?"

"O.K."

"And I'll think that you're thinking it and so it'll be all one thought and that thought will be a great send-off."

"A great send-off."

Then he went away, so small and fair, with his funny teeth and his funny baldness, his anchor and his courage, and to me he seemed very tall now, and he didn't seem funny any more.

"Bye to you too, Theodore. So long."

"So long and anyway if we don't see each other again . . ."

"What do you mean, Theodore, 'if we don't see each other again'!"

"Well, all I meant was even if we don't see each other again you be careful with those ugly drive-ins won't you?"

"I'll be careful, Theodore."

"Because you know I understand that we have to eat and drink but to eat and drink we don't have to spoil things, see what I mean?"

"We'll try not to spoil them, Theodore."

"Even if there aren't leaves flowers birds and you know how much I love leaves flowers birds we have to treat things with respect, see what I mean?"

"We'll try to treat them with respect, Theodore."

"Well it looks as if there's no more to be said. So long, eh?" And he held out his hand to me.

To him I couldn't speak of the Moon, I couldn't say: I'll cry when you go to the Moon, Theodore. I wonder why. To him I'd have liked to say something special, beautiful, something that would tell him what he had given me, grace, goodness, purity, that's it, the story of old Moses, for example, a story of Siodmak's, the one I like so much, I've read it I don't know how many times and I've almost learned it by heart. But it was suddenly kind of clouded over and I could no longer remember how it went. Let's see, I kept saying to myself, there's old Moses who lives alone on a mountain and then there's the green creature who's a being from another world, made like a plant, and nobody knows what it is, whether it's a man, an angel, a tree. So this creature arrives and is wailing because it has broken the silver cage in which it travels, but the people don't understand and don't listen, instead they laugh. But old Moses listens to it, this green creature, and picks up the silver cage. And then? I couldn't remember what next. Then there's the green creature that can't express itself, it emits only the strangest sounds, but eventually it makes its meaning clear and asks old Moses to mend its cage with his pieces of silver money. So old Moses takes his pieces of silver, all the wealth he possesses, and melts them over the fire and mends the silver cage. And then? I couldn't remember the next either. Then there's the green creature that inside its trunk hides a green crystal that is its traveling companion, its seed, through which it can be born again if it should happen to die, and before leaving it commits a great folly, it gives the crystal, its companion, to old Moses . . . And then? I couldn't remember, Father, no, although I was old Moses, I could only remember that then old Moses goes away clutching this crystal that for him is only a crystal and he doesn't know what it's for but he knows that it gives him great joy. It was very strange that he should feel happy because he had no reason in the world to feel happy: he was old and the green creature had left him forever and he no longer had his silver pieces. Maybe, he told himself, he was happy because the creature had stopped and given him a gift. It was a gift, however useless it was. And for many years nobody had thought of giving him a gift.

"There's something I want to say to you, Theodore: that knowing you has been a gift."

"Oh!" said Theodore happily.

"A great gift."

"Oh!"

"I shall also think of you tomorrow morning when that thing goes up. I shall think that one day there'll also be you inside the thing and—"

"You mustn't see it like that," he said, "it's of no importance whether I go or not. You must see it as a prayer because when we launch that thing it's like praying."

It was the last thing he said and I was never to see him again, this brother of mine called Theodore: never again after that June evening on the edge of a swimming pool at Cape Kennedy, and around us people were laughing, talking, wondering whether the Saturn would go.

It went after four hours' delay. The usual breath of wind stirred mockingly by God deflected a plume of smoke on some screen or other and countdown kept stopping at "fifteen minutes." From the press box, three miles away from the launch pad, the smoke couldn't be seen: but it could be seen very well, shining white against the blue, and this time it wasn't a condemned man, it was an enormous candle waiting to be lighted to the glory of ourselves and of God. Never mind if God was amusing Himself humiliating us, making fun of us. Sooner or later He would let us celebrate this rite greater than any Mass, than any sacrifice to a Holy Ghost, than hymns sung inside churches. The church was these three square miles, with the sky for a roof. The altar was the blockhouse, where stood the high priest with his priests, von Braun with the astronauts and technicians. The hassocks for the believers were the grass on which I stood with two hundred other journalists, a round plot of grass enclosed by a wooden rail, with a lot of booths like confessionals. Inside each booth there was a telephone on which you could call any city in the world, and for a second I was tempted to phone you, Father, to tell you I was at Cape Kennedy and over there stands the Saturn, an enormous candle waiting to be lighted to the glory of ourselves, not of God. We've been here for three hours, four hours, and we're held up because God is stirring the wind and throwing a thread of smoke across some screen or other, but we don't feel humiliated, Father: it's a beautiful morning, the sun is warming like a promise, and when noon sounds you'll see we'll light that candle . . . I didn't phone you, I know. Everybody was phoning news to radio stations, television centers, newspapers, there was a lot of din, and you wouldn't have understood me. I stayed there instead, thinking that you wouldn't have understood me, and then noon came and God stopped making fun of us and He commanded the wind to move over, and countdown went on again, and our prayer began. As in a church. The priest called out his invocation from the blockhouse: "Fifteen . . . fourteen . . ." A loudspeaker transmitted it to the press enclosure, the journalists on their telephones picked it up and repeated it in unison: "Fifteen . . . fourteen . . ." In unison, you know, with solemn voices, with composed faces, and they were no longer numbers, those numbers, they became words, those numbers.

"Minus one minute . . ."

Te rogamus, Deus, audi nos . . .

"Nine seconds . . ."

Te rogamus, Deus, audi nos . . .

"Eight seconds . . ."

Te rogamus, Deus, audi nos . . .

"Seven seconds . . ."

Te rogamus, Deus, audi nos . . .

"Six seconds . . ."

Te rogamus, Deus, audi nos . . .

"Five seconds . . ."

Te rogamus, Deus, audi nos . . . Te rogamus, Deus, audi nos . . . We pray Thee, God, hear us . . . We pray Thee, God, hear us . . . hear us . . . hear us . . . hear us . . . hear us, liftoff! Hallelujah!

The white volcano opened, robbed the sky of all its petals of clouds, made a great crown of them and placed it around the Saturn, a white candle crowned with white: and for a while it stayed there, swaying, as if it couldn't face the dare, the blasphemy of going up, and then it rose with exasperating slowness, separated from the crown, leaving it all forgotten on the ground, and went up toward the heavens, leaped away out into space, and even its roar was glorious, it was no longer a roar but Easter bells, the Easter when we are happy and free and good, the Easter we spent together when the war was over, Father, and you were alive, I was alive, Mother was alive, everyone around us was alive, and the sun was hot, the bread was white, white as our candle that was rising straight, leaving its orange-colored comet, and now it was no longer a candle, it was a rocket, and the rocket was no longer empty, they were all inside it, my brothers, my friends, and Pete who was laughing, laughing, joyfully clapping them all on the shoulders, Frank and Tom and Gordo and Wally and Jim and Gus and John and Scott and Dee and Deke with stars in his eyes at last, Theodore who was saying oh! oh! and how happy he was, how happy they were, so happy that they were forgetting me, leaving me here on Earth. Don't leave me, I wanted to shout, I don't like it here, people are unhappy here, they break everything, please take me away, take me up there with you. But they were too far away, they couldn't hear me and they couldn't turn back, because there is no turning back, Father. Once you've started, you have to keep on going, on and on, and as they kept on going they disappeared with their comet, they became a little flame, the tip of a lighted match, a silvery speck that penetrated into the stratosphere, they got lost in infinite darkness, and they left me here on Earth. Sadly I made for a telephone. I dialed my New York office number. I told them I'd be there that evening. Yes, make a reservation at the hotel.

I could have seen them again, obviously, convinced myself that they hadn't left me down here alone. I would only have had to hurry over to one of the buses that were going back to the Holiday Inn. But I preferred not to see them again, to think of them up there in the sky, and this was why I loitered, watching the crowd move away as after a village fair. I loitered for about two hours in the now empty church: until von Braun came. Von Braun had put on a little weight, he looked very satisfied and puffed out his chest, and every now and then he threw me a questioning glance. In fact, I was the only one who wasn't asking him anything. At a certain point he raised his brows, smiled, as much as to say: but what are you doing, what do you want? I'm not doing anything, I answered silently, I don't want anything, I only want to pass the time. And I stood up, made my way to the last bus. In the bus there was only the soldier who was driving it. He asked me if I liked being alone in the bus and I told him I liked it very much because it made me feel as if I owned the bus and I could think things over. "Here, the usual things. Princess Désirée has got married, Princess Margarethe is about to get married, Khrushchev is coming here on a visit. The rest is silence." And, thinking things over, I reached the Holiday Inn, where I alighted in the hope that they would all have gone. They had all gone except Gordon Cooper, who was paying his bill and was wearing his flying suit. Gordo said that the others had

looked for me, Theodore had left me a note and Pete a gift, then they
had gone off shouting: Where's the filthy spy?

"Where were you, though?"

"I was there," I said. "Thinking."

"Thinking what?" Gordo said.

"Things. The things that happen here, the things that don't
happen there. Your life, our silence."

"I see," Gordo said, not understanding.

"So long, then, Gordo."

"So long. Here's the note and the gift."

He handed them to me laughingly with that beautiful smile full of
teeth. Pete's gift was a nasty mug for root beer, with a handle and the
words *Root Beer*. Theodore's note said: "Filthy spy, remember to give
my greetings to Tonati, here's the formula you were looking for for the
Russians: five, four, three, two, one . . ."

"Thank you, Gordo."

"Well, I'll be going, then."

"Go on, go on. It's getting late."

Damn it, why had he taken away my illusion? But perhaps it wasn't
Gordo, it was someone who looked like him. Gordo was flying with the
others up there: a silvery speck that was going around the Earth, around
and around, while I was clutching an ugly root-beer mug and a note that
was a prayer. "Five, four, three, two, one . . ." In my room I
found your letter, Father, the one telling me you'd saved the life of a
tree, you'd bought me a tree. "I've bought you a tree, by the way:
remember the oak tree overhanging the spring? The big one, with its
roots uncovered, where you used to climb when you were a child? Well,
the owner wanted to cut it down for the wood. And I bought it so it can
stay there. Mother didn't approve—all that money, she kept saying, for
a tree in somebody else's field. But I knew you wouldn't like it if I'd let
him kill it, so I bought it and it's a gift for you. You'll find it when you
come back, it's there waiting for you. Still in its usual place,
overhanging the spring. A big hug. Your Pa."

I shook my head as I read it. I thought how crazy he is, my father.
Buying me a tree. Saving the life of a tree. How crazy he is, my father:
I don't understand him any more.

32.

The way I heard it, that last day of October, and the final lesson I learned from it: I've never told you about it. In an article I wrote that I had heard it in the street when I was hurrying to Madison Square Garden to listen to Lyndon Johnson and Bob Kennedy; the Presidential election campaign was winding up. Well, that wasn't how it happened. It happened in a much more cruel way.

I had returned to New York, naturally. You know that now I spend more time there than with you, Father, that my choice is made. In New York I have a home that seems like a General Motors car, air-conditioning, microphones, levers, buttons, chutes, portable television sets, and you'd be staggered to see how nonchalantly I move around in it: without any sense of embarrassment or irritation. You'd also be staggered to see in what a nonchalant manner I go to Cape Kennedy. I often go to Cape Kennedy, roughly every time my friends are flying in the cosmos, and when the great candle goes up with those men inside, two lives maybe going to their death, I don't weep, I don't shiver, I don't get worked up. It seems so normal to me now. Besides, many things that used to make me cry or shiver or get worked up seem so normal to me. By now even the fact that a cross has to be disinfected. When Pete went up with Gordo and stayed up eight days I thought it would be nice to send him a cross to take into the sky with him, and I gave Paul Haney the cross Grandmother gave me, remember, yes the seventeenth-century silver one with the black patina, but do you know what happened? Paul brought it back, grumbling: Pete says you're crazy, it'd have to be disinfected, decontaminated, weighed, did you suppose you could take a cross on board that wasn't disinfected, decontaminated, weighed? And I: by God, Paul, Pete's right, I hadn't thought about it. You see what I mean, Father? A year before, I'd have thought it crazy to disinfect a cross. I'd have written a whole chapter about it, a very long story, an entire book maybe. But now it seems so normal to me, I relate it just like that. I'm no longer different from them, at times I feel I'm one of them. When I go to Houston, for example, when they invite me to dinner with their wives and children, and if I had to tell you what it is in them that strikes me today, I wouldn't be able to. Everything seems so

normal to me now. I arrive and the wife is in the kitchen, anxious as
Mother is when we have a guest for dinner, then the wife comes out of
the kitchen and says dinner is ready: we take our places at the table and
we eat and we talk of many things. Just like home, understand? We talk
of Vietnam, of Sophia Loren, of China. Never about the Moon, about
Mars, about obvious subjects. Loren, for them, is a less obvious subject
than the Moon: understand? Don't forget that we're in Houston, that
is in the provinces, it's a provincial life in Houston, where Sophia Loren
is considered important, and to go into the cosmos you fly direct from
there, skipping straight over the cynicisms, the intellectualisms, the
sophistications of Rome, of Paris, of New York, the ghosts of a world
that no longer has anything to give. Nothing. Not even memories, not
even regrets. Talking to them about days we do not forget and do not
forgive, that we cannot forget and forgive, is like talking to you about
the surface of Mars: believe me, Father. The other evening at the house
of Richard Gordon, the one who's like Berto, remember, there were
also Chaffee, McDivitt, Cernan, Cunningham, Scott, and we had an
argument. I mean an argument arose, over von Braun. You know how
it is: von Braun, Germany. Germany, Nazis. Nazis, Mussolini, Mussolini, you in prison. You in prison, hunger . . . and fear . . . and
firing squads . . . and my dead, your dead, our dead . . . "What I
don't understand," said Richard Gordon, "is your hatred, your perpetual resentment. I got to know the Germans in Germany and they were
really decent, really democratic." "They were not," I muttered, "they
were not, at that time." "Well, you used to shoot at them," he said.
"Yes," I muttered, "we used to shoot at them." "Then why all this
hatred?" he said. "Why?" I muttered, "you can't understand why." "All
right. Maybe for us to understand what it was like we'd have to go back
to the Civil War," he said. "Oh, are you trying to be funny?" Chaffee
interrupted, "The Civil War was the most atrocious, the most cruel civil
war that there has ever been." "Chaffee," I replied, "haven't you ever
heard about the civil war in Spain?" "Oh!" said Chaffee, "you certainly wouldn't compare the civil war in Spain with our Civil War!"
"Chaffee," I replied, "haven't you ever heard either of what happened in
Poland, in Yugoslavia, in France, in Italy, in Germany, in places called
Dachau, called Mathausen?" "Yes, but the Civil War was the most
atrocious, the most cruel civil war that there has ever been," Chaffee
concluded. You see, Father? They live in a state of limbo, these men
who will go to the Moon or to Mars, and they don't even know what
happened in Poland, in Yugoslavia, in France, in Italy, in places called

Mathausen, called Dachau, they don't even know what the Spanish civil war was like, they don't even know about hunger prisons fear firing squads hatred rancor the inability to use that stupid useless illogical coward word forgiveness. And it's right, Father, that it should be so. When we embarked in our wooden ships to seek other shores, other hopes, we didn't carry with us any resentment against those who had hurt us. There was no time for it. There was no room for it. Everything superfluous had to be thrown aside like that cross. What use is a cross, Father? Can a cross steer a ship, a spacecraft? Can a cross replace an electronic computer? Come on, Father. Honestly. Answer me, Father. Look me in the eyes, Father . . . And now we have come to the point, to the way I heard it, to the final lesson I learned that last day of October and the days that followed.

I had returned to New York, as I was telling you. And as soon as I'd got there I'd phoned a certain pilot who's been working on the LEM for years now and keeps Grumman Aircraft and the astronauts in touch with each other: his name is Smyth. The LEM, by the way, is being constructed at Grumman Aircraft, a factory on Long Island, less than an hour from New York, and during my second journey Smyth often invited me to go there and take a close look at the spacecraft that will land on the Moon: but finding one excuse or another I had always declined his invitation, I was tired of meeting machines, I preferred to postpone the meeting. And the meeting finally came about on that last day of October, on a Saturday afternoon. On Saturday in America people rest. I thought this was why Smyth was on edge. He isn't, as a rule. Partly on account of his job, which requires coolness, control, partly on account of his Nordic phlegm, he's always indifferent, ice cold, the type that accepts any setback, any misfortune, without batting an eye. Including the misfortune of being friendly with a wretch who doesn't respect Saturday afternoons. But that day he was numbed by a strange anxiety, you know, an anguish that from time to time kept exploding in nervous gestures very unusual in him, kicking at a piece of paper on the floor, for example, flinging a pencil onto the table, coughing. His frozen withdrawn face wore a very hard burning expression. His pale sleepy eyes seemed suddenly awakened by repressed rage. At the least little thing he gave way to the gesture he makes only in the rare moments when something's wrong: the sudden shake of the head to toss back a fallen lock of fair hair.

"After all, is it so dreadful that I've asked you to show me the LEM on a Saturday?"

"No, no."

"Has something bad happened?"

"No."

"Have you got a toothache?"

"No."

"You must realize I couldn't come to Long Island before today."

"Here's the LEM."

Brusquely he flung wide the door of the big shed. And there was the LEM: a creature of shining aluminum, erect on its four legs, it really looked like a bug, like a spider. With a head, a stomach, four legs. The stomach was the fuel tank, latched onto the legs. The head was the box to hold the two astronauts. And in its head it had eyes, the two portholes; it had a mouth, the round hatch below the portholes; and ears, the antennae on its right and left. With its eyes it watched us, with its ears it listened to us, with its mouth it would soon say something: the robots of science-fiction tales were made more or less like this. I almost yelled.

"God, you were right! It is alive, it is gorgeous! How big it is! It's more impressive than the rocket, than anything! When I think it'll land on the Moon carrying characters like Pete and Theodore—"

He cut me short, speaking tersely.

"It's twenty feet high, twelve feet wide. It weighs fifteen tons. We've been working on it for four years. There are six of us studying it. It cost twenty billion dollars."

"I seem to see them inside it, can you believe it? Pete looking around, all suspicious, and exclaiming, man, good God, man! Theodore looking around in delight and saying, beautiful, oh! how beautiful, what beautiful lava, what beautiful sand, what beautiful rocks—"

"The aluminum is to deflect the rays of the sun. The windows have been made smaller for the same reason. It will shine so brightly in space."

"Then Pete exclaiming, who's going to get out first? will you get out, Ted? should I get out? But you can tell he wants to be the one to get out and Theodore says, go on, go on—"

"The four legs are to distribute the weight in such a way that the spacecraft on the ground exerts a pressure of only half a pound to every square inch and won't sink if it should happen to land on a deep layer of dust."

"Let's go inside it, eh? Let's go inside. God, I'm so happy! To be going into the LEM, like them! It's a little like going up with them.

Let's go inside, come on!"

"O.K."

We climbed up a ladder and wormed ourselves inside through the round hatch. Inside, it was about as big as the control cabin of a commercial aircraft. In the ceiling there was the hole through which the two of them would lower themselves and later re-enter the Apollo spacecraft. Below the little windows were the controls and the electronic brain. There was nothing to sit on.

"I can almost see Theodore—"

"You'll notice that there are no seats. They aren't necessary. Being weightless means you don't get tired standing and it will be the same on the Moon, where gravity is reduced to a sixth of what it is here. Seats would add unnecessary weight and take up precious space. This vitreous substance on the floor is called Velcro and sticks to their shoes to prevent them from floating."

"Extraordinary! Isn't it extraordinary? I'd like to phone Theodore. Isn't it funny? I can't get Theodore out of my mind today. Did I ever tell you what happened at Cape Kennedy when Pete told him—"

"This is the alarm system."

He pressed a button sharply and a very faint but piercing *blip-blip* tore my heart and my ears. *Blip-blip. Blip-blip.* God, what a sound! A sound never heard before, inexplicable, other-worldly. A sound that came from nothingness and led to nothingness.

"Turn it off, please!"

He turned it off. And tossed back that lock of fair hair.

"Listen, Oriana . . ."

"I am sorry, Smyth. But that sound. That sinister terrible sound. It seems to portend evil, I don't know."

"Listen, Oriana . . ."

"When I think the alarm could sound for those boys: for Theodore, or Pete, or Wally, or Frank, or Gordo, or the others . . ."

He tossed back that lock of fair hair again. Then he gave me another look made somber by some repressed rage. And he spoke.

"I was called before you arrived."

"Oh, yes?"

"I was called from Houston."

"Oh, yes?"

"I have some bad news for you: Theodore died this morning."

He said it all at once. Quickly, without mercy. Like doctors when they tear out a diseased nail.

"Killed by a wild goose while he was flying over Houston in his T38."

That sound.

"He was coming in to land on the Ellington runway."

That sinister sound.

"On a Saturday morning, it's very strange."

On a Saturday morning, Father, he never used to fly. He used to take his bicycle and go to Nassau Bay with Faith and little Faith to see the geese as they came down to drink. Everyone knew it, they used to tease him about it: are you going to see the geese on Saturday morning, Theodore? Even the previous evening someone had said to him: are you going to see the geese tomorrow morning, Theodore? And he had answered: no, not tomorrow morning, I'm a bit behind with my flight hours, I'm going for a spin in my T38. He took off at one minute past ten, from the Ellington runway. The sky was hazy because of the heat. In Texas it's still hot in October. At 1800 feet there were scattered clouds: those little clouds that look like snowflakes or birds. He flew for thirty-six minutes and then asked the control tower if he could land. The control tower replied: wait, there's traffic on the runway. He climbed again. At ten forty-six he lost height again and asked the control tower if he could land this time. The control tower answered yes and he came down to 2100 feet, then to 1800. He was approaching from the southwest. Suddenly he turned and said he would approach from the southeast, and he said nothing else and did come down from the southeast. The goose came looking for him from the southwest, at exactly 1800 feet. Right in his corridor. It was a very big goose. When they measured its remains later, they established that it must have weighed at least twenty-six pounds. And it must have had a wingspread of no less than a yard. From a distance it looked like a scattered cloud. Theodore went into the cloud that instead was the goose. And the goose crashed against the cockpit, on the port side. The mouths of the T38 engines are beneath the cockpit. One wing of the goose went into the mouth of the port engine. A double explosion was heard, then the plane caught fire. It caught fire like a match, but Theodore kept it under control. He tried to land on the Ellington runway all the same. He was a very good pilot, a test pilot. Many were the times he'd landed with engines in flames. Theodore turned, lowered the undercarriage and came down toward the runway. But the flames were high. By now they were surrounding the cockpit on every side. Theodore couldn't see and realized that he couldn't land. He could only abandon the plane.

Bail out with his parachute. Theodore turned again, drew away from the runway, looking for a spot where he could abandon the plane and bail out. On the ground everyone was waiting for him to bail out. They were only hoping that he wouldn't bail out over any houses. At that moment he was over some houses, the astronauts' houses. Theodore didn't bail out over the houses. He couldn't see them, but he knew they were there. He made for a field of clover about three miles from his house. And so he lost precious seconds. The plane was losing height. When the cockpit opened and Theodore's body shot out, the plane was at 900 feet; everyone realized that the parachute wouldn't open in time. The truth is that Theodore had shot out badly. Downward instead of upward. The parachute didn't open. Theodore dropped like a stone into the clover field. And here Pete found him—shattered like glass.

"Pete was the first to get there, to see him."

"Let's get out," I said. "Let's get out of here."

"He was shattered like glass."

"Let's get out," I said. "Let's get out of here."

"Pete was given the job of reconstructing the accident. Pete and Deke Slayton. They're out in that field together."

"Let's get out," I said.

"I asked Pete if I ought to tell you."

"Let's get out, please!"

"I decided to tell you."

"Enough! Let's get out. Christ!"

We got out and the aluminum creature in which Theodore had never been able to picture himself stared at us with its big glass eyes. But Smyth was looking straight ahead and seemed like someone liberated from a weight. No longer numbed, he was once more walking with his long absent-minded stride and ignoring the lock of fair hair that tickled his eye. His face looked frozen again, indifferent. His voice was calm. In that calm icy voice he asked me what time I had to be at Madison Square Garden. He seemed surprised when I said I no longer wanted to go.

"But you were supposed to go."

"I was."

"Nothing's changed. You still have to go."

"Nothing's changed?"

"Nothing's changed, considering you still have to go."

"Still go? But Theodore is dead!"

"Theodore is dead and you must go to Madison Square Garden just the same."

"But aren't you sorry he's dead?"

He looked at me from some far-off remote point, the lock of hair over his sleepy eye.

"It could have happened to me. It could have happened to any of us."

Then he took me to Madison Square Garden to listen to Lyndon Johnson and Bob Kennedy. At Madison Square Garden there were thousands and thousands of people. They were waving flags and throwing confetti at each other. Johnson was flinging wide his arms at the crowd and the crowd was shouting in response: "Lyn-don! Lyn-don!" Bob Kennedy stood waving, together with his wife. His wife was wearing a dark brown coat and was eight months pregnant. I was seeing things as if I were underwater and I was thinking of Theodore, of his prayer "five, four, three, two, one," and suddenly I remembered that I had never given his greetings to Tonati. The address Theodore had written on the scrap of paper was no longer any good, to find the right one had taken a good while and when I'd found it Tonati was away on his honeymoon. I told all this to Smyth and he said to stop thinking about it, to stop thinking about it for goodness' sake.

———

The funeral took place four days later in the Arlington National Cemetery. I reached Washington the evening before and, as with a rocket-launching, they were all gathered in the same place—this time the Georgetown Inn Hotel. The group of astronauts was there in full force, the remaining twenty-eight plus John Glenn. They moved around between the restaurant and the bar, greeting their friends, receiving congratulations and good wishes. In the coming months White and McDivitt, Cooper and Conrad, Armstrong and See, Schirra and Stafford, Borman and Lovell would be going up into space, they too would see the brilliance of the Sun beyond the obscuring veil of the sky, they too would return to receive tributes, medals, streamers, parades, or perhaps, Christ, someone else too would find one day that atrocious death that suddenly shatters you as if you were a glass even though you may be young, strong. And as if they knew this, as if they were already thinking it, as if they found it quite normal, obvious, they were calmly replying to the congratulations, the good wishes. "Congratulations,

Eddie. Congratulations, Jimmy." "Thanks, yes, thanks." "Good luck, Gordo. Good luck, Pete." "Thanks, yes, thanks." "Let me congratulate you, Neil. Let me congratulate you, Elliot." "Thanks, yes, thanks," and each of them wore the same expression as Smyth when he'd said to me: "Yes, he's dead and you have to go to Madison Square Garden." The first to come up to me was the Chief. He was smiling. He had a glass in his hand.

"Hi, dolly! How are you?"

"Hi, Deke."

"We'll soon have the election results, eh? It looks as if Johnson's made it in almost every state."

"Yes."

"Maybe even in Arizona."

"Yes."

"You're in Washington for the elections, eh?"

"No. I'm in Washington for Ted's funeral."

"I see."

"It's atrocious, Deke."

"His parachute shot away wrong. It shot away like this instead of like that."

He spoke with an impassive face.

"It's terrible, Deke," I repeated.

"It could have happened to me. It could have happened to any of us."

The second to come up to me was Frank. Dressed in dark blue, clean-shaven, he looked like a student who's happy because he's passed his exams.

"Look who's here! Hi! Congratulations!"

"Congratulations for what?"

"I've seen a book of yours in English. My wife's reading it. She says you say bad things about American women. When are you coming to Houston?"

"I'm not coming to Houston."

"You've got to come. Absolutely. My wife wants to ask you to dinner and show you that American women aren't the monsters you think they are."

"O.K., Frank."

"And your new book about the Moon, have you written it?"

"I'm working on it. But I've not been working for the last few days. Ted's death . . . it's terrible, Frank."

"It could have happened to me, it could have happened to any of us."

The third I saw was Tom. He greeted me even more noisily than the others. Even his bald head was laughing.

"Now, this is a nice surprise! So you're here! We were just saying, it feels as if that filthy spy is somewhere around, but where is she, where is she? And then she's here, she's here! How are you?"

"How are you, Tom?"

"Fine! Great!"

"I'm not."

"Why? What's happened? What have you done?"

"I feel so full of grief, Tom."

"It could have happened to any of us."

The fourth I saw was Wally. I had not seen him since that day in Houston. He came over to me with his cheerful husky voice, with his bright American smile.

"Hi! Glad to see you. Hi!"

"Hi, Wally."

"You know, I was talking about something, a while ago, that would have interested you, about the messages to Alpha Centauri. The feller says: are you expecting a reply? I say: I'd be very disappointed if nobody replied; every morning when I wake up I'm expecting a reply from somebody. The feller says: all right, so we send them messages, but what do we say, what language do we use? I say: obviously not 'Hi, boys, how's it going in Alpha Centauri, would you like a Martini?' We use code symbols that don't require translation or interpretation, feller. For example: dip-dip-dip-da . . . dip-dip, dip-dip-da . . .'"

"How are you, Wally?"

"Fine, great, thanks. Of course if you receive them and you're an intelligent creature, what do you do? You don't send them back exactly the same, do you? You realize that if you send them back exactly the same they'll be confused with an echo. Which reminds me: you know the old joke, don't you? You're in an echo valley and you shout: Hellooooo . . . And the echo answers: Hellooooo. No surprise. But if you shout: Hellooooo . . . And the echo answers: How do you dooooo? . . ."

"Very funny."

"Yes, I understand, I know what you're thinking. It's hateful being killed by a machine. To be killed by a man, that's fair enough.

But by a machine, no, it's really hateful. Well, it's also our job. I mean: it could have happened to me. It could have happened to any of us."

One by one. All of them. They all said the same thing. Like a password, a set comment. And not a sign of grief, not half a word of regret. And so I didn't understand them, just as I hadn't understood Smyth. I didn't understand them and I grew indignant, just as I'd grown indignant with Smyth. What did they have in place of a heart, these men, Father? Didn't they realize their comrade was dead and lying in his coffin, shattered like glass? Wasn't even one of them capable of dedicating a tear to him? And were these the men I had held in such esteem, so admired, so envied? Were these my heroes, the heroes whom I had invested with my childhood dreams of glory, the heroes with whom I had replaced even you, Father? And Pete? Would even Pete answer like this? Pete was coming into the bar with the inseparable Jim. He saw me. He gave his cat-like leap, his usual irresistible smile.

"Filthy spy! How are you, filthy spy? By the way, the wine hasn't arrived. You lousy liar. Tell her, Jim, it hasn't arrived."

"It hasn't arrived," said Jim obediently.

"Pete . . ."

"Boy! Shall we have a Martini?"

"Pete . . ."

"What, don't you like Martinis?"

"But, Pete . . ."

"I like 'em. And then I need one. Four whole days, four damn days I spent in that clover field. Without drinking, without eating. I want a Martini."

Maybe, I thought, it was the tension of those four days that had wound them up like this. Maybe it was the way they'd been brought up. For certain people, showing grief is rude, ill-bred. Maybe it was because they'd all been drinking and that was why they were so worked up.

"Pete, you were the first to find him, weren't you?"

"Yes, I was."

"You were fond of him too, weren't you?"

"What do you mean, was I fond of him? Everyone was fond of him. Could you help being fond of a character like that?"

"Exactly, Pete."

"But what's the matter? What do you want?"

"I . . . Nothing, Pete. I'm only saying . . ."

"Only saying what?"

"God, Pete! What a terrible, unfair thing!"

"It could have happened to . . ."

"But it happened to him, Pete! It happened to him! Tell me, Pete: what do you feel when you think that he's dead?"

He became very white, Father. Oh, Father, I have never seen such a suntanned face become so white. It seemed like marble. And his voice, a slap in my teeth.

"If your father dies, do I ask you what you feel?"

"No, but . . ."

"For you he was a character in a book, for us he was more. Do you really think it leaves us cold knowing he's shut up forever inside a coffin? Tomorrow morning, I could have been lowered into that grave. If it were possible to make a swap, maybe I'd do it. I haven't asked myself, but maybe I'd do it. But since you can't make swaps with death, I'm alive. And since I'm alive, I'm not going to wallow in Greek tragedy. And since I'm not going to wallow in Greek tragedy, I'm going to have a Martini, a double. Drink one yourself and laugh, by God! Laugh because you're lucky, you're alive!"

A beautiful woman walked past us, dressed in white, with a black hat, a black veil, her face impeccably made up, dry of tears. She stopped by somebody, smiled charmingly, held out her hand as when you are introduced to somebody at a cocktail party. Then she proceeded as before and sat down to eat with a silent elderly couple. She was Faith, Theodore's wife, and the elderly couple were his parents.

"Well, do you want this Martini or don't you?" Pete repeated.

"Yes, I want it."

"O.K.! To your health, to mine. You know I'm going up with Gordo? We're going up for seven days, floating around, seeing you tiny, tiny, tinier than me! Haven't they told you?!"

"They told me, Pete."

"They told you and you don't even say blow up, Pete? Go and blow up, Pete?"

"Go and blow up, Pete."

"Well, now! Well! Another Martini."

On the television they were transmitting the election results. Drinking whiskey and Martinis, the twenty-nine stayed there watching, discussing; every now and then there would be a burst of laughter. They stayed there until three in the morning, you'd have said that they wanted to stay awake, that they were making the effort to stay awake, I don't know, almost as if by staying awake they were making themselves feel more alive; and the name of Theodore was never spoken. They made no allusion, no reference to him at all. Only Jim at one point said what a bore, tomorrow morning, having to wear a uniform. And Pete added the uniform's nothing, it's the cap. Have you ever seen us, Oriano, with our caps? I'll put my cap on later and give you a laugh. And then I understood that theirs wasn't indifference, wasn't coldness. Nor was it shyness. It was an acceptance of life. Because only by accepting life can you accept death: and we have to accept death, Father, however it comes, at whatever moment it comes, death is a part of life, death is the price we pay for life, try to realize it, to comprehend, please, that crying about death is for children. And for those who are weak. And irrational. And old. And merciful, if you prefer, but the future doesn't need merciful people who buy a tree so it won't be cut down: "Remember the oak tree overhanging the spring, the big one with the uncovered roots where you used to climb when you were small?" The future needs men who are strong and rational and young and cold, if you prefer, because the world is full of oak trees and for every oak that's cut down another one is being born or is already born or will be born. A single tree doesn't count, remember. Get into your head that a single tree doesn't count and you'll understand that death doesn't exist, Father. This was the decisive lesson I learned from these men who are strong, full of tomorrow. And until I had assimilated it, it was useless to say prayers over a rocket that's going up. Tomorrow morning, when the funeral procession would move off, no tears.

The funeral procession moved off at ten o'clock, a line of slow-moving automobiles that drove along the paths of Arlington and never seemed to arrive. But eventually it arrived and there was Theodore, shut up in his coffin. The coffin was covered with the flag of the United States and was placed on the grass near a tree. In the tree there was a squirrel. Faith, little Faith, his parents and brothers stood in the front now; Faith was dressed as on the previous evening, in white. The twenty-eight astronauts stood behind, together with John Glenn, who was also wearing his uniform of colonel of the Marines. There were no crowds. With the elections over, the city was exulting in the Johnson victory and nobody had the time or felt the need to enter a cemetery. There were only a few photographers, even fewer journalists. The ceremony was short. The Presbyterian minister said a prayer and the military guard fired the last salute. At the sound of gunshots the squirrel took fright. He slithered down the treetrunk and jumped onto the coffin, where he stayed staring with astonished eyes at the little girl in a pale blue coat, a red ribbon in her golden hair, who looked so much like her father and was weeping desperately. She wept until someone told her that was enough, and these were the only tears one could see shed over Theodore Freeman, astronaut, dead at the age of thirty-four without going to the Moon, killed by a wild goose while he was flying in the sky over Houston, less than three miles from home. Then the squirrel jumped down. Tom, Frank, Ed White and Bean came forward and raised the flag that was covering the coffin, folded it five times and gave it to Faith. The group broke up, the automobiles drove off again in haste, and Theodore was left there alone, inside that coffin that was gleaming like the LEM, I ran away to go to the airport and return to New York. Goodbye, Theodore. Perhaps tomorrow I'll have to say goodbye to others of you; tomorrow others will be gone also. But we'll meet again, all of us, meet again, I don't know where, I don't know when, but I know we'll meet again, some sunny day. One Sun out of many: there are millions, billions of Suns in the cosmos, all the sand on Earth does not amount to the number of stars in the skies, Theodore. Heaven doesn't exist, Hell doesn't exist, goodness doesn't exist, but life exists, and continues to exist even if a tree dies, if a man dies, if a Sun dies. Didn't you believe it too, Theodore? I do, now. I do. And you must too, Father. Believe it, please, Father. Believe it together with me. Don't leave me alone to believe it alone with them. They've convinced me, they've bent me, they've converted me, they've made me join them, and they frighten me so, Father. Because reason is on their side. And reason is always so frightening.

"Now is it all clear?" the husky voice asked while I ran away.

"Yes," I said.

"If it had happened to one of the others, he would have behaved the same way as everyone else. Now do you understand?"

"Yes" I said.

"Life is made of death too."

"Yes."

"Life doesn't end because one man goes."

"Yes," I said. "But I'm sorry all the same."

"So am I. But I can't stop to think about how sorry I am. I mustn't. I don't have time. And the others won't have time to stop and think about how sorry they are when I die."

"But it's cruel," I said, "it's inhuman."

"It's the war," he said. "You don't stop to weep over your fallen comrades in the battle. You push ahead, trying to dodge the bullets and shoot in place of those who are dead."

"But we aren't at war," I said.

"Yes we are," the husky voice said. "Every day is a war."

Every day is a war.

It is a war from the start: from the moment we land in this world, Father . . . After the baby has spent his appointed 266-or-so days in the tranquillity of his mother's womb, he is abruptly shoved out by a 100-pound propulsive force into the hostile world full of startlingly unfamiliar conditions. The first shock is the drop in temperature from the mother's cozy 98° to a room temperature some 20° lower. His eyes, which have been open to nothing but darkness, are suddenly assailed by light. He moves from a wet world to a dry one. It is a war from the start, Father. For each of us. Always.

Every day is a war.

———

"That's exactly what he told me, Ray."

"Indubitable," Bradbury smiled. "Obvious and indubitable."

"Great truths are always obvious and indubitable."

"Not always," Bradbury smiled.

We had met, Bradbury and I, at the opening of a bookshop in New York and now we were walking along an avenue and I was telling him the story.

"A great lesson, however, Ray."

"You couldn't avoid it," Bradbury smiled.

"I didn't want to avoid it. I wasn't trying to avoid it."

"And now what are you doing in New York?"

"Waging war."

"And don't you get tired of waging war?"

"We who come from the other side of the world are so accustomed to war, Ray. When we wage it, we wage it better than others. Even if we lose it."

"Do you think you'll lose it?"

"I don't know, it doesn't matter. What matters is believing in it."

"In what?"

"In what you believe in too. In life, in tomorrow. In the drive-ins we'll open on the Moon, on Mars, on Alpha Centauri, to continue life, to continue tomorrow."

"I find you changed."

"I am."

"Not as good as you were."

"I'm not."

"But with no doubts any more."

"I no longer have any."

"And your father?"

"He still hopes I'll go back to what I was before."

"Will you?"

"No, I don't think I will."

"You'll have to pay a high price for it. You'll suffer a lot, my dear. You'll curse yourself in regret. They're ugly, the drive-ins. They always spoil the landscape."

"I know, Ray. I also know that those who build them are often as ugly."

"But we'll need them. We'll need them desperately."

"Exactly. And since we'll need them, it's useless to get bogged down in doubts, yes or no, Ray? Let us put it like that: we'll try to spoil as little as possible, not to pee in the golden sarcophagi."

"In what?"

"Nothing. Anyway there's always someone who pees in the golden sarcophagi. It isn't, after all, much worse than peeing against trees."

And we went on walking along an avenue.

At the corner of a street and the avenue a drill was excavating a big hole, and people were looking curiously at a strange torpedo-shaped object that was dangling from a crane and would soon be lowered into the hole. I asked Bradbury what it was and Bradbury told me it was a Time Capsule, constructed to last until 6965. I asked him what a Time Capsule was and he said it was a thing for our descendants: to leave for them so they would know that we had existed and how we had existed. I asked him what it was made of, what it contained, and he replied that it was made of copper, chromium and silver fused in a metal tougher than steel and able to withstand erosion, fire, atomic explosion: Cupaloy. Inside, protected by electronic systems, it contained the evidence of our civilization, such as it appeared to be on the threshold of the year 1965 after Christ, the eve of the flight to the Moon, in a society in which grief and death are life. I asked him what this evidence consisted of and he replied that there was a little of everything, thirty-five articles in common use, from a woman's hat to an alarm clock, a safety pin and a camera, a doll and a scalpel, and then seventy-five samples of metals, fabrics, plastics, synthetic materials, and then twelve kinds of seeds, from corn to roses, from cypress cones to coffee. And then a thousand microphotographs of automobiles, of aircraft, of rockets, of cities, of bicycles, of girls in bathing suits, of mothers with babes in arms, of astronauts with spacesuits, of martyrs before the firing squad. And then the *Encyclopaedia Britannica,* reduced to microfilm. And then the Bible, the books of Confucius and Mohammed. And then many textbooks of medicine, pharmacology, mathematics, physics, astronautics, biology, reduced to microfilm. And then Shakespeare and Homer and Dante and Sappho, reduced to microfilm. And then an assortment of fifty newspapers, magazines, brochures, catalogues, all reduced to microfilm. And then fireproof photographs of the masterpieces of Giotto, Leonardo, Raphael, Michelangelo. And samples of money, cigarettes, chewing gum. And then the history of the last fifty years of our planet up to Project Apollo. And lastly the *Book of Memory,* a grandiose code so that all the writings can be understood in the languages to come and translated and saved. And so, amazed, I asked who had invented the code, whose idea was it, whose sublime effort, and he replied that the code had been invented by a certain Mr. John P. Harrington, the idea had come from a group of engineers with the Westinghouse Electric Corporation, the sublime effort had been made by the Smithsonian Institution of Washington.

"And what happens next?"

"Something beautiful."

"What?"

"You'll see if you stay here and watch and listen."

So I stayed there and watched and listened. And I saw a man dressed in dark blue who stood still on the edge of the hole beside some other men dressed in dark blue, I heard an absorbed silence, barely disturbed by the rumble of the subway. Cars were passing by, slow, distant, because policemen were diverting the traffic. Then the crane moved, bent forward as if to bow, and accompanied the Time Capsule toward the great hole. Slowly, solemnly, the Capsule was lowered into the great hole, and when it was right inside the man dressed in dark blue stepped forward, spoke these words: "Time Capsule, may you rest in peace. May you awaken five thousand years from today. May your contents be found and prove a good gift for our remote descendants to come."

He spoke these words and the pouring cement soon after descended on the Capsule: heavy as the age in which we live, voracious as the future which we are entering. It was a beautiful evening in New

York, a cool and limpid evening. We were separated from each other, Father, maybe lost to each other, but I felt full of hope, of desperate optimism. A man, a brother had gone. Other men, other brothers would go, suddenly cut down like a trunk of a tree struck by the axe. I too would go, God knew where, God knew when the axe would strike and cut me down too, I who want to live, and hate death, but the world remained a long promise and the sky was offering thousands of lighted homes. And if the Earth dies, and if the Sun dies, we shall live up there, Father. Cost what it may: a tree, a billion trees, all the trees that life has given us.

Index

Oriana Fallaci

I was born in Florence of Florentine parents on the 29th of June under the sign of Cancer. I am the eldest of four sisters, all of them journalists with the exception of the youngest, who is four and who writes poems. I grew up in an anti-Fascist family, and during the Nazi occupation of Florence I fought in the Underground Movement: Corps of Volunteers for Freedom. At fourteen I was honorably discharged by the Italian Army as a simple soldier, with the equivalent of $23.50.

I got started on my own with a crime column in an Italian daily paper. At the same time I studied medicine at the University of Florence. I have traveled widely, around the world more than once, covering revolutions and royal marriages, interviewing people of every kind. Because of this I live alone and enjoy it. I have several houses, but the one I always go back to is a quiet old villa near Florence, occupied by my parents and two thousand books, in the middle of a beautiful farm which produces Chianti. In 1965 I came to New York City to stay. The place where I live is a noisy cage in Manhattan. I survive taxes and other disasters by writing for the Italian magazine *L'Europeo* and for some other magazines in Europe and in South America.

My books include *The Useless Sex,* a book on women; a novel, *Penelope at War;* and *The Unlikables,* a series of profiles of famous people.